'You know what a ⸻
learning you should ⸻
I'm telling those son⸻ ⸻ ⸻
they can have you!' He grabbed the backporch railing
and leaned drunkenly out into the blackness. 'They
can have you! You hear me, you bastards? There's
my daughter! There's Mary! Take her!' He put his
arm heavily around Minna's bare shoulder and the
two staggered back into the house.

The girl stood in the night, alone. The silence had
descended. She could feel the moisture start to build
in her eyes, then brim over her lids and run hotly
down her cheeks.

Then she felt the writhing in her insides. The
churning of her stomach. Felt the contractions in her
abdomen and the sudden intake of gasped air to her
lungs.

Then she felt the stuff moving up her throat and into
her mouth. She opened her lips and gagged
repeatedly as the wet slimy balls of feathers, small
bones and fur poured out of her, splashing onto her
bare feet and staining the green grass a dark brown.
Some of the disgusting stuff was absorbed into the
warm earth but other, larger chunks of it wriggled
away into the shadows as if, transformed by the hot
air, they had suddenly assumed a life of their own.

Also by David St Clair

CHILD POSSESSED
MINE TO KILL

and published by Corgi Books

The Devil Rocked Her Cradle

David St Clair

CORGI BOOKS

For
Marian Armstrong
(it's her book)

THE DEVIL ROCKED HER CRADLE

A CORGI BOOK 0 552 12705 1

First publication in Great Britain

PRINTING HISTORY
Corgi edition published 1987

Copyright © David St Clair 1987

This book is set in 10/11 pt Mallard
by Colset Private Limited, Singapore.

Corgi Books are published by Transworld Publishers
Ltd., 61–63 Uxbridge Road, Ealing, London W5 5SA, in
Australia by Transworld Publishers (Australia) Pty.
Ltd., 15–23 Helles Avenue, Moorebank, NSW 2170, and
in New Zealand by Transworld Publishers (N.Z.) Ltd.,
Cnr. Moselle and Waipareira Avenues, Henderson,
Auckland.

Reproduced, printed and bound in Great Britain by
Hazell Watson & Viney Limited,
Member of the BPCC Group,
Aylesbury, Bucks

The common people of the country of my birth have a proverb of a child grown to a troublesome man. They say the Devil rocked his cradle. By which they would say, he is not so much to blame for his perversity as some malign accident of nature.

A Maggot by John Fowles

In short, when after years of trial and observation she had reached her fortieth year, the ecclesiastical authorities were finally convinced that here was a clear case of demoniacal possession.

Begone Satan by Rev. Carl Vogl

With Thanks

No author really writes a book by himself and this one would have been impossible to complete without the help of many people: especially that of the Roman Catholic Church in North America. I'd like to thank the following Franciscans: Father Jeremy Harrington, O.F.M., Minister Provincial of St John Baptist, Cincinnati, Ohio; Father Harry Speckman, O.F.M., Vicar Provincial, Province of the Sacred Heart, Chicago-St Louis; Rev. Urban S. Wagner, O.F.M., Archdiocese of St Paul and Minneapolis, St Paul, Minnesota; Rev. Joel Schmolke, archivist, Chicago-St Louis Province of the Sacred Heart. In St John's Abbey, in Collegeville, Minnesota, a special thanks to Father Oliver Kapsner O.S.B. and to the Abbey's archivist Rev. Vincent G. Tegeder, O.S.B. To Rev. Msgr Roy M. Klister, the Catholic Diocese of Green Bay, Wisconsin. Thanks to Rev. Stephen L. Orr, Chancellor, Diocese of Des Moines, Iowa. Special thanks to Sister Barbara, the head archivist of the School Sisters of St Francis, in Milwaukee, Wisconsins for sorting out all the Earling Sisters for me. In the town of Earling, Iowa, itself, I'd like to thank Mr James Schimorowsky and Mrs Benita Langenfeld. And a warm thanks to Mr & Mrs Ambrose Muenchrath who ventured into the local cemetery even though it was below freezing to verify some dates for me.

I'm especially honoured that John Fowles gave his permission for the quote from his book, *A Maggot*.

Thanks to that noted author of metaphysical books, Martin Ebon, for his information and guidance. He said research on this story would not be easy: and it wasn't. To writer and friend Barbara Dreimiller of Solon, Ohio for her guidance. To newsman James Breig, editor of *The Evangelist*, the publication of the Catholic Diocese of Albany, New York. To newsman Sal. J. Miragliotta of the National Catholic News Service in Washington, D.C. Special thanks to Father Frank Horvath, Christ Our King Catholic Church in Warren, Ohio, for setting me straight on ritual and dogma. To Mattie Marie Brainard, my typist in the States and Kate Fraser for typing the rest of the manuscript in London. To my mother, Mrs Ruth St Clair, for answering a multitude of questions about grammar, history and just for putting up with me as I wrote the book. To Patrick Janson-Smith of Corgi Books. If he hadn't said 'yes' none of this would ever have been put into motion.

And a very special thanks to Sister Nedine Ferris in the convent at Earling. By her refusal to give me any information she made me dig deeper and come up with a much better story.

Read This First

This story is true.

It is based on names, dates and events that have all been verified by the Roman Catholic Church. The background facts first appeared in a German language Catholic magazine called *Lieb Frauen Bote*. The editor, Rev. Carl Vogl, was an old friend of Father Theophilus Reisinger and obtained the story from him, first hand. Rev. Vogl was a responsible editor as well as a responsible Catholic. As a canonist, his rank in the Catholic Church was equivalent to that of a bishop. The exorcist, Father Theophilus, corrected the text, editing out the more unsavoury parts. After all, he had been there, it was *his* story. The English language version appeared in 1935 in a translation entitled *Begone Satan* by Rev. Celestine Kapsner, O.S.B., duly censored by the *Nihil Obstat* of Rev. Alexius Hoffmann, O.S.B., and with the approval and *Imprimatur* of Joseph F. Busch, Bishop of St Cloud, Minnesota. The Catholic Church in North America has never denied the story. The English language booklet, reprinted many times, can still be purchased from Tan Books of Rockford, Illinois, one of America's most influential Catholic book publishers. In other words, this story, told by those who lived through it, is true.

Therese Wegerer, sister and housekeeper to the younger exorcist, Father Joseph Steiger, said upon reading the original text: 'I was a witness to almost the whole period of the exorcism of the Earling possession case and I can truthfully say that the facts mentioned in *Begone Satan* are correct. There is not the slightest doubt in my mind that the devils were present and I will never forget the horrible scenes, vile, filthy and dirty, as long as I live.'

Much time and effort has gone into researching and augmenting that basic story. Dozens of letters and phone calls have been exchanged with Catholic priests, nuns and archivists. There has been correspondence with Rev. Kapsner's octogenarian brother Rev. Oliver Kapsner: 'My brother was indeed a zealous missionary and was determined to let the devil have it, for which I'm sure he has been greatly rewarded.' There has been fine co-operation with residents of Earling, Iowa, who remember it all happening in their small town. There was no co-operation, however, from the Sisters of St Joseph presently in charge of the convent in Earling. They would like to have the event forgotten.

Those who read this and doubt that the conversations between the devils and the priests are too glib, too informal, must take other published exorcism cases into consideration where verbal debates have been recorded. During almost all exorcisms, the language and exchange of ideas flow easily. It is not solely scenes of screams and howls and green vomit. Down through history the Church has reported these dialogues with the devil and they are usually infernal tennis matches, each side trying to win their points.

Those who read this and wince at some of the language used, must remember it comes from the voices of the demons and those possessed. Again, in all chronicles on exorcism, the language (when faithfully reported) is foul, debased and always pornographic. In this book that kind of language has been toned down a *great* deal. Not eliminated, for that would diminish the atmosphere of reality, but most certainly toned down.

Finally, this book is not meant to be either anti-

Christian or pro-demonic. It was not written to take sides. It was not written to destroy beliefs nor convert unbelievers. It was written to tell a story . . . and to let the reader make up his or her own mind.

Part One

Part One

1928

'Piss on your church! And piss on you, too, priest!' The woman lying on the bed, hands and legs bound to the sides, twisted her body and pulled at the leather ropes. 'I don't give a damn what you want, Who cares what you want, you old monkey?' The voice that came from the woman's body was low and harsh, more like a man's.

'Your names don't hurt me,' said the white-bearded priest. 'I can take all the slander you try to throw at me.'

'Then take this, you old bastard!' The woman's lips drew up in a tight circle. Then the green hot liquid shot out of her mouth and spattered across the old man's chest. A nun hurried forward and dabbed at the mess with a cloth. She shuddered involuntarily. Even though this had been going on for days she wasn't yet used to the stench or the sacrilege of it all. Especially the sacrilege.

'Your venom can be wiped clean,' the old man said. 'Your filth can be erased. We can erase it. And we can erase you.' He paused and looked at the unconscious woman in front of him. 'And we will, you know. We'll erase you and defeat you and you'll leave this woman yet. We'll make sure of it.'

'Even if it kills you?' The masculine voice inside the woman's body laughed.

11

The woman's lips did not move, yet the voice and the laughter came from within her.

'Yes,' the old man said softly, 'even if it kills me.'

'Well,' said the voice. 'I just might do that.'

'No,' the younger priest spoke up. 'You don't have the power. Not to kill a priest. We'll get rid of you first.'

The woman's head twisted, her closed unconscious eyes stared at the young priest. 'Go away, you stupid ass! Nobody's talking to you. Go outside and play with yourself.'

The head turned back in the direction of the old priest. 'What a fool. Where did you find him? In the seminary toilet?'

'You can't talk that way to me!' The young priest came nearer the bed, his face scarlet with anger.

'I can talk to you any way I please!' the voice said. 'You're not important. You're an insect. If I could get off this bed, I'd step on you like an ant. No, like a cockroach. You're more like a cockroach. Dumb and frightened and eating shit.'

'I said stop that!' the young man shouted.

'You stop it,' the voice said. 'Take your rosary beads and go save a soul. Do anything but just get out of here and leave me alone.'

'Father Steiger!' The old priest put out his hand and stopped the younger man from getting nearer the bed. 'Prudence,' he said, 'and caution.'

'But I don't have to take this!' the young man said loudly.

'Yes you do,' the white-bearded priest replied. 'Yes you do. Just as I have to take the vomit and the insults.'

'It's been going on too long. This was supposed to be over in a week!'

'It will go on as long as necessary,' the old man said. 'Until the devil has gone.'

The body on the bed laughed, even though the lips didn't move. 'Well then, it looks like we're going to be

12

together for a long time because I don't intend to go anywhere! I'm going to stay right here. Right inside this body. I like it here,' The laugh came again. 'I may decide to fix up this place. New paint and curtains, you know, make it *livable*. You nuns won't mind if I do some decorating, will you?' Blind eyes turned to the four Sisters standing near the wall. 'You're nice girls but you've got terrible taste. Your clothes and your accessories are for the birds. Bright colours, that's what I like.' The laugh came again. 'Especially red.' The laugh was louder now. 'Oh yes, *especially* red!'

1896

Mary sat with the doll on her lap, the small comb running through the yellow wiry hair on the doll's head. 'It'll be all right,' she whispered to the doll. 'It's over now. It'll be okay.' She patted the doll on the face and smiled down at it. 'He won't do it again. I'm sure he won't.' She picked the doll up and held it against her cheek. 'He didn't mean to do it. You were just in the way, that's all. He just didn't see you.' She smiled at the doll, trying not to notice the dull grey spot where the paint had chipped from the doll's tiny nose. 'He didn't mean *you*,' she soothed in her little girl voice. 'You were just in the way.'

Mary cradled the painted wooden doll in her arms and rocked silently with it. She sat in the darkness with the only light coming from the gas streetlight just outside the house. There were four lampposts on her street and she always thought how lucky she was to have one of them right outside her bedroom window. It chased away the night, kept the shadows confined. In the light the neighbour's yard across the street gave her something familiar to stare at when she awoke in the middle of the night.

There was a lamp in her own room but she hardly ever lit it. It was an oil lamp, one of those glass bottom ones that had a wick and a shade and could be carried from the kitchen to the dresser and down the hallway to the bathroom. Mary didn't like going to the bathroom at night, in the dark, so she used the pot under the bed. Her mother had shown her how to squat on it in the darkness and then how to toss out its contents and wash it clean in the morning. Her mother called it a 'potty'. Her father always called it a 'thunder mug'. Mary thought that was a funny name for it but her mother refused to explain.

Her mother. She could hear her even now, through the wall that separated their two bedrooms. She was still crying. She had hoped – prayed – that when she heard the front door slam her mother would stop crying and come to her. She didn't tonight. Most nights when this happened, she did. But she didn't tonight.

Her mother had fixed supper, as usual, and as usual they had waited for her father to come home and eat it with them. As usual, he didn't appear.

'We might as well start without him,' her mother said. 'Sit in your place and let's eat before everything gets ruined.'

Mary pulled out the wooden chair and climbed up on it. She was eight years old but small for her age. Most other kids in her class (Sister Berta's third grade class) were bigger than she was. Other kids had grown but she had remained as small as she was when she went into first grade. It wasn't that she was dwarfed or deformed, it was just that she was small. Once when Sister Berta talked about a mother dog giving birth, she told of the smallest puppy and called it the runt of the litter. Some kids laughed and one boy said aloud: 'Like Mary?' and then all the kids laughed. The name stuck and almost everyone called her 'The Runt'. She didn't mind. It gave her attention. It made her special. She had been signalled out by her peers and it made her glad inside. She needed the attention. She got so little of it at home.

'Are your hands washed?' her mother asked and Mary held up both palms for her mother to see. The woman nodded. 'Bow your head,' she said. Mary did. 'Oh Lord, bless this food we are about to eat. Nourish us with it and make us grow and make our bodies strong and give us strength to do your will. And Lord,' she paused and glanced at her small daughter who was sitting with her eyes closed and her head bowed, 'Lord, give me the strength to endure whatever this is that you've put upon me. Make Jacob see the error of his ways and what he's doing to himself and his family. Please Lord protect us because I am sorely afraid. Yes Lord, I am sorely afraid. Thank you.' Mary raised her head and looked at her mother. The woman's eyes brimmed with tears. They didn't fall down her cheeks, they just sat there shimmering on her bottom eyelids catching the light from the oil lamp on the table. The woman shoved a bowl in the girl's direction. 'Take some potatoes before they get cold. I saved some in the oven for your father.'

They did the dishes afterwards but her father's place setting remained on the table. Her mother washed and Mary dried. She was good at it and the towel sped around the plates and her small hand was able to get the towel deep into glasses and cups. Because she was so short she just put the dried dishes on the table and her mother put them away in the cupboard. The last pot had been washed and her mother had just returned from throwing the dishwater off the back porch when they heard the front door open. They glanced worriedly at each other and held their positions like actors in a church tableau.

They could hear his unsteady, shaky footsteps, clomping down the hallway linoleum toward the kitchen. The small house seemed to shudder as he lurched and came to a full stop against the kitchen door frame. 'I suppose,' he said, 'there's nothing to eat in this damned place.'

Mary's mother didn't even glance at her husband. 'I've saved you your supper,' she said quietly. 'If you'll sit down, I'll serve it.'

'You couldn't wait till I got here?' his deep voice was slurred.

'It's getting late,' the woman replied wiping her hands on her cotton print apron, 'and I wanted the child to have her supper.'

'The child,' he mimicked her voice. 'You wanted the child to have her supper! And me?'

'I said I have your supper ready.' She sighed, still not looking at him. 'Now sit down and I'll get it for you.'

'I suppose it's cold,' he muttered and weaved his way to the kitchen table. He pulled out his chair and sat at his place, plate and silverware waiting for him. 'If I wanted to eat cold food, I could have eaten cold food at Sam's. Sam's got cold food. Right at the end of the bar. Sam's got a platter of it there, Sam does.'

'I said I kept your dinner warm for you.' His wife took his plate and filled half of it with the fried potatoes and the other half with the ham loaf. She set it in front of him.

'I could have eaten *cold* food at Sam's,' he muttered again. He took a forkful of ham loaf and shoved it into his mouth, chewing and swallowing but not tasting. Another forkful followed, to be quickly crammed inside his mouth by a heap of potatoes.

'Is it warm enough for you?' the woman asked. He nodded. 'Good,' she said. 'All right Mary, it's getting late. I think you should get ready for bed.'

'Bed?' Jacob raised his head and looked around the small kitchen. 'What zis about bed?'

'Mary's bed,' his wife replied. 'It's time for Mary to go to bed.'

'It's early,' he said, bits of chewed ham falling from his mouth, 'I just got home.'

'It's almost nine p.m.,' his wife replied. 'Tomorrow is a school day.'

16

'Not for me, it isn't.' He laughed. 'It's not any nine-pee-emm,' he mimicked her again. 'I got off work at four thirty. I just got off work. If I just got off work,' he stared at her but didn't see her, 'if I just got off work how come it's nine-pee-emm already?' Mary laughed at her father's pronunciation and her mother glared at her.

'It's already nine o'clock,' she said, 'because you went to Sam's Bar before you came here. And you sat at Sam's Bar and spent your money on Sam's liquor and when you got too drunk to drink any more, Sam took you outside and pointed you down the street in the direction of your own home. That's why it's so late.'

'Did I go to Sam's?' He tried to focus on her face. 'I went to Sam's? How d'ya know? Was you there dearie?' He laughed and grinned in the direction where he thought his daughter would be. 'Was you there?'

'I don't have to be there,' the woman replied a little loudly, 'I can smell Sam's wares on your breath.'

'Sam don't yell at me,' he said softly. 'Sam don't yell at anybody.'

'Because Sam makes money off of you,' she said louder. 'I don't. I barely have enough money to put that food on the table because Sam treats you so well!' She took Mary's arm and started from the kitchen. 'Say good night to your father.'

'Wha d'ya mean good night?' he muttered. 'Too early go to bed. Just got off work. Just got home f'Chrise sake.'

'Mary, go to bed,' the woman said.

'I said no,' the drunk at the table shouted.

'It's bedtime and she has school tomorrow!' the woman shouted back.

'I just got home!' He pushed himself away from the table and lunged for the girl. She pulled away and he fell across a chair. Chair and man went crashing to the floor. Mary and her mother screamed at the same time.

17

'Get your doll and get to your room!' the woman shouted. The woman picked up the doll that had remained seated in the doll's highchair next to the table and shoved it at the girl. 'Go! Now!'

Her father staggered to his feet. His face was beet red and the fall seemed to have sobered him a bit. 'I said it's early! Mary, you stay here with me!'

'It's time for her bed!'

'I said stay with me!'

Mary looked from one parent to the other, equally frightened as they stood glaring at each other. Her mother nodded and she started toward the door. The man grabbed her with both hands and swung her into the air. 'I said stay here and God damn it, when I say "stay here", you stay *here*!'

'Mama!' Mary screamed as her father swung her high above the floor. 'Mama!'

Her mother hurried to the man and started beating on his back. 'Put her down! You're going to hurt her! Put her down!'

'Wha?' Feeling the pounding on his shoulder blades he turned around, trying to see, like a dog trying to catch something tied to it's tail, what was happening to him. The sudden turn swung Mary and she collided with her mother. The woman grabbed for her child, caught her, and the man released her sending mother and daughter reeling across the room, falling against the sink board, then sliding down onto the floor. Mary was screaming, her mother was moaning and crying from the pain.

'Now you can go to bed!' her father shouted and pulled her up by her hair. Mary hollered in agony mixed with terror. 'Go on!' he yelled. 'Mama's precious little jewel! Get your skinny ass out of here! Get it to bed!'

Mary could barely make out his outline through her tears. 'Here!' he shoved her doll into her arms. 'Take this damn thing with you!' She was staggering towards

18

the door when she heard the swooshing sound; then she heard the noise his open hand made as it caught her on the side of her head and sent her sprawling into the hallway. It didn't really hurt until she was halfway across the living room. Then, it was all she could do to find her bedroom, make it inside and shut the door.

She sat in the middle of the floor feeling the stinging against her ear and could still hear the roaring sound inside her head. She cried until she saw that her doll had also been hurt. The doll was worse off than she was. The doll had fallen on her face and had lost some paint off her nose. Mary forgot about her own pains and worried about her doll's. Even though her chest still heaved with the force of her sorrow, she soothed and calmed her doll.

Because the kitchen was on the other side of the house and because Mary had shut her bedroom door and because her mother had become used to this and deliberately kept herself from screaming out each time her husband hit her, Mary didn't hear much of anything until her mother's muffled sobs came from the other side of the wall that separated the two bedrooms. Then she heard the front door slam. She knew her father had left the house. She guessed he was headed back to Sam's. He had sobered up enough from the food and the beatings he had given out. Sam would serve him more booze. In spite of the sounds her mother was making, the little girl knew things would be quiet for the rest of the night. She knew that when she got up in the morning she'd find her father stretched out on the living room sofa, fully clothed and fast asleep. She knew that would be one more day of work he would miss.

'He didn't mean it,' she crooned to her doll. 'You were in the way. That's all. You got bumped because you were in the way.' She stopped and stared at the gaslight at the edge of the street. 'Just like I am,' she said slowly. 'In the way, just like I am.'

*   *   *

19

Jacob never got to see the Statue of Liberty. He liked to brag about it, in bars later, that he never set foot on Ellis Island with all those other 'im-grint bums'. His ship, the ship his parents had boarded in Hamburg, Germany, was called the Auslander and it's specialty was hauling furniture from Europe and bringing raw cotton back from the southern U.S. Now that the war between the states was over in America the ship was free to haul immigrants along with bureaus and chairs. The Leurens family bought passage in the upper hold. It contained two wide mattresses and a charcoal brazier screwed to the floor so it wouldn't spill the burning coals when the ship pitched into waves. The family was expected to supply it's own bed linen, it's own cooking pots and dishes and it's own soap and towels. The ship's commissary (actually one overcrowded room near the captain's quarters so he could keep an eye on the comings and goings there) had charcoal for sale as well as such staples as dried beans and peas, flour and rice, potatoes and dried meats, sausages, eggs, salt and cooking oil. The prices were outrageous but the immigrant passengers – many like the Leurens with small children – had to eat. They were told, when they paid for their tickets, that it was against 'international health regulations' to bring their own food on board. Water, as a courteous gesture on the part of the shipping line, was free.

The trip should have taken less than two weeks but a severe windstorm in the middle of the Atlantic set them back four days. During those four days everyone got seasick and three passengers died. The captain said a few words as each body was tossed over the side. When they got within two days arrival of the port of New York, the Morse Code operator took the message that another storm – this time on land – had closed down the docks and was sending waves up onto the loading platforms. The captain, wanting to unload his furniture in Norfolk anyway, headed south. When

20

they got to the Virginia coast, the storm winds had subsided and they docked without incident.

The passengers were unloaded along with the furniture. All of them had expected to land in New York. Most of them had friends and family waiting for them to clear Ellis Island. The captain didn't care. He had been paid to take them to the United States and that's where they were. So, everybody off.

The immigration officials in Norfolk weren't as careful as those in Manhattan.

'Last name?' the man in the dark blue jacket with the silver badge over his heart asked Otto Leurens.

'Leurens,' Otto replied haltingly in a phrase he had been practising for weeks. 'We are Leurens Family.' He paused, searching the man's face to see if he understood his English. 'We are from Badgastein. Badgastein in country of Austria. You know Austria?'

'Lawrence,' the man said and wrote on their entry papers L-a-w-r-e-n-c-e.

'I Otto Leurens. This is my wife Sonia. This is my son Karl. This my other son Wilhelm. This my last son Jacob.'

Jacob, the youngest at three years old, stood close to his mother's long dark skirt. His brothers, because they were older, seven and nine, stood a little further away and tried not to look worried. All the way over in the dark and musty hold of the Auslander they had been drilled on how to act when they came into the presence of this American who, quite literally, held their lives in his hands. Sonia had washed them all, thoroughly, before letting them get dressed in the clean clothes she had saved especially for this moment. She had trimmed their hair and dug under their fingernails. Their shoes had been rubbed with cooking oil to make them shine. She had combed her own hair and her husband's as well as brushing out his full black beard. She had scrubbed at his large hands but no amount of soap and water could ever get out the dirt in

21

those work-worn creases. Her husband's hands were nothing to be ashamed of, she told herself, he had always worked hard, had always put food on the table and a roof over his family's head.

The blue-jacketed official handed Otto the slip of paper he'd been writing on and pointed at an open door. 'Thank you. Thank you,' Otto mumbled as he shepherded his wife and three small sons in the right direction. Inside a large room were most of the passengers of the Auslander. A few of them sat despondently on one side, their heads in their hands. Others stood smiling expectantly in a line by a table. A large woman in a white jacket and the same kind of metal star over her heart motioned to the newly-named Lawrence family to approach her. On cue, they all smiled. Sonia had been told by someone: 'Make sure you smile a lot. Americans don't want citizens with sad faces!'

The woman cupped Karl under the chin, stared at his face, then moved her thumb so that it pulled up the lid of his left eye. She glanced at it, then pulled up the lid of his right eye. That done she picked up his hands, turned them over a couple of times and with a slight shove pushed him on to the rear of the room. Then Wilhelm went through the same procedure and finally Jacob. The woman looked in Sonia's eyes, put pressure on her jaws so she opened her mouth and then studied Sonia's hands. Next she took a stethoscope and listened to Sonia's heart.

Otto was next. Sonia held her breath as the woman stared at his work-calloused hands. All the other hands had been clean and neat. Would Otto be refused because of dirty hands?

'Looks like you're a hard worker,' the woman said. Otto kept smiling. He had no idea what the woman was talking about. She wrote something on the paper and handed it back to Otto. Then she pointed to the right side of the room. Sonia almost collapsed with relief.

Outside with their luggage, standing on a U.S. street

22

for the first time in their lives, a boy with a horse and cart offered to take them to a hotel where everyone spoke German. The boy himself spoke German. Otto and Sonia both agreed this was a most auspicious sign.

They stayed five days in the hotel, resting up from their trip and relaxing now that they had been admitted into America. They then left for Chicago. Otto had a cousin living in Chicago and he had written to them while they were still in Austria telling them they could stay with him and his wife – for a while – until Otto got a job and started making his own money. The cousin was a carpenter and worked steadily. Otto was a plumber, a joiner and a fitter of water and sewage pipes. Now that the war was over there was a building boom all across the U.S. Chicago, the nation's second largest city, was getting bigger day by day.

'Otto, I am trying to keep my voice down, but you must listen to my point of view!'

'I don't want every guy who works here knowing my business. Just bring me my lunch and go home. That's all I ask.' He tugged at the cover on the handled tin lunch bucket. 'That's all I ask,' he sighed.

Sonia sighed, too. 'This is the only place I can talk to you,' she said in a loud whisper. 'You know she listens to everything that's said in the apartment.'

'It's her apartment,' the man said. 'She has a right.'

'And I don't have a right?' She waited. 'And I don't have a right? I'm asking you, Otto, don't I have a right?'

'You have a right but you don't have a right to stir up trouble. It's not your apartment. The place is Cousin Mark's and his wife's. Not ours. I've told you that.'

'And I've told you I don't want to live there anymore. Not with her. I can't.'

'Sonia, she doesn't mistreat you. She treats you fine. Just like a sister.'

'Hah! Like a sister? Then I can't imagine how her entire family ever survived! You're not there all day. I am. I have to put up with her. You don't see any of it. You stay here ten hours a day and . . .'

'You think I like it here ten hours a day?'

'It's better than being *there*, with her.' Sonia shook her head. 'Otto, I can't take it any longer. You have to find us another place to live. For me and the boys.'

'And me. What about me? You don't care where I live?' He stopped munching on the sandwich and looked at her. 'It's not my home, too?'

'It's not anybody's home. Not for our family! It's a small apartment and it belongs to Mark and Katia and she doesn't let one hour go by without reminding me of it! I don't want to stay there. Not any more. It's bad for the boys. They feel the tension. They hear what's happening there.'

'So what do I do? Huh? Tell me what? I tell Katia she is a cow and we pack up and take the boys and go to live where? Come on,' he gestured with the half-eaten sandwich, 'Tell me where?'

'There's lots of places in Chicago. There's places all over the place. We could rent one. We could move out and have our own place.'

'I'm not making enough money for that,' he said keeping his voice down so the other men on the lunch break wouldn't hear.

Her voice rose. 'Not making enough money? You're making more here than you ever made in Badgastein and in Badgastein we had a *house* to live in! Not a piece of a box set on another box set on another box with stairs to climb and no grass to look at. I want my own things sent over, Otto. I want my brother to send me the stuff we had in our house. Send it over here so we can have a *home*. We don't have a home here. We have a corner in a piece of a box on top of another box. I can't even put my mother's bedspread on our bed. Katia says the colours don't look right with her curtains.'

'She's right,' Otto said simply.

'She's right and I'm wrong. That's what you're

24

saying? Katia, the woman who married your cousin is more right than me, Sonia, your own flesh and blood wife. That's what you're saying?' She glared at him. 'Yes, that's what you're saying. All right my dear husband, all right.' She started walking away from him, lifting her skirts to step over the lengths of lead pipes and the pots of sealing tar that were strewn across the entrance to the new building. 'You'll see what's right!' she shouted.

Sonia got back at Otto. Each night she got into bed, alongside her husband, wearing a man's long woollen under garment. She had triple stitched the flap on the seat, and the fly in the crotch and sewn up the front where there should have been buttons. She managed to wiggle into this body-stocking before he came back to the apartment each evening. She refused to get out of it and threatened to start screaming if he tried to tear it off her. After six long weeks of this, Otto told Mark he had rented an apartment for Sonia and the kids.

'We were counting on the money,' his cousin said unsmilingly. 'You know Katia and I were counting on the money you pay us for rent.'

'I'm sorry,' Otto shrugged. He didn't tell Mark about the nightly longjohns. 'It's better we have our own place.'

'But you promised us, Otto,' Katia broke in. 'You promised to stay two years and pay half the rent. Now you're going away? It's not even a year and a half yet. What are we supposed to do?'

Otto shrugged again. He hated confrontations. 'I'm sorry,' he said. 'It just seems better this way.'

'And after Mark got you your job and everything,' Katia continued. 'Without him, you would never have got that job. He went to the foreman, he and the foreman are friends. He gets you settled in a new country and in a new job and saves your hide from living in Austria and this is how you thank him?' She glared at Otto and at Sonia, who was leaning, listening, against the kitchen. 'My Mark gets no more thanks than that?'

'You want a thank you?' Sonia said, her features expressionless, 'So we'll send you a thank you note. With our new address on it.'

The next day when Otto went to work, the foreman told him he wasn't needed any longer. A new man had been hired in his place. When Otto started yelling that it was Mark's doing, the foreman just looked blank. 'I don't owe you no explanations,' was all he said.

When he returned home, he found Sonia and the three boys on the front steps of the brownstone building. Sonia had been crying. The tears were dry but he could see where they had run down across the thin coating of powder on her face. She gestured to their packed suitcases. 'Katia did this this morning. She and her friend Marie Vrettas from across the hall. I go out for groceries and when I come back. . . .' She shrugged. 'The valises on the steps. The kids on the steps. The apartment lock changed.' She pointed to a door key that had been tossed into the gutter. 'It won't work in the new lock.'

'I lost my job,' was all he could say.

'I know,' she replied. 'Katia yelled it to me from the other side of her door. She said you deserve it. Your cousin Mark got you fired.'

'I know,' he said and sat heavily on the stone front steps.

That afternoon, with their luggage and their three kids around them, they sat waiting for the 8:32 train for Milwaukee. There was a lot of building going on in Milwaukee. It was just a few hours to the north. Besides, there were a lot of German-speaking immigrants there; someone had told them that you heard more German on the streets than you did English. The train fare wasn't that much. It would have cost about the same to rent a hotel room for them all for the night. And it was away from Mark and Katia. That was the real plus in Milwaukee's favour.

That night as the train rattled upward along the shores of Lake Michigan, most of the passengers in the car fell asleep. The three boys were curled up on the seat opposite their parents, exhausted from the emotion of being thrown out of one place and the excitement of heading for another.

'Otto?' Sonia said softly. 'Here. Give me your hand.' She glanced across the aisle making sure the passengers over there were asleep. 'Here,' she repeated. 'Your hand.'

He put his hand in hers and she guided it up under her suit jacket. Then she moved it down, under the band of her skirt. He knew she must have unbuttoned the waistband on the skirt. His fingers touched warm smooth flesh.

'What's that for?' he asked.

'Don't you see?' she whispered and then giggled softly. 'The longjohns. They're gone.'

In April of that year, 1874, Jacob had turned six. So when September came Sonia enrolled him in first grade. She chose St Aloysius Academy for him as well as for nine year old Wilhelm. Karl, at eleven, wanted to go to public school so he 'could be with American kids'. His complaint was that at St Aloysius most of the pupils were children of immigrants and religion was stressed over 'useful things'.

Most of the priests and nuns at St Aloysius were German or Austrian and so most of the classes were taught with heavy German accents. The few Italian or Irish kids ended up speaking English as if they had come over from Hamburg instead of Sicily or Galway. Little Jacob spoke German at home with his parents, spoke German at school with the nuns and scattered German in his English with his schoolmates. Those formative years made such an impression on him that he never lost his accent, even though he had only been three years old when Otto and Sonia emigrated to America.

Jacob wasn't sure he liked school. The nun would slap his knuckles if he made a mistake and paddle his behind if he really caused trouble. Sister Berthudas taught music and she was thin and small, just a little bigger than most of her elementary age charges. She found it difficult to command respect and even more difficult to slap a ruler with enough force to make it felt. That's why she wore a heavy wooden cross with metal edges and a heavy metal figure on it. When a student acted up she grabbed her beads, bent back her body and let the Lord and His cross thump against the head of the offending child. The kids agreed it hurt twice as bad when you were hit by Jesus.

Otto hadn't found any difficulty in getting a job. He had gone around commercial buildings that were being put up and asked, in German, about work possibilities. The fourth place he went to, a shoe factory under construction, he was hired on the spot. It was a complicated plumbing job and he was one of several German-speaking fitters and joiners. The job took almost ten months to complete. By the time it was over, he had lined up another job, this time with a contractor who was puting up three-storied apartment blocks. The pay was good and none of it had to go to cousins.

They rented an apartment for several months until Sonia, at church, heard about a house that was for sale. The German who had started to build it had been called back to Germany to help settle his father's estate. While he was gone his wife, who had remained behind in Milwaukee, got the flu and, after just three weeks in the hospital, died of pneumonia. Their two small children were taken in by relatives and then sent back to Germany to join their father. He never came back to the States and the empty house, albeit uncompleted, was for sale.

Sonia and Otto went to see it. Both agreed it needed a lot of work. Some of the exposed wooden beams had started to decay and quite a bit of the poured concrete

28

needed replacing. But the main structure was sound and the neighbourhood was mostly European and growing, so after about four months of letters going back and forth across the Atlantic, Otto purchased the property and started fixing it up. When the first days of spring arrived, Otto kept Karl out of school to help him on the house. After all, the boy was almost thirteen and could do the work of one man. Wilhelm was almost eleven, and while Otto didn't take him from school he did insist he work almost every evening and always every Saturday on the project. Jacob, who was eight, carried nails, swept up sawdust and helped chip old concrete from bricks and paving stones. By the onset of the winter of '76, the house was ready to move into. The rooms hadn't all been wallpapered but the gas lines were laid (no more kerosene lamps to clean or candle drippings to peel away) and the water pipes went upstairs as well as down. Otto was proud that his house was the only house on the block that had a flush toilet and a bathtub upstairs as well as down. Because of his expertise, he was able to install the very latest contraption: an overhead toilet tank that would fill with water so when someone yanked the wooden handle on the metal chain, six gallons of water would come rushing down the tube, crashing into the toilet bowl, it's sheeer force shoving everything down the drain and leaving the bowl filled with fresh clean water. Sonia had to flush the toilets several times a day, in the beginning, so curious neighbours could marvel on how wonderfully they worked. The Lawrence's were pleased that being a plumber had its social value after all.

When the school year was over, in May of '77, Karl announced he wasn't going to go back in September. He would be fourteen by then and was too old for more schooling. Otto got him a job as a hod carrier and he started to work as soon as weather permitted cement to be poured.

There was no question about Wilhelm getting a steady job. He wasn't quite twelve and he liked school. He brought home good grades and was active on St Aloysius' baseball team: The Defenders. He didn't mean to change his first name but everyone automatically called him 'Willie'. Sonia held out the longest, not wanting to have him lose his last links with the Old Country. After all, her father's name had been Wilhelm. But she, too, started calling him 'Willie' and only when she got angry at him or wanted to impress her point of view did she revert back to 'Wilhelm'.

Jacob wanted to quit school. He didn't like it. He didn't like the nuns. He didn't like going to Mass every morning before classes began. He didn't like confession and he didn't like doing homework. He argued that he was almost as big as Karl (and he had grown within three inches of his older brother's height) and could do the same amount of work that Karl did. Sonia told him, in no uncertain terms, that it didn't matter if he grew as tall as the house: he was only nine years old and that hardly made him a man.

'I don't like to read,' he told her. 'I shouldn't have to read if I don't want to.'

'I don't care,' she replied. 'I have to do lots of things I don't like to do. You don't hear me complaining, do you?'

'No,' he admitted, 'but you don't have to do what those nuns want all day long either. They're mean. They hit you for doing nuthin'.' He stared at her, wanting sympathy.

'Then imagine how they would hit you if you did "something",' she said. 'You're staying in school. Now go and do your homework and let me see it before you go to bed. I don't want to hear anything more about quitting school.'

'Life isn't fair,' he said as he grabbed his schoolbooks and started for his room. 'It isn't fair.'

His mother didn't even glance up. 'Nobody ever said it was.'

And it wasn't.

Two years later Sonia, exactly like the woman who

had planned to live in that house, caught the flu. She kept at her work for a few days and then finally fell, exhausted, into bed. Otto went to see the doctor and he ordered the hospital horse and ambulance to come at once. In a hospital bed, the verdict was the same as for the original lady of that house: pneumonia.

'I want her to get better and come home, Sister.' Jacob said to Sister Berta who was sitting before him. 'I don't want her to die in the hospital.' Tears welled up on his lower lids. 'I don't know what we would do if anything happened to her.' The tears slid silently down his cheeks.

The nun took out a handkerchief and wiped his face. 'Jacob, it's times like these that try our faith. Do you believe in our Lord?' He nodded. 'And do you believe in His mother the Blessed Virgin Mary?' He nodded again. 'Then talk to them about your mother, they will do everything in their power to make sure she gets better and comes home soon.'

She stood up and took him by the hand. They walked down the school corridor and went into a room that was the nuns' own chapel. Jacob had never been in there before and he looked around at the statues and the benches and the stained glass and the burning candles. 'Come on,' she said, 'down here in front.'

She motioned him to kneel on the padded rail before the altar. Directly in front of him was a marble pulpit with a cross of gold sunk into it. If he raised his eyes higher, and craned his neck back, he could see the statue of Our Lady. She was all in white with a blue robe and a crown of gold. In her arms, she carried a bouquet of red roses made of plaster.

'You talk to her,' the nun said in a soothing voice. 'You tell her what you told me. She'll listen and she'll help. You'll see.' She patted him on his head and he heard the sound of her long skirts moving away from him. Then he heard the door close. He was all alone with Our Lady.

'Oh blessed Virgin Mary,' he said and made the sign of the cross. 'My mother is in the hospital. She's sick. The doctor says she has pneumonia. People die from that. They die from that all the time. Please Lady,' the tears started welling up again, 'don't let her die. I don't want her to die. She's my only mother. I love her. I don't know what I'd do if she died.'

He moved backward just a bit. He wanted to get a better view of the lady he was talking to without having to crane his neck. She didn't look directly at him, but gazed out over the empty chapel with painted blue eyeballs and a painted red smile. 'Sister Berta told me that if I asked you you'd save her. The doctor told my father last night that he couldn't do anymore for her. He said it was out of his hands. Please Virgin Mary ask God, ask Jesus' father to save my mother. Her name is Mrs Sonia Lawrence and she's in St Mary's Hospital, room number one sixteen. Please save her. Sister Berta told me you would. She promised you would. And I'll do anything,' he swallowed hard as he said this, 'I'll do anything you want if you save her. You want me to study harder, I will. You want me to stay in school, I will. I'll go to Mass every Sunday and if you want me to volunteer to be an altar boy, I will. Please don't let her die. You can save her. Sister Berta said you could. Please Virgin Mary, I have faith in you.'

When he got back to the house, the living room was full of neighbours. Mrs Baumgartner rushed over to him and grabbed him and hugged him and started crying. He thought she was saying 'I'm so sorry, I'm so sorry.'

At the funeral, Jacob sat with his arms crossed and stared at the priest. He hated that man up there in the white robe and he hated that other man hanging there on that cross. They strung Him up, they killed him? Good! He deserved it. He gives promises and then doesn't keep them. He makes sure people give Him money and crawl on their knees to Him and tell Him everything and go without meat on Fridays and then He doesn't keep a promise. Then He doesn't keep a woman alive. He doesn't keep a poor mother alive. Oh sure, you have to bow down to *His* mother and kiss *her* gown and repeat *her* name over and over again in the Rosary. He makes you do that. But He didn't let His *own* mother die. He just took her straight up into Heaven. She rose up off the ground and went through the clouds and arrived in Heaven. He could do that for His *own* mother but He couldn't do it for *Jacob*'s mother. And this was a mother who worshipped Him and believed in Him and made her kids get up every Sunday and go to church because *He* was supposed to be there. The Romans nailed Him on a cross and then, like dummies, let somebody roll away the stone. Hell, they should have chopped His body into little pieces and burnt them and then tossed the ashes into the sea! That way, they would have made sure He was dead. He should have been killed dead and not have been able to get up again. Just like He let Jacob's mother die and didn't lift a finger so she could get up. Some Saviour! Some phoney! Some lie!

And Jacob never went to church again.

'And I'm not going to school anymore, either,' Jacob confronted his father. 'I don't need all that shit they teach there. I can read and write and do my numbers and that's enough. I ain't going.'

'How old are you?' his father put down the glass of whisky and stared at his youngest son.

'Fourteen,' the boy replied. 'I'll soon be fifteen.'

'Already?' the man shook his head and shakily picked the glass back up. 'Your mother wanted you to finish.'

'Well, she's not here.'

'I know,' Otto said and drew more of the whisky into his mouth. 'I know.' He shook his head, trying to clear the fog that had been inside it ever since Sonia had been pronounced dead at the hospital. Sometimes the fog clouded over his eyes and made everything blurry. Sometimes it settled on his tongue and nothing tasted right. Sometimes it grew heavy, so heavy, and pressed down around his shoulders and his heart. Sonia had gone. The whisky had taken over.

'And you drink too much,' the boy said.

'That's okay,' Otto replied. 'It'll be all right soon. Your mother didn't think you should quit school. She wanted you to grad-u-ate,' his words were slurred.

'Karl and Willie didn't graduate,' Jacob insisted. 'She let them quit.'

'Thass was diff ... difference. Thass was big differ ... Oh, hell, I gotta piss ... Gotta get to the ... Gotta piss real bad ...' He managed to push himself up out of the overstuffed armchair and as he took a step he stumbled over the small table beside the chair sending his glass and the half-empty whisky bottle crashing to the floor. 'Oh, shit! Look what you done!' He lunged for the bottle to stop it draining into the wool carpet. 'Look wha you done and I gotta take a piss ...' He fell over onto the floor and lay unconscious. As Jacob watched, Otto's urine soaked out of his trousers and into the threadbare carpet on the floor.

Jacob never went to school again.

'Hey Lawrence!' the foreman shouted at him. 'I thought I told you to get that pile of stuff out of the way!'

'You did,' Jacob replied carefully. 'I was going to do it as soon as I cleaned the brushes.'

'The brushes can wait. We're gonna be cartin' door frames through here and we can't have that pile of junk in the way.'

'Yes sir.' Jacob shoved the dirty paint brushes back into the bucket. He didn't mind picking up the mound of shavings, paper, ends of lumber and rags. It was easier and cleaner than getting paint out of those wide wall brushes. He positioned the empty wheelbarrow and as he reached toward the pile he stopped to examine his hands. They were dirty from several different colours of paint, and were calloused where the early blisters had formed, broken and reformed until the skin thickened over those spots, they were also full of tiny scars that had been caused by nail points, sharp edges and removed slivers and they smelled like turpentine.

Jacob's father Otto didn't work hardly at all since his drinking had worsened. The housing complex where he had been employed when Sonia died was completed a month or so after the funeral and Otto went looking for other jobs. In the beginning he found some, then they found he was drunk most of the day and he got fired. Nobody wanted a drunk hooking up their sewer lines. He sat – or lay – around the house, occasionally doing some plumbing for one of the neighbours. There were a few rare stretches when he went without a drink three or four days. Then he would take his plumber's box and go from door to door offering to do odd jobs. But then he would stop at the saloon on the way home, spend most of what he earned on booze and be lucky to find his way back to the house by midnight.

During the first weeks Jacob lay awake in bed waiting to hear him stagger into the house and stumble up the stairs and collapse into bed. Then the boy would go to sleep. After a while Otto took to sleeping on the sofa in the sitting room and then, when the weather turned warmer, he'd fall asleep on the front porch. More than once Jacob got up to see where his father had fallen. After awhile, he didn't care.

'Let the son of a bitch sleep in the gutter!' Karl told him. 'He's older than you are, don't worry about him.'

'Right,' Willie added, 'not to worry. One day he'll get real drunk and wake up dead. That's not your responsibility.'

'But I have to live here,' Jacob argued. 'You guys are

going to be gone and I have to stay here with him. He is my responsibility! You walk out and leave me all alone to take care of him!'

'It won't be for long,' Willie said. 'As soon as we get there and get our first couple of paychecks we'll send you the money. We promise.'

'And Papa can take care of himself,' Karl added.

'Remember Bubbala,' Willie smiled at his youngest brother, 'We are your family. We won't forget you.'

'No, Jacob,' Willie assured him, 'as soon as we get settled we'll send for you.'

The olders boys had told their father they were going to California but he had forgotten about it, so when he awoke from the sofa that morning and staggered into the bathroom he was surprised to see his sons' beds were empty. He splashed water on his face, scowled at how grey his dark beard had become, scratched his crotch and clumped downstairs. He knew Jacob had the coffee pot on, he could smell it.

Jacob was packing his own dinner box. He nodded to his father but didn't look directly at him. He didn't want the old man to see that he had been crying. No one would see that. Not even Karl and Willie. He had got up early with them, had taken coffee with them and stood and waved from the porch as the horse-drawn dray took them away to the train station. When they were out of sight, he sat on the steps and let the tears flow. They were silent tears making no sound as they ran down his cheeks.

Otto looked at the table, set for just himself. 'Where are the other cups?' he asked.

'They had their coffee earlier.'

'They did?' Otto looked at his son. 'They go to work early this morning?'

Jacob shook his head. 'They went to California. To Sacramento.'

'Oh.' Otto sat down and reached for a piece of bread. He stopped. 'To Sacramento? Karl and Willie?' Jacob nodded, his face turned away, still intent on packing his dinner box. 'Come on,' Otto grinned, 'why'd they go to work so early? I thought they couldn't do anything until this afternoon when the cement floor dried.'

'They quit that job yesterday,' Jacob said evenly. 'They took the train from Union Depot.'

Otto put down the bread, untasted. 'They quit that job? That good job they quit? I don't believe you.'

'So don't,' the boy replied. 'But it's true. They told you about it.'

'Oh, no,' he shook his head. 'They never told me they were going to quit that job.'

'They told you last week they were going to go to California and get a job. They told you there was lots of work in the State Capitol.' He put an apple in with his sandwiches. 'I was right there when they told you.'

'I don't remember nothing about California!' Otto shouted. 'Don't tell me I was told when I'm telling you I wasn't!'

'I'm not going to argue with you, Papa. They told you and I heard them tell you and now they're gone.' He snapped the round lid onto the box. 'That's it.'

'That's nothing! That's what it is. Nothing! Those two worthless whelps! Running away. Leaving me all alone here to take care of you!' He got up from the table and stood there deciding whether to go to the train station or not. 'What time did they leave?'

'Before sun up.'

'They they're gone.' He sat back down.

'Yes, Papa, they are gone.'

'And for money?' Otto asked, his hands starting to tremble with the realization of this news. 'What are we supposed to do for money? Those worthless boys gave us money to run this house. Now what? You know it's difficult for me to work. You know how hard I try but what with my illness and all . . .'

'I know about your "illness",' Jacob answered. For the last six months Otto had been blaming his condition

37

on a strange interior malady. It wasn't the booze it was 'the illness' that kept him home most days, 'the illness' that forced the boys to support him with their small salaries. 'They will send you money when they get situated,' Jacob said.

Otto snorted. 'And when will that be?'

'Willie knows a man who has promised to put him on a work gang when they get there. Both of them, Karl too. It'll take about a month for them to get settled but when they do, they'll send enough money to keep you.'

'They told you that?'

'Papa, they told you that. Last week. Right there in the sitting room they told you and you agreed.'

'I don't remember.' He shook his head, trying to clear it. 'It's the illness,' he said slowly, 'you know what tricks it plays with me sometimes.'

Jacob picked up his dinner box and headed for the door. 'Anyway, we'll be hearing from them soon and they'll send money. We won't starve. We still have my salary.'

'The salary of an apprentice?' Otto snorted. 'How long can we live on the salary of a "pick up boy"?'

'We won't starve.' Jacob replied. 'It'll be enough for food until they start sending.'

'Enough for food, maybe, but I have to have more than that. I need money to take care of . . . my illness. You know what happens if I don't have a drink or two to steady things.'

Jacob could see already, this early in the day, that his father's hands were starting to shake from 'the illness'. He opened the back screen door and brought himself up to his full size as a man. 'I'll take care of you for now,' he said. 'I'll see you have what you need until Karl and Willie start writing.'

But the letters never came. Months went by and neither father nor little brother ever heard from Karl and Willie again.

* * *

It ate away, deep inside him, that his brothers had abandoned him. He thought they had been close; they had been a family when they came from Austria and continued to be a family in the United States and were a family even after Sonia died. But only for a few months until Otto caught 'the illness'. Then everyone grew up at the same time. It was like watching daffodils in new March sunlight. One day they were stalks, the next day they were blossoms. Then they developed their seeds and they were gone.

That spring and summer of 1884 was the longest stretch Jacob could ever remember. He'd get up in the morning, check to see where his father had fallen the night before, make coffee, pack his dinner box and go to work. Each time he cleaned a paint brush or pushed a wheelbarrow or held a two-by-four while a carpenter cut it, he hoped it would be the last time he did that particular job. He knew that when he got home there would be a letter waiting for him from California and the letter would have money for his father, money for his train ticket and an address to head for. But each evening there was no letter. In his alcoholic haze, Otto berated his worthless older sons, berated them for abandoning him to the care of little Jacob. Berated them for not writing, not sending any cash and for not honouring their mother's memory with at least a note telling him they were all right.

Every Friday evening, Jacob would pull his salary out of his pocket and put it on the kitchen table. Then Otto would separate what the house needed for food, what the coal bill and the water bill would be, and put the rest into his own pocket. There was never anything left over for Jacob.

The worst night was Thursday. That was the night before payday and Otto often had spent everything. Then Jacob was accused of being a rotten son, the ne'er-do-well who couldn't get a decent job that paid, who didn't care enough about his own father to try a little harder. Otto would wander around the small house, rubbing his grey beard, muttering through his stained teeth and unconsciously opening and closing his dirt-creased hands.

Jacob started holding back a dollar for Thursday nights. Just a single bill to place, unseen, on the sitting room floor or Otto's dresser or the bathroom sink. He'd let Otto discover it and then sigh with relief as the man hurriedly slammed the screen door as he almost ran to the local saloon.

Then, around mid-August, Jacob started putting two dollars away. One for Thursday night and the other for himself. He had been given a raise, a whole dollar more a week, and hadn't told his father. By the end of September he had six dollars saved, by the end of November fourteen dollars. He kept the money in the pocket of a dress that belonged to his mother. The dress hung in the bedroom closet, the same bedroom Otto hardly every slept in. All Sonia's clothes hung exactly where she had last put them before they took her to the hospital. Otto never touched them, didn't even want to look at them, but refused to sell them. Jacob knew it was the safest place in the house to hide things.

It was especially cold that first week of December. Milwaukee was always catching icy hell from the winds off the lake but this year the winds seemed to have edges honed in a knife sharpener. The house was cold. There was no coal.

Jacob didn't even attempt to take off his dirty coat or the torn work-sweater under it. The house was freezing, almost as cold as the uninhabited house he was helping to build. 'They didn't come again today?' he asked his father.

Otto shook his head. He was curled up on the sitting room sofa, wrapped in a patchwork quilt Sonia had made. There was an almost empty whisky bottle beside him. 'I waited,' he slurred, 'but they didn't come. All day I waited and they . . . didn't come.'

40

Jacob glanced at the front window to see if the red and white sign was still in it, the sign to let the coal company know they were to stop and fill the coal bin. 'Did the sign fall down today or what?' he asked.

Otto shook his head again. 'Don't think so,' he said slowly. 'Isn't it there?' He managed to turn his body far enough to see the cardboard hanging in the window. 'Yes,' he smiled, 'it's there. Didn't fall down. Can't fall down. There's a nail. It's hanging on a nail.' He blinked his eyes several times and smiled. 'I put that nail up there. Did you know that? I did. I put that nail up there because your mother wanted it. "Hang it right there", she told me and I got a nail and I put it there. That's why I know it's there,' he managed to turn again and stare at the sign. He took a swig from the bottle. 'That's how I know.'

Jacob glared at his father and started for the door.

'Where you going?' the man asked.

'To the coal yard. Maybe there is somebody still at the place. Maybe they can still deliver some here tonight.' He angrily slammed the door and almost ran down the street.

'Sign's in the window,' Otto said to nobody. 'On that nail I put there myself. Always been there. Where Sonia wants it. Sign's there.' He lowered his chin into the quilt and fell asleep immediately.

'Wake up!' Jacob was shaking him. 'God dammit, wake up!'

Otto opened his eyes quickly, startled by the unexpected movement and yelling.

'Why didn't you pay them?' his son shouted at him. 'Why did you do that?'

'Wha you talking 'bout?' Otto needed some time to form his words.

'The coal money!' Jacob shouted. 'The man at the coal yard told me you didn't pay for the last two loads! He showed me the books.'

41

'I paid,' Otto said lamely. 'I paid.'

'You didn't!' Jacob yelled. 'He showed me the books. You should have given them the money when they delivered the coal and you didn't. That's why they don't stop anymore!'

Otto tried to get off the sofa but the quilt was tangled around his body. 'I paid,' he said loudly. 'The man's a liar!'

'You're the liar!' Jacob heard himself say and for a second he stopped. He had never used such language with his father before. Never mind. 'You're the liar!' he said again. 'I gave you the money to pay for the coal. Both times! You didn't give it to the driver. Now they won't deliver until those two loads are paid for! What did you do with the money? Where is it? In your fat gut? Is that where it is?'

Otto kept trying to rise. 'Don't you talk to me that way! I'm still your father and don't forget that fact!'

'Oh, shit, how can I ever forget *that*?' Jacob yelled. 'I gave you money for the coal and you drank it up. You did, didn't you? Isn't that what you did with it?'

'I don't owe you no explanation,' Otto yelled. 'What I do is my own business.'

'Not with my money you don't do what you want,' Jacob was near tears but refused to let them flow. 'And the money I gave you yesterday? For the load they were supposed to deliver today? Where's that?' He grabbed his father and started shaking him. 'Where's that? In the bar? Long gone, too?'

Otto struggled to get out of the clutches of this quilt which seemed to have engulfed both legs and the arm he didn't use to tilt the bottle. 'I'm going to thrash your ass!' He yelled. 'Don't you touch your father!'

'You are shit! Old man, you are shit! And I am sick unto death because of it!' He turned and ran toward the staircase, knowing he couldn't look at that drunken old man on the sofa without wanting to kill him.

'Come back here,' Otto shouted. 'You come back

here and apologize to me! I'm your father and I deserve . . .'

Jacob sensed it coming at him rather than actually seeing it. He stepped to one side and the empty whisky bottle sailed past his head and struck the wall. It didn't break but fell with a thud onto the uncarpeted part of the floor. The boy ran for the bottle, grabbed it by the neck and ran back to the sofa. 'You're an old shit!' he screamed. 'I'm sick of you! I'm sick! Sick! Sick of you!'

With each word 'sick', he brought the heavy glass bottle down against the side of Otto's head. Then he threw the bottle across the room. It hit a door frame and shattered. He ran upstairs, threw open the door to his mother's closet and found the dress. He yanked the dollar bills from the pocket and stuffed them into his own pocket. He ran back down the stairs. As he headed for the front door he stopped – just for a moment – and looked at the man sitting on the sofa. His eyes were closed, there was blood coming from his ear and he wasn't moving. He didn't know if his father was dead or not. He didn't care. 'Old shit!' he said aloud, then ran from the house and into the dark December night.

Occasionally when someone would ask Jacob why he came to Minneapolis he would shrug and say 'That's where the train stopped.' And it was almost true. He had run from his father's house all the way to the train station, his vision blinded by tears. His heart pounded in fear: the police would soon be after him for the old man's murder. He wasn't sorry he had hit him. He was only sorry that maybe he would get caught and be put in prison, or worse, be deported back to Europe. He had almost forgotten Austria and the little town and the inconvenience of life over there. He spoke English better than anyone in the family.

As he ran, he tried to block out the thought that kept forcing itself into his mind: his father was dead . . .

But that blood-stained, grey-haired lump sitting on the sofa hadn't been his *father*. It had been the corpse of a stranger, the man who had come into the house and taken over the day of Sonia's funeral. His father had been a good, kind and hard-working man. Although he had been strict, the boys had realized that this was for their own good. The man who had returned to the house after the funeral although he looked like his father had been a different person, a drunk, evil man who had destroyed the family. This stranger had had to die.

He got to Reed Street and ran across it and into the railroad station waiting room. There weren't many people around at that hour. He could see a train outside, on the track, and could see a few people standing beside it, talking to passengers who shouted from open windows. He stood in the waiting room, looking for a ticket-seller, but all the windows were shuttered. He needed a ticket. To *anywhere*! The train gave a blast of it's whistle. It sounded shrill even inside the station. Then a puff of steam gasped loudly out from under the engine. Jacob dashed across the waiting room, sped through the doors, ran across the wooden platform and jumped up onto the steps of the passenger car just as it began to move. He stood there for several minutes, outside in the black coldness, and watched as the lights of Milwaukee got fainter and fainter and until all was blackness around him.

A half hour later he was sitting inside in the softness of the car. Two small wood-burning stoves – one at each end – kept it warm. Small glass bulbs glowed with a strange reddish light from the ceiling and on the wall between the seats.

A uniformed conductor came into the car and chanted 'Tickets . . . tickets . . .' from seat to seat until he got to Jacob.

'I don't have a ticket,' he explained. 'All the seller's windows were closed in the station.'

'Where are you going?' the man asked.

Jacob took a deep breath. 'How far does this train go?'

'Minneapolis.'

'Then that's where I'm going.' The fifteen year old boy reached into his pocket for his dollar bills. 'I'm going to Minneapolis.'

'Another one?' The priest looked up from the papers on his desk. 'That's four this week.'

'Yes, Father,' the large man in the tight-fitting policeman's coat replied, 'I know. I brought them all in myself.' He beamed as if he were telling of a successful hunting trip rather than patrolling his beat in the back alleys of the city.

'Do you have a name, boy?' the priest asked.

'Jacob. Jacob Lawrence.' His voice was low, almost a whisper.

'Speak up, boy,' the policeman prodded him. 'The Father wants to help you.'

'I don't need any help,' the boy said. He tried to keep up his bravado, his defiant attitude, but now seeing this priest confused him. He was positive when the cop shook him awake that he was going to be taken to the station and booked for the murder of his father. Instead, he was taken through the back door of a church and told to take off his cap in the presence of a priest. 'I'm perfectly capable of taking care of myself.'

'I'm sure you are,' the priest said. 'Where did you come from?'

'From Austria,' he answered automatically. Americans always wanted to know what part of Europe foreigners came from. He could never figure that out.

'Don't lie to the Father,' the policeman admonished. 'There ain't no train service from Austria to Minneapolis.' The priest smiled, wearily. 'I found this stub on his person, your Grace. It's for a railroad ticket from Milwaukee to Minneapolis. Dated yesterday.'

'So you came from Milwaukee?' the priest asked. Jacob nodded. 'I have a good friend at St Mary's in Milwaukee. Do you go to his church?' Jacob shook his head. 'Are you Catholic?' Jacob shrugged then nodded. 'What church do you attend in Milwaukee?' Jacob shook his head. 'None? You don't go to church?' Again, Jacob shook his head. 'Too bad,' the priest added.

'Lawrence,' the cop said. 'That's an Irish name, isn't it?'

Jacob glared at him. 'It's Austrian,' he said firmly. 'We came from Austria!' He had seen enough Irish immigrants in Chicago to know he didn't want to be mistaken for one of them. 'The name was something else before it was changed,' he admitted. 'It wasn't always Lawrence.'

'Oh?' The priest was interested. 'What was it then?'

'I don't know,' Jacob said, 'I was only three.'

'Certainly your mother and father must have told you the real name,' the cleric said. 'It must be on your papers.'

'I don't know where my papers are,' the boy replied, 'and my mother is dead.'

'I'm sorry,' said the priest.

'So am I,' replied Jacob with a glance of hatred at the large wooden Christ on the wall.

'But your father,' the man insisted, 'where is he? Back in Milwaukee?'

Jacob was about to tell him and then stopped. Maybe that was what this was all about. A trap to get him to confess that he had killed his father. Someone must have found the body by now and the neighbours must have told the Milwaukee police about Jacob and everyone must be looking for him. Well, he wasn't going to do their work for them. 'My father went back to Austria. Last week. He was in bad health and he decided to go back. So he did.' He paused. 'He left me and I came here.' He stared at the priest's face and then looked directly into the policeman's face. If they suspected he

46

was lying, he would read it on their faces, it would be reflected in their eyes.

'I'm sorry to hear that,' the priest said. 'There's no use sending him back to Milwaukee if there's nobody there to take care of him.' The officer nodded. 'Take him over to Mrs Ginert and tell her to make a place for him. 'Boy,' he spoke directly to Jacob now, 'go with the officer and he will show you where you will live for a month. The lady runs a respectable Catholic boarding house and she'll give you a dry place to sleep and warm food to eat. The church will take care of you for a month over there. After that, you'll be on your own.'

Jacob took a deep sigh of relief. They didn't know he had killed his father. 'Fine,' he said.

'Do you have any money?' the cleric asked.

Jacob shook his head.

'He don't, your Grace,' the policeman said. 'I only found a dollar and some coins in his pocket.'

'You'll have to get a job,' the priest said. 'There's lots of work here in this city for a young man who's not afraid of it.'

'I'm not afraid of work or anything else,' Jacob said. 'I can survive on my own.'

'I'm sure you can.' The priest put on his professional smile and reached into a desk drawer. 'Here,' he said holding out his hand, 'take this and wear it. It'll protect you and guide you and make you remember your Lord.'

Jacob looked at the small cast metal crucifix. 'I don't need this to remember the Lord,' he said. 'I remember him and everything he's done for me quite well.'

'Spoken like a good Christian boy,' the priest said, 'but wear it anyway and keep in good health. I expect to see you at Mass next Sunday.' He smiled and went back to his papers. The officer took Jacob by the arm and started toward the door.

'Don't you have something to say to the good Father?' the policeman asked.

Jacob smiled, turned in the doorway and looked at

the black-robed priest. 'Fuck you,' he said softly.

The officer bristled. 'What was that?'

'I said "thank you",' Jacob was still smiling. 'Why? What did you think I said?'

Mrs Ginert, a small middle-aged woman with enormous breasts, showed him his room. There were four beds in it. His was the one farthest from the door. She explained where the bathroom was, what times meals were served and how he was to behave while in her house. She reminded him that everyone who lived there met early on Sunday morning and marched as a group to 7:30 Mass. After they had taken communion and the service was completed, they returned as a group for breakfast and readings about the lives of the saints. The church would pay to keep him with her for a month.

After she left him alone, he closed the door and quickly took off his pants. Then he reached for the soiled handkerchief that he had stuck to the inside of his thigh with chewing gum. Damn, how that thing pulled at his skin! He unfolded the cloth and took out the bills. He looked at the wad. There was over two hundred dollars in large bills. On the train, during the night, he opened the pocketbooks of the two elderly women who slept in the seats across the aisle from him. It had been pure luck that these two were carrying so much money. He only took part of what they had so if they opened their purses while on the train they wouldn't get suspicious. They got off hours before Minneapolis, never checking their handbags even once.

Jacob put a couple of the bills into his trouser pocket, then neatly folded the rest into the handkerchief. He unclasped the safety pin Mrs Ginert used to keep the doily fastened to the back of the one chair in the room, and pinned the handkerchief to the inside of his trouser leg. Then he put his pants back on, walked down the stairs and out the door.

As he crossed the street, he dug into his pocket and

took out the metal crucifix the priest had given him. 'And fuck you again!' he said, and threw it away. He laughed aloud. He was rich. He was free. He was going to make it without his father and without his brothers and without the Goddamned church. He was going to make it! He laughed aloud again.

'I don't know why you don't move in with us,' Jack Brannigan said. 'It's sure cheaper than where you are.'

'I'm happy where I am,' Jacob smiled. 'Anyway, one of you probably snores and I'm a light sleeper.'

'We don't snore! Either one of us.' Carl Sontag laughed. 'Now maybe the sounds of creaking mattresses would keep you awake, but not our snoring.' He signalled and the bartender refilled their beer glasses. 'It would help us out. Come on.'

Jacob shook his head. 'I don't want to live with anyone. Not my father and not my brothers and not you two.'

'But you're not rich!' Carl protested. 'You make the same money we do and we can't afford to live alone in one room all to ourselves.'

'There's some of us that are special,' Jacob said with a smile. 'Some of us that don't need to do what everybody else does.' He grinned at them. All three were still teenagers, all three had no family and all three needed each other. Except Jacob didn't need them when it came time to going home at night.

'It'll only cost you four dollars a month,' Jack said. 'The rent is twelve a month for the whole place. Come in with us and we can save you the money you're paying now. Didn't you say you were paying ten a month just for yourself alone? Well, hell we could save you six whole dollars a month! That's a lot of money!'

'I agree,' Jacob said, 'but I can manage it.'

'How?' Carl demanded, 'You make the same thing we make. *How* can you manage it?'

Jacob shrugged and then smiled. There was no way they were going to know about his two hundred dollars. He bought some clothes, lived alone and managed every penny of it very carefully. By working during the day and playing poker for dimes and quarters almost every night, he had managed to keep his cache at almost the original two hundred dollar amount. If he told them – or anyone else – about it then he would have to tell them how he got it. And that he wasn't about to do.

'Are you sticking it to the landlady?' Carl grinned. 'Is that how you're paying your rent?'

Jacob laughed. 'If you saw her, you wouldn't ask. She looks like a lizard! Skinny and with no behind and big ugly eyes.'

'But at night with the light out?' Carl nudged him. 'Who can see then? A lot can happen in the dark.'

'With her,' Jacob laughed again, 'it could never be *that* dark.'

'Well, it seems damned strange to me that you stay there all alone. Must be another reason.'

'I just like to be alone. Isn't that permitted in this town? Can't a person live alone if he wants to?' He motioned to the bartender. 'My God, I'm seventeen years old! I'm not a baby.' The bartender came with the pitcher of beer and filled their glasses. 'I had enough living with people. I'll never never live with anyone else again.'

'And a wife someday,' Jack said. 'Someday there'll be a wife and you'll have to live with her.'

'When that time comes,' Jacob replied seriously, 'she'll have to live with *me*.'

There was another reason he didn't want to share his living quarters with anyone – not just for the stolen money – but for what was happening around him. The strange things that bothered him. The strange things that happened only at night when he had blown out the bedside candle and had pulled up the covers.

It was a low rasping sound, like something being dragged across the wooden floor. It came from the far corner, came toward the bed, crossed the small braided rug next to him and then went under the bed. The first time he heard it, he sat straight up pulling the covers to his chin. It startled him. It was a low sound, not high-pitched, a low sound that only gained in strength by the time it crawled under his bed. Yes, 'crawled', that was how he felt about it. It didn't scratch or slide, it – the sound – somehow 'crawled'. He tried to explain it to himself but couldn't and he sure as hell wasn't about to try and explain it to anyone else. No sir, this noise was *his* secret.

He never heard the sound during the day. Sunday was his one free day, the one day he didn't have to report to the construction site. Yet that day, all that day and through Sunday night, there was never a sound. Everything seemed normal. Whatever 'normal' was anymore.

The third time he heard the sound he had been ready for it. He had a match and a striking surface ready. The sound came out of the darkness and he rose up, and struck the match and instantly there was a chasing of shadows in his room. The sound stopped. He shook the match out, lay down, pulled the covers up to his chin and waited. There! The sound started again. Once again in the far corner. He sat up, grabbed for another match, struck it, there was the sudden light and the sound stopped. He lay back down, waited, the sound came, the match was lit, the sound stopped. Useless. Whatever it was, was smarter than he was. It didn't want to be seen. The hell with it, he thought. If it doesn't like light, then it'll *get* light. He struck another match and lit the candle. Then he got out of bed, placed the lit candle in the far corner where 'it' was and then got back under the covers. He glanced once more at the corner and the candle, then pulled the blankets over his head and fell asleep.

He thought about it the next day while he carried the

51

heavy wooden hod full of cement from the mixing trough to where it was to be spread. The sound had strarted in the corner, made that 'crawling' sound across the floor yet even as it passed over the rag rug it still made that identical sound. The rug should have softened the sound or at least changed it, yet the sound remained the same. Then it got louder as it came nearer the bed, then it stopped as it got under the bed. He would look under the bed when he got home that night. He had planned on doing that this morning but he overslept and didn't have time. He'd do it tonight. Maybe there was a rat hole under there. Maybe that's all it was, a very smart rat who avoided light and who had the same right to live in that room as he did. Jacob wasn't afraid of rats. He told himself he wasn't afraid of *anything* anymore. For his seventeen years he had gone through a great deal and he was afraid of nothing. He had seen his mother buried. He had been abandoned by his brothers. He had *killed* his father! He had taken a train all by himself. He had robbed two old ladies. He had arrived in a strange town all alone and had found a job all alone. He had found a place to live on his own and he had told Jesus *and* the Catholic Church to go to Hell! No scurrying rat was going to frighten him after all that.

There was no hole under his bed. There wasn't even a loose plank. Jacob stared at the tightly nailed boards. He scratched his head. 'Now how in the hell did he manage to disappear like that?' he wondered aloud. He pushed the bed farther from the wall. The small porcelain wheels groaned. He got on his knees and searched along the siding. There must be an opening there – somewhere – where the rat was able to squeeze through. He ran his hands along the skirting board. It was nailed tight. He checked the plaster above the skirting board, maybe it was loose and there was a hole underneath the wall paper. But there was no hole, no opening, no escape for 'his' rat.

That night the sound came again. Jacob was ready for it. Instead of lighting a match he crouched on top of the bed, and waited for 'it' to get close enough. When he heard the sound just at the edge of the mattress he thrust down a hand, and grabbed something soft and mushy. He shouted gleefully. He rolled over, struck a match with his free hand and lit the bedside candle.

He noticed the stench before the candlelight showed it to him. It oozed through his clenched fingers, small pieces dropping onto the blanket he had to sleep under.

'Shit!' he shouted. And that's what he had. A fistful of warm, reeking, human faeces.

There was no more 'crawling' after that. It was as if it wasn't necessary to frighten him, to concern him, to disgust him any longer. He still awoke every night, listening to sounds that weren't there. It had taken him almost three days of washing with lye soap to get the smell from between his fingers. Often at lunchtime, when he raised a sandwich to his lips, he imagined he could still smell that excrement under his fingernails.

He never stopped to rationalize that it was impossible for a handful of shit to manifest itself in an unoccupied corner and to come scratching and slithering across a floor and to squish between his fingers when he grabbed it. Jacob didn't analyse. He didn't talk it over in his mind. He just accepted it.

'Nice place,' she said and shivered slightly as she let her long skirt fall to the floor. He nodded and watched as she put the skirt with her blouse and shoes cn the one chair by the window. 'I knew a girl what lived in this neighbourhood,' she went on, 'over by the street-car barn. You know? That was a nice place, too. How much rent you pay?' She didn't wait for an answer. 'Hard to get places with one room like this anymore what with everybody looking for space.' She sat on the edge of the bed, wearing just the white cotton top and white cotton bloomers above her black stockings. 'Lived here long?'

'We came to America when I was three.'

'No,' she laughed, 'I mean here in this place. In this room.'

'Oh. About a year. Yeah, just about a year now. Came here from ...' He was about to tell her 'Milwaukee' but decided it wasn't really a whore's business where he had come from.

'It's three dollars,' she said not smiling now. 'In advance.'

He still had his trousers on and reached into a pocket and brought out three silver dollars. He preferred them to paper money. It felt like he had something when he heard the silver clink. He put the coins into her hand.

She started slipping off her bloomers. 'Put the candle out,' she said with a smile. 'It's better in the dark.'

He bent over and blew out the flame. The small furnished room became lost in dark shadows. He unbuttoned his trousers, dropping them on to the floor. He was excited and he stood there, extended, waiting for her to tell him what to do next. Then he felt her hand on his bare leg. It was tugging. He moved toward the bed, felt the edge of the mattress against his skin, reached out to steady himself and then climbed up there with her. He stretched out his hand and could feel her. That was a leg. That was her belly. That was a breast. The other hand started feeling now, tracing in the first hand's path of discoveries.

'That's nice,' she murmured. 'Just keep it nice and gentle. You do this often? Bring girls here?'

'Not often.'

'Such a nice boy, you are. Don't you have a regular girl?'

He shook his head, no, but then realized she couldn't see him in the dark. 'No. I don't have a girl.'

'I'll wager lots of girls would like to be your lady

friend,' she said. 'That's right. Right there. Uh. Huh. Yeah. Lot's of girls would give their eye teeth for a young steady beau like you. Not too fast, now. Yeah. That's better. You have a job?'

He wished she'd just shut up and let him do it to her. 'Yeah. I do.'

'In what? Oh. Yeah, like that. Just like that. In what? I mean, what do you do? You're not a banker, are you? Uh. Huh. Uh. I would like to do it with a banker sometime. If he kept his vest on. That's the only way I'd want it done. You know what I mean?'

Jacob didn't answer. His muscular legs were too busy pumping up and down for him to stop and make conversation.

'That friend of mine, you know, Judy? The one that was with me when you stopped to talk to me on the corner? Well, her. She once went with a banker and he took her into the bank building. Really! It was after hours and all and she told me they did it on sacks of money. Instead of a mattress, they did it on money bags. Do you believe that? I don't know if I do or not. When she first told me about it, I said "Oh come on Judy . . ." Hey! Go easy! I ain't made of iron, I ain't! Calm down a bit, buddy! There. That's better. Anyway, I said to her "Judy, I find that whole episode perfectly difficult to believe." I did. I told her. But it is an exciting way to do it. Don't you think? I mean, right there in the bank and with all that cash! I had another friend. . .'

Jacob stopped moving. 'Could you just stow the gab?'

'Whatd'ya mean?'

'Just be quiet. Shut up while I'm doing it. That's what I mean.'

'Well! I didn't come with you to be insulted, you know. I have some rights, too. Ain't I supposed to get any enjoyment out of this?'

'No. I am.'

'Oh, really? Mr Big Shot in diapers! Mr Astor in a rented room! Oh, really?' She moved under him suddenly, trying to roll away but his body held her down. 'I don't have to be insulted, you know!' She pushed at him, trying to force him off with her hands. 'I'm not some piece of beef you buy and bring home, you know!'

'Shut up!' he said loudly. The extra movement excited him and he worked the muscles of his legs faster.

'I won't shut up! Get offa me you big dope! I've had enough!'

'Well, I haven't!' he said loudly. 'I ain't finished yet.'

'You are as far as I'm concerned!' She was shouting now. 'You want your three dollars back! You can have 'em! I ain't the kind to be insulted!'

Jacob raised himself up on both hands, feeling the energies mounting up inside him. In just a few seconds, he would be ready. He kept pumping. Just a few more times, he could tell. He was about ready.

'Let me up! You son of a bitch, let me out of here!' She pounded on his chest, trying to reach his face but the spread of his shoulders and arms blocked her punches. Then she howled. 'Ow! God damn! What are you doing? Hey! Jesus! Wh... the hell... Ow! Stop it! Please... Oh, please stop it! You're hurting me!' She started to sob. 'Not my face! Please don't hurt my face! Not my *face*!' She was sobbing heavily now. 'Oh my God. Not my face!'

Jacob raised his head, stretched his neck, clenched his teeth and made one last final plunge into her body. Then he stopped, relaxed his legs and arms and fell slowly on top of the girl. Exhausted.

She rolled his body off of her and managed to get to the edge of the bed. 'You bastard!' She shouted. 'You bastard!' Her hands groped on the bedside table for the box of matches she had seen him use. She found them, struck one and lit the candle. She grabbed the candleholder and hurried with it over to the mirror that hung above the dresser. She peered into it, holding the candle closer for a better look. She screamed. 'You bastard! You worthless bastard! Look what you did to my face! Why?' She was screaming through her sobbing sounds. 'Look! Just look!' She hurried back to the bed, holding the candle close to her face 'Look!' she screamed.

Jacob raised himself up on one elbow. She was holding the candle near her face. He could see them, the deep X marks cut into her cheeks were now filling with blood, and the straight pins that stuck out from her cheeks at all angles. 'I didn't . . .' he said. 'I didn't do that.'

'You did this to me!' she shouted. 'Look at me! Why did you do that? I *need* my face! What did I ever do to you! I mean, *why*?'

'I didn't,' he said. 'I didn't do that. I mean, I couldn't have done that. My hands were . . . were on the bed. I didn't do that to you. Honest.'

'Now what am I gonna do?' She was still hysterical and she sat on the edge of the bed, pulling the bloody pins from her face and rubbing the marks that were starting to puff up. 'I need my face. In my line of work, you gotta have a nice face. Look what you did. Oh, my God, why did you do this to me? Why?'

He put his arm around her but she shook him off. 'I didn't do it,' he said. 'My hands were on the bed. I *couldn't* have done it. I . . . I . . .' he stammered.

'Well, then *who*?' she screamed. 'Of course, it was you! Who the hell else if not you? Huh? Tell me!'

'But it wasn't me,' he insisted. 'I had both my hands . . .' He started feeling sorry for her as he watched the blood start seeping from the cuts and stream down toward her chin. 'Believe me,' he said, 'it was not me.'

'Then who else, you son of a bitch? Who else is in this room? Who?'

'I'll take one more,' Jacob said.

'Just one? Whatta you got?' the large man dealing the cards looked up quickly.

'You'll find out,' Jacob smiled. 'Just give me one more card.'

The single card spun across the rough-hewn table, landing face down in front of the eighteen year old boy. He picked it up, smiled ever so slightly and put it in place with the other cards in his hands.

'I've seen that look,' thought another young man at the table, 'I'm folding,' he said aloud.

'Me too,' another slightly older man said and he put his cards down on the table.

'Just you and me, Jacob, me boy,' the large man said. "Whatta you go? I'm callin'."

Jacob eyed him seriously. 'You really want to know?' The man nodded. 'Well then, Bucko, look at this royal flush.' Jacob broke into a wide grin and spread all those colourful face cards in front of him. 'I win,' he said. 'Again.'

'Again!' the large man snorted. 'That's the fifth time in a row. I've finished. No more money on me. You know, my lad, I can't afford to play cards with you. You've got the luck of the Irish or of the Devil. I don't know which.'

'Well, I'm not Irish,' 'Jacob grinned as he pulled the pile of silver coins toward him, 'I'm Austrian.'

'Then it must be of the Devil,' the older man snorted. 'I never saw anyone with your kind of luck.'

'Well, it sure isn't from the Virgin Mary.' the other young man laughed. 'I know how Jacob feels about luck from *that* side of Heaven!' and he laughed aloud.

'Amen!' Jacob laughed with him. 'If I've any luck at all, it ain't Irish and it ain't from any of the saints. It's gotta be from the Devil.' He laughed again.

'I don't think I'd be taking the Holy Virgin's name in vain like that,' the large man said, not smiling at all. 'Playing a good game of poker is one thing but talking against Our Holy Mother is quite another thing.'

'She may be *your* mother,' Jacob grinned, 'but she ain't mine. I don't claim anybody in that family: father, son or mother. If the Devil gets the credit for my winning ways,' he stood up, the coins bulging in his front trouser pocket, 'then more power to him. At least, I don't have to go to his church on Sunday and give some of this to him. The Devil don't ask anything of me. He just lets me win.'

'That's blasphemous talk!' the large man scowled. 'You'll get in trouble for it.'

'From who?' Jacob was still smiling. 'From the priests! Shit! They don't have anything to do with me! I'm my own boss. I make my own rules. If I listened to them, I wouldn't have *this* now,' and he patted the coins in his pocket. 'There'd be a rosary there now instead of silver dollars if they had their way.'

'You shouldn't be blasphemin' like that, anyway,' the large man admonished. 'No good can come from it.'

'This is good, isn't it?' Jacob jangled the coins.

Two hours later, Jacob returned to his furnished room, weaving slightly from the effects of the three pitchers of beer the four men had consumed. There was a full moon illuminating the shabby furniture as the young man leaned toward the dresser. Not bothering to light a candle he took his billfold from his back pocket and put it on the dresser top. He took his comb from the other back pocket along with a white handkerchief. Then he reached into his front pocket for his night's winnings. Had to be at least seven dollars in there. Hell, that was almost a month's rent. If he kept up his lucky streak, maybe he wouldn't have to work at all.

His fingers dug into the collection of hard metal and closed around the coins. Then he felt them move. They squirmed in his hand. He let out a yell, brought his clenched fist out of his pocket and flung whatever it was that was in it in the direction of the window. 'Ahhh!' he shouted, starting to yank at his belt buckle and the buttons on his fly as his trousers suddenly became alive with squirming life. As he kicked at the trouser legs in an attempt to get them off his body, he could see thick white maggots crawling out of the pocket. Maggots crawled in the window curtains and the wooden floor in front of the window. Maggots! Dozens of them. More than he had thrown. Maggots doubling in number, reproducing in front of his eyes. Maggots filling the floor space between himself and the wall. Maggots tumbling out of his pocket, dozens and dozens of them. Maggots crawling toward the dresser, toward his bed, toward *himself*. He shouted again, something wordless and without meaning, but a shout of pain, a shout for help. Still they doubled in number, still they came at him, the floor white with them, the window covered with their fat squirming slippery bodies.

He started moving backward, back toward the door. He bumped into the bedside table and the sound of the candlestick falling over brought him slightly out of his panic. He groped for the candle, then for the box of matches that was always beside it. The maggots continued in his direction, the floor and rag rug now covered with them. He grabbed a match, struck it and found the candle wick. It took a second to catch, but it did and as it did he held the flame over his head, sending light into the far corners of the room.

The maggots had vanished. They were gone. It was as if they had never been there.

Jacob sat on the edge of the bed and started to shake. He put the candleholder on the table and pulled himself up onto the bed. He started to cry, cry and shake, with the unexplained terror of the moment just passed. He put his hands over his face and pulled his legs up, curling his body like a ball. The candle continued to burn for the remainder of the night.

'Now when they get here, don't become crazy,' Carl Sontag shook his finger at Jacob. 'No filthy stories and no tall tales. You promise?'

Jacob grinned. 'I promise, but this girl had better be a real tomato if you want me to be extra-special.'

'She is,' Carl said. 'Jeanette's the nicest girl I've met since coming to Minneapolis. And wait'll you see her hair! A funny kind of red. Like a fire that's just about to go out. You know, deep like glowing coals.'

'Sounds like you're on fire already and this is only your first date with her!' Jacob laughed, 'Take it easy, my friend. Don't let her rush you into something you'll be sorry for tomorrow.'

'She's not going to do any rushing,' Carl said. 'If anybody does any rushing, it'll be me. I've wanted to go out with her ever since I saw her at church. It's taken me almost three weeks to find a girl who knew her and who would introduce me to her.'

'And the other girl is going to be my date for the afternoon?' Jacob asked, even though he knew the answer. 'This messenger of yours is supposed to make me happy.'

Carl took out his comb and ran it through his short blond hair one more time.

'You look fine,' Jacob smiled, 'just like the willing suitor in the magazine drawings.'

'Don't laugh,' Carl said quickly, 'this could be serious. I think I'm in love.'

'Oh, God,' Jacob grinned, 'you haven't even met the girl and already you've got a ring to buy and a priest to pay! Maybe she won't like you. Did you ever think of that!'

'Can't happen,' Carl grinned, 'I'm irresistible.'

'I don't know about that,' Jacob answered, 'I've been places with you where the girls have resisted you. That one brunette who slapped your face over by the railroad station. Remember her?'

'Well, I was drunk. Anyway,' he shrugged, 'that was only going to be for the night. Jeanette is for the rest of my life.'

'The only thing certain for the rest of your life is

shitting,' Jacob said, 'and you don't even do that unless you eat regularly.'

'Now that's what I mean,' Carl shook his finger in Jacob's face again, 'that kind of talk. Don't do that in front of the girls. Especially Jeanette.'

'Okay. I promise . . . maybe.'

Carl was about to continue the lecture when he glanced toward the door. 'There they are! See them? The two girls in the white dresses?' He stood up and waved. 'The one with the red hair. That's Jeanette.'

'I kind of figured that,' Jacob said. 'And the dark haired one is mine.'

'Please be good,' Carl said worriedly.

Both boys were now standing, watching the two teenage girls pick their way around the chairs as they headed for their table. The ice cream parlour was crowded, as always, on a Sunday afternoon. It was the place for the young set to gather even though many adults worried that such open public meetings would lead the new generation into immorality. If a girl started eating ice cream in full view of everybody, where might it end up?

Jacob was against these ice cream parlours, too. He thought it a terrible place to meet a girl. A guy couldn't move in on a girl in a joint that didn't serve beer or booze.

Carl almost fell over the chair as he pulled it out for Jeanette. 'My name's Carl,' he said quickly. 'Carl Sontag.'

The redheaded girl put out her white gloved hand and Carl held it reverently. 'I'm Jeanette Prosser. Pleased to make your acquaintance.'

'Likewise,' Carl said. 'Hello Louise. Nice to see you.'

'Thanks,' Louise smiled at Carl and glanced at Jacob. 'We can only stay a little while. Jeanette has to be back home early.'

'Sure,' Carl kept grinning at Jeanette, 'sure. We'll make sure she is.'

'And I'm Jacob Lawrence,' Jacob stuck out his hand, first to Louise then to Jeanette. 'Carl's good friend.'

There was a momentary silence which Louise interrupted. 'Jeanette's going to be a teacher, she's going away to college in September.'

'To Oberlin College,' Jeanette volunteered. 'That's in Ohio.'

'Going away?' Carl's voice raised again.

'To study music,' Louise said. 'Jeanette plays the piano and wants to teach it. To children.'

'This September?' Carl couldn't get over the bad news. 'That's just two months from now. This is already the end of June.'

'Carl is going to teach calendar reading,' Jacob said. 'To children.'

'That doesn't give us much time,' Carl said.

'For what?' Jeanette asked.

'To have an ice cream sundae,' Jacob replied seriously. 'It takes at least one month for Carl to make up his mind what kind of ice cream he wants and another month for him to eat it. By the time it's all gone, it's September already.' He laughed and the girls laughed and Carl glared at him. 'I suggest we place our order,' Jacob continued, 'or else we'll still be sitting here when they put up the Christmas decorations.'

Jeanette laughed but kept her attention on Jacob's face. She knew she had been brought there this afternoon to meet Carl (she had seen him at Mass and knew he had been asking abut her), yet this other young man was strangely interesting. 'I don't believe I've seen you around town, Mr Lawrence,' she said.

'Probably not. We don't travel in the same circles.'

'What high school did you attend?' she asked.

'None,' he replied.

'Jacob came here from Milwaukee. About a year or so ago.' Carl gave the information.

'Do you have family here?' she asked.

'I don't have family anywhere,' he replied.

'Not even in Milwaukee?'

'All the family I have is dead,' he said. 'Or should be.'

Louise sucked in her breath. 'Oh, my!.'

'Indeed,' Jacob said. 'My mother and father are dead. I have two brothers in California and, frankly, I don't care if they are alive or not.'

'You sound bitter,' Jeanette said, her eyes still on him.

'Not bitter. Just practical. A family can hold a fellow back. I didn't start to succeed in life until I got rid of mine.'

'And where do you go to church?' the red-haired girl asked.

'I don't,' he replied.

'Ever?'

'Never.'

Carl raised his hand and signalled to the white-aproned waiter. 'I think we better give him our order now,' he said, 'Jeanette has to get back early.'

'Nothing for me,' Jacob said, 'I have another appointment.' He got up from the small metal chair. 'Ladies, it was a pleasure meeting you both.' He smiled at them. 'Carl, see you tomorrow at work.'

'Why do you have to rush off, Mr Lawrence?' Jeanette asked and Carl thought he detected disappointment in her eyes.

'He is a very busy fellow,' Carl answered. 'Don't beg him to stay. If he says it's necessary to go, then it is.'

'Wise fellow,' Jacob said and patted him on he shoulder. 'They're all yours, Carl.' He tipped an imaginary hat at the girls and walked quickly from the shop.

'What a rude fellow!' Louise said.

'He can be, at times,' Carl agreed.

'Is he always that?' Jeanette asked.

'Rude and in a hurry?' Carl questioned.

'No, a bit frightening.' She shuddered.

Carl felt a new emotion surging up inside himself. It

64

felt like anger. 'Jacob is almost always impossible,' he said. 'He's fun for a little while but not for a long term. I try not to have a great deal to do with him.' He patted Louise's hand, yet his remark was aimed directly at Jeanette.

The next day, at the building site, Carl looked up to see Jacob coming in red-eyed and unshaven. 'What happened to you?'

'Nothing. Didn't get much sleep. That's all.' He looked through the supply boxes for the tools he would need that morning.

'You be okay?'

'Sure. Just need to wake up a bit.' He grinned. 'She was a nice girl.'

'Who?'

'The girl at the ice cream place yesterday.'

'You mean Louise? The one who was supposed to be your date?' Carl asked.

'No,' Jacob grinned. 'Jeanette. The one who was supposed to be yours.'

'You *did* startle me a bit, as a matter of fact,' she said. 'I didn't expect anyone to be waiting out here.'

'Trees are for waiting under,' he replied. 'And for getting out of the rain.'

'It's not raining. At least, not on this block and not in my front yard.' Jeanette wasn't happy that Jacob had been loitering around her parent's home. 'You could have rung the bell,' she said rather sharply.

'And your father would have answered it,' he replied.

'That's the way normal people do things,' she said.

'Nobody's ever accused me of being *that*,' and he laughed.

'Well, you'd better come in now.' She glanced back at the front porch where both her parents were standing, watching, from behind the screen door. 'Good thing I spotted you first. Mother would have thought you were a prowler.'

'You got my note?'

'I did,' she replied. 'I decided not to answer.'

'Why?'

'I told you. I'm going away soon. To college. I have lots of things to do to get ready.'

'And no time for boyfriends. New boyfriends.'

'No time for any boyfiends. New or old.' She blushed slightly. 'There aren't any old ones, anyway.'

'I'm glad,' and he reached out to touch her.

She pulled back. 'I really think you should come in. My folks will want to know who you are.'

'You can tell them who I am,' he said simply.

'I don't know anything about you,' she answered truthfully. 'We've only met once.'

'That was enough,' he said smilingly.

'Enough for what?' she asked and raised an eyebrow.

'Enough for me to know that I want you.'

Her face turned crimson and she was glad the gas street lights weren't bright enough for him to notice. 'I really don't know what you're talking about,' she said. 'I must be getting back inside.' She turned to go back up the sidewalk when she felt his hand on her arm. Her parents, still in the doorway, stiffened.

'I'll see you again,' he said.

'I don't think so,' she replied. 'I don't have the time.'

'Then make it.'

She stared at him through the shadow of the maple tree. 'That sounded like an order.'

'It was.'

'Young men don't give orders to young ladies they hardly even know.'

'I do.'

'Then you are very rude.' She turned her back to him and started toward the house.

'I'm many things,' he called. 'Only one of them is rude. You'll see.'

'No I won't,' she called back.

Her father stepped out onto the porch. 'Jeanette, is that young man bothering you?'

'No,' she replied. 'I can control him.'

'No she can't,' Jacob called.

'Then *I* can control you, sir!' her father started down the steps.

'No you can't,' Jacob called. 'Nobody can control me!'

'Get off this property!' the older man shouted. 'Stop bothering my daughter!'

Jacob stepped backward, into the middle of the quiet street. 'I'm off your property, now.' he said. 'But I'll not stop bothering your daughter because she's bothering me.'

'Father ...' Jeanette put her hand on the man's arm. 'It's okay. He's a friend of some friends I met through Louise. He's just a homeless boy. Don't worry about him. Please.'

'He's not coming in, is he?' Jeanette's mother called from the safety of the porch screen.

'No, he's not!' her husband replied loudly.

'Not tonight, anyway,' Jacob called. 'But I'll be back another night, Mrs Prosser, and then I'll come in.'

'That'll never happen,' Mrs Prosser yelled out.

Jacob laughed from the darkness. 'There's no such thing as 'never'. You'll see, I'll be back and when I come back you'll invite me in. That's for certain.'

'Over my dead body!' Mr Prosser shouted.

'That, sir,' Jacob shouted back, 'can be arranged!'

'Are you crazy?' Carl stepped in front of Jacob as he entered the building site. Jacob stared at him, uncomprehending. 'Are you crazy, or what?'

Jacob pushed past him but Carl grabbed his wrist. Jacob looked down at the boy's hand. 'Take it off,' he said quietly.

'I want to know what's the matter with you!' Carl

67

was shouting now. 'Louise and Jeanette came over to my place last night and told me what an ass you made of yourself in front of Jeanette's mother and father.'

'I didn't do anything to them,' Jacob said softly, 'so let go.'

'Jeanette said you loitered in front of her place like a common criminal and didn't try to ring the bell or anything and then when her father came out you sassed him and threatened him.'

'I didn't threaten him. He shouted at me and I shouted at him. That's all and now take your damned hand off my wrist. It doesn't belong there.'

'You're gonna get me in trouble,' Carl said loudly. 'Louise and Jeanette are my friends and I want to remain friends with them.'

'Go ahead. You can be friends with anybody you want.'

'Stay away from Jeanette!' Carl ordered and tightened his grip as his voice rose.

'She is none of your God damned business!' Jacob shouted and reached to unlock the boy's fingers.

'Jeanette is going to be my girl!' Carl was breathing heavily, hanging onto Jacob's wrist tighter than before.

'You're an ass!' Jacob twisted his body knocking Carl off balance. 'You don't own Jeanette! You won't ever have her!'

'And who will?'

'I will! Now get the hell off my arm!' Jacob's right hand went across and grabbed the fingers on Carl's hand. Carl tightened his grip. 'Son of a bitch! I said let go!' A glaze seemed to cloud over Jacob's eyes. 'You are not part of our plans!' he shouted and his fingers swiftly pried up Carl's fingers, bending them backward, bending them unnaturally. Three workmen heard the sounds of bones snapping and saw the expression on Carl's face as he fell to the ground, screaming in pain and holding his crippled hand. By the time the foreman managed to get Carl to a hospital, the boy was unconscious; his hand had swollen up into an enormous blue balloon of bruised flesh.

'You frighten me,' she said. 'You did from the very first time I met you.'

'Then what are you doing here with me now?' he asked.

'I don't know. I told myself I shouldn't be here, yet here I am.'

'You didn't tell your parents?'

'Oh no! They would never understand.'

'But you don't understand either?'

'No,' she shook her head, 'I don't.'

'Maybe it's love,' and he grinned.

'No,' she shook her head, 'I don't think so. From everything I've read about love, it should be different from this.'

'I just fascinate you,' he said matter-of-factly.

'Like a python with a small animal,' she said. 'I read about things like that in high school. One animal with power, the other animal frightened.'

'Yet the frightened one doesn't run away.'

'No. The frightened one knows it should but it's fascinated. So it stays.'

'And what happens to it?' he asked.

'It gets destroyed,' she said simply. 'But then you knew that.'

'Yes,' he replied, 'I knew that.'

'They had every right in the world to tell me!' Mrs Prosser stood in front of her daughter, barring her way up the staircase. 'You can't reproach them for 'snitching' as you call it. It was their duty as your friends!'

'Oh, mother, please.' Jeanette leaned wearily against the papered wall. 'It's late. I really need some sleep. I have many things to do tomorrow.'

'The reason it's late is because you were out till almost midnight with that awful Jacob person! If you had gone to the concert with your friends – as you *lied* to me that you were going to do – you would have been home over two hours ago!' The woman sat heavily on the carpeted stairs. 'Why have you started lying to us? You were always such a good girl.'

'Mother, if I had told you I was going to see Jacob, you would have had a fit. I thought it was easier this way. That's all.'

'Easier on who?'

'On you and father,' she replied.

'You keep your father out of this,' the woman bristled. 'He's in his room. He won't come out. He said he's heartbroken and can't face you. That's what he said and I believe him.'

'I've done nothing to break his heart,' Jeanette protested wearily.

'You went off with that awful boy after you lied to us and said you were going to the concert.'

'He's not such an awful boy. You don't even know him.'

'He insults your father and he breaks all the fingers of your friend Carl and you don't call *that* "awful"?'

'Father started the insults and Carl refused to let go so Jacob had to use force. That's what happened.'

'So much force that poor Carl's hand is still in a cast and doctors don't know if they set the bones properly or not and poor Carl lost his job over it. That much force was needed? He's not an "awful" boy? Really, Jeanette, we didn't raise you this way. We raised you to be a good girl.'

'Mama, I *am* a good girl. You did an excellent job raising me.' She gave her mother a light peck on the cheek. 'But I'm also a young woman now. I've graduated high school and I'm off to college soon and everything will be fine. I'm an adult now, mama, even though you still think of me as a child. I'm a big girl. I can take care of myself.'

70

'But you don't have any experience with men like this awful Jacob,' her mother insisted. 'You don't know what path he will try and lead you down.'

'Mama, I'm not going down anybody's path but my own. Jacob is different. He fascinates me. And I've done nothing with him to be ashamed of.'

'You've not . . .?'

'Mama! You raised me better than that!' Jeanette turned beet-red. 'How could you think. . .' she stammered.

Her mother relaxed visibly. 'Then let's go up and see your father,' she smiled. 'He'll sleep better if you stop in and say goodnight.' She stretched out her hand and as Jeanette took it they walked upstairs together.

Two weeks had gone by and they had managed to be together almost every day. She told her mother she had shopping to do for her college trip, then would meet him at noon near the building site. Often they held hands, always they talked, sometimes he gave her a light kiss on the cheek. Then she would run to a nearby notions store and buy some small thing she really didn't want but would at least be put in a store bag as proof to her mother that she really had been shopping.

Her father never mentioned Jacob. The man wanted nothing to do with this brash almost nineteen year old immigrant boy and didn't want his daughter to have anything to do with him either. He was from the school that believed once the child knew the father's wishes, the child should obey. Once both mother and child knew the father's wishes, it was up to the two of them to make sure his wishes were obeyed. If he was the voice of authority in his household, then there was no need to issue his commands but one time. It did no good to shout the same orders over and over. As husband and father, he was to be obeyed the first time. Not the twentieth.

Jeanette's mother fussed at her and pried at her but

never came out and actually told her she doubted Jacob was out of her daughter's life. Jeanette had been raised to be obedient and truthful and, so the woman reasoned, it would be a breach of the faith that had built up over the years between them to doubt – openly and vocally doubt – her daughter now at this age. After all, the girl had graduated from high school and was on her way to college. At that age, her mother recalled, she herself had been married and expecting her first child, Minna.

Minna had been a bit of a disappointment to the Prosser family. She had been pretty but not very bright. She hadn't been on the honour roll or active in school functions and never attended Mass regularly the way Jeanette had done. Minna had been bossy and argumentative. Jeanette had been the opposite. Minna had run with a 'fast' crowd. Jeanette chose her friends wisely. Minna wore shocking styles like red stockings that called attention to her ankles. Jeanette dressed the way ladies should. Both parents had yelled and threatened and punished Minna, but she did as she pleased. As Jeanette grew up, they saw she was different from Minna and gave thanks for it. Instead of forcing Jeanette to do their bidding (the way they had forced Minna and failed), they soft-pedalled their own wishes knowing, trusting, that Jeanette would have the sense to do the right thing without being intimidated into it.

About three days before high school graduation, Minna had run off and married (at least she married him, thank God!) a West Virginia dirt farmer who had come north to work in the factories. He was a good fifteen years older than Minna and they had a child right away (so who was counting the months?) and then another one and then a third one before he became discouraged with the low pay and the city noise and moved back to his pa's mountain farm. His pa died soon afterward and then not long after that he himself died, suddenly, out in the field. Minna buried him beside his pa and took over the farm. From the few brief notes the Prossers received (Minna didn't write very often or very well) they were sure she was coping and was being a success. Together, with Jeanette, they marvelled that a lone woman could handle those acres and those animals. Minna never wrote them about the passing strangers who helped her around the place. She couldn't pay them in cash but she could move over and let them share her bed. When she got tired of one, out he went and another came by to take his place. Minna ran the farm but it was always the way *she* wanted it run. Her parents were pleased that she had made something out of herself. Minna's neighbours could have told them exactly *what* she had made. Jeanette would be a success, too, the Prossers were sure of it.

'Bless me, Father, for I have sinned.'

The priest adjusted his robe that had bunched up under him causing him to squirm on the confessional seat. 'What did you do, my child?' He wished they'd either make the seats wider or let him wear just his trousers inside the confessional box.

'I had sexual knowledge with a young man,' the girl replied, barely able to control the trembling in her voice.

The priest yanked at the hem of his robe. 'How many times?'

'Twice, Father.' She shut her eyes expecting a lightning bolt to shatter the church roof at any moment.

He scowled because he was supposed to scowl, even though she couldn't see it. He couldn't see her, either. There was a red cotton curtain hanging over the slatted window. It kept out the smells of garlic and beer and cooked cabbage on the penitent's breath, but also muffled their voices making it difficult to hear those who insisted on whispering.

'Once could have been an accident,' he said, 'twice was deliberate.'

'Yes, Father.'

'Are you sure it was only twice?'

Only twice? She had sinned and he said 'only'? 'Yes, Father. Twice.'

'Do you plan to marry this young man?' he asked.

'No, Father.'

'Why?' His voice rose trying to show some interest. 'Is he already married?'

'No, Father.'

'Are you already married?'

'No, Father.'

'Then why aren't you planning to marry this young man? Is he not a . . .' and he paused for special sinful emphasis ' . . . not a Catholic?'

She raised her head now. Glad she couldn't see his face. 'He's a Catholic, Father, but he doesn't go to church.'

'But he *is* a Catholic?'

'Yes, Father.' The tears started now and he hoped she'd find a handkerchief. How he hated runny noses! 'He never goes to church but that's not the problem. My parents don't like him. They would die if I married him.'

'Do they know him?' He really didn't care, there was so much of this happening among all these factory people. 'Have they met him?'

'Sort of,' she replied. 'They've seen him. They haven't been introduced to him. If that's what you mean.'

'It is,' he sighed. 'Maybe if they met him and got to know him they'd change their minds. After all, he *is* a Catholic.'

'Yes, Father.'

'Are you . . . with child?'

'I don't think so, Father. It only happened this week. That's too soon to tell. Isn't it?'

'Yes, too soon. Did you use any . . . precaution?' Now *that* would have been a sin all by itself. All these new products on the market plus all the old-wives things girls were using nowadays. He had had a real education in birth control since coming to this parish. She didn't reply. 'Nothing?' Again no reply. 'Where did this happen?' he asked.

'In his room. Where he lives. He lives by himself.'

'He forced you into his quarters? Did you go willingly?'

'Willingly, Father.'

'Knowing what he had in mind? Knowing what would happen if you went with him?' Sometimes these stories got juicier as they went along. 'Knowing he had sinful thoughts on his mind?'

'Yes, Father. I went knowingly.' There was a silence while he hoped she would decide it was time to go. There were others waiting after her. 'I couldn't help myself. I knew what he had in mind, yet I was anxious. I'd never done . . . that thing . . . before.'

'You were pure before going with this young man?'

'Yes, Father.' The tears started again. 'Now I feel dirty.'

'Didn't you feel dirty after you went with him the *first* time?' She whispered yes. 'But not dirty enough not to go back and sin the second time.' This time she was silent. Didn't young people ever consider their actions until they completed them? 'Will you see this young man again?'

'See?'

'See. Yes. *Go* with him. Sin with him again?'

She shrugged. 'I don't know. I've thought about it. Part of me says stay away but the other part keeps pushing me forward.' She tried to imagine his face. 'You asked me, Father. I have to give you my honest answer. I just don't know.'

'You *are* honest,' he said, 'but you have also sinned. To repeat it would be piling sin atop sin. You *do*

75

understand that, don't you?' She murmured that she
did. 'It doesn't do any good for me to absolve your sins
here in the confessional if you go right back out and do
it again. You understand that?' He paused wondering
if he could catch a short nap before supper time. Had
to get these people in and out in a hurry. *Ego te absolvo
a pecates tuis.* God bless you. Go in peace.'

'Yes, Father.' She rose and her knees cracked from
the cramped position.

'You have made a promise to God. Are you aware of
that?'

'Yes, Father.' She opened her purse and took out a
handkerchief.

'Now go with God,' he said, hoping that when she
finally blew her nose, it would be out of his earshot.

'Thank you, Father.'

When she walked through the heavy front doors and
down the stone steps, she saw him. He was across the
street, leaning against a store front waiting for her.
She sucked in her breath, frightened at seeing him, yet
pleased he was there to comfort her after her ordeal.
What should she do? If she went to the left, she could
catch a streetcar directly home. If she went to the
right, she could be safely at the house of one of her
friends in a couple of blocks. She shook her head,
trying to clear it so the right decision could be made.
She wiped her eyes, put her hankie in her purse and
crossed the street to join him.

They had pulled the blinds so that the sunlight was able
to penetrate the small room only around the edges and
through some scratches in the green window shade
fabric itself. Jacob had often lain there, in bed, watching the sun struggle to enter the strange marks that had
appeared on the blinds. They had been newly installed
when he rented the room but now they were marked
with off-centre circles, small cubes, incompleted
crosses and squiggly lines that had no definite shape at

all. Jeanette had noticed them the first afternoon she spent there with him. She had asked him why his landlord didn't put in new shades. He claimed he could see meaningful symbols in those scratches but she just laughed and pulled him closer to her.

He was awake now after having dozed for a half hour or so. He had probably lost his job, this time. The foreman had threatened if he skipped any more afternoons he would be fired. Jeanette had stopped by at lunch time and she had looked so good and he had felt all those stirrings in his guts that he didn't give a damn what the foreman wanted. He had brought her back to his room, they had quickly undressed, had caressed, had kissed, had climaxed and had slept. He turned to look, and marvel at her long reddish hair spread out across the white pillowcase. Yes, she was beautiful and yes, she was worth all the trouble.

He put his own arm next to her arm. His was tanned from the outside work and the hairs on it had turned golden. Hers was of pale skin and so smooth it could have been velvet. She breathed steadily through slightly parted full lips. Lips that even in sleep were smiling, lips that were remembering how *his* lips felt on them. He let his fingers wander lightly across her face. She didn't even move. He smiled, wanting to kiss her, but instead got up carefully so not to awaken her.

He got up and stared down at her. For the first time in a long time, he was not alone. For the first time since his mother died, he had someone who loved him. She had *said* she loved him and she had certainly *proved* she loved him. Here it was almost time for her to leave for college and she had spent every afternoon with him. She told him she should be spending it with her parents and her other friends but she *wanted* to be with him.

He hated the idea of losing her to that school in Ohio. He knew there were boys there who would see she was pretty and would want her in the same way he wanted her. He doubted she would let them have her the same way she had let him have her, but he couldn't be sure. She was very pretty and she would be lonely away from him and she might give in. At least, her parents wouldn't be there to talk against him to her. But at the same time, he reasoned, they wouldn't be there to keep her from other boys, either.

'Don't let her go.' the voice said.

'What?' Jacob turned, startled by the masculine voice. But there was nobody there. The room was empty. Hell, he knew the room was empty. Just himself and Jeanette, that's all. 'They' . . . whoever 'they' were . . . were playing games with him again.

'Don't let her go to that school.' the voice repeated. 'Keep her here.'

Jeanette didn't stir. 'Get out of here!' Jacob whispered. 'I don't want you here! Not with her here!' He pointed to the sleeping girl. 'Please,' his tone was pleading now, 'please don't do anything. Just let me alone!'

'She'll go off to school, meet lots of new people and forget all about you. It happens all the time.'

'No she won't! She loves me! She'll wait for me or else I'll go there and get a job and be with her there. Did you ever think of that?' His voice rose slightly and Jeanette moaned in her sleep. He lowered his voice. 'Get out! I don't want her to know anything about you!'

'You'll tell her one day.'

'No I won't!'

'Yes you will, She'll find out about us. If she stays with you, she'll *have* to find out about us. Sooner or later.'

'No!' he yelled and Jeanette rolled over suddenly, opened her eyes and sat up. He hurried to the bed. 'I'm sorry,' he mumbled and started kissing her, 'I'm sorry I woke you. I must have been dreaming and had a bad dream. I'm sorry.' Oh God! He didn't want her frightened. He didn't want her to know about the voices. He didn't dare do anything at all that would make her leave him. She was the only thing in his life that made any sense. She was the only thing in his life, period. He needed her and he understood, at that moment, that he could never permit her to go away to school and leave him.

'I never thought I'd see you sitting in this room,' Mr Prosser said looking at Jacob and Jeanette side by side on the living room sofa. 'I should have taken care of you long ago, the first time I ever laid eyes on you.'

'Father, please!' Jeanette said. 'We didn't come here to argue.'

'No,' said her father, 'you just came by to tell us your life has completely changed.'

'For the better,' she added.

'Time will tell about that!' the man replied.

'And all those new things for school,' Mrs Prosser had stopped crying and was holding her damp hankie to her still red eyes, 'all those new clothes . . . what good are they now?' She couldn't look at Jacob. She tried to make her eyes focus only on her daughter.

'I'll still need them,' the girl replied. 'I'll have to wear clothes whether I go to school or not.'

'Until she changes them for maternity clothes,' Jacob said. His eyes rested cautiously, on the old man. 'They'll serve until the baby comes.'

'Oh,' Mrs Prosser moaned into her handkerchief, 'a baby! That's all we need.'

'No,' Jacob put in, 'that's all Jeanette and I need. To make us complete,' he added.

'There's no need to rush into having a family,' the older man said, 'you don't even have a job. Take your time about having a family.' He was still glaring at Jacob.

'That's been taken care of already,' Jacob said. 'Jeanette is pregnant.'

At this, Mrs Prosser let out another flood of tears

and Mr Prosser stiffened as if he had been instantly encased in concrete. Jeanette started to cry and didn't know if she should go to her father or her mother for comfort or stay beside her husband.

'That's why you did this so suddenly and so sneakingly,' the old man said. 'That's why it was a justice of the peace and not a priest!'

'I thought you wanted to be a grandfather,' Jacob smiled.

'I already am a grandfather. I didn't need you for that!' Prosser growled.

'No, but Jeanette did,' and Jacob smiled again.

'You just run off and get married,' Mrs Prosser whimpered. 'No priest, nothing. Just a peace justice and no flowers!'

'Under the circumstances, mother, we thought it was the best thing.' Jeanette said.

'Whose circumstances?' her father demanded.

'Ours and the baby,' Jeanette said. She rose and went to put her arms around her mother. The older woman stiffened. 'I couldn't have been married in a church,' she said, 'and in white. Not now.'

'So who's fault's that?' her mother cried.

'Mine,' Jacob said loudly. 'All mine!'

Her father exploded. 'You get out of here!' he shouted. 'Out! Out of my house! This is a terrible thing you have done to this family, a terrible thing and I will not have you in my house one more minute! God, how I wish I had a gun!'

'Father!' Jeanette shouted. 'Jacob is my husband now! I love him and you have to love him, too!'

'I don't *have* to do anything where this despicable cur is involved. I want him out and then we'll see about having this farce annulled.'

'I don't want it annulled,' the girl started crying.

'You want to be married to this piece of . . .'

'Yes. I do. Jacob is my husband and I *want* him to be my husband.'

'Then when he leaves you had better leave with him,' the man said quietly.

'When things calm down,' the girl said, 'you'll feel differently.'

'I'll never feel differently.' The man walked toward the staircase and the refuge of his upstairs bedroom. His wife was crying softly now. 'When your husband leaves this house, you will please leave with him.'

Mrs Prosser hugged her daughter. 'You come back for visits, you hear?'

'She will not come back,' the old man said, 'not as long as she is still married to that . . . that thing!'

Jeanette stared at her father and then at her husband. 'Jacob,' she pleaded, 'do something. Please!'

'Sure,' he said and he stuck the index finger of this right hand into the air and waved it at Mr Prosser. 'Here, old man. Fuck you!'

They lived in Jacob's furnished room for over a month until the landlord heard about it and told them they'd have to get out. He was running a house for single working men, not for wives and definitely not for children who would cry in the middle of the night and wake up the paying tenants. One glance at Jeanette's swelling belly told him that the peace in the place would be disturbed very soon.

Jacob had lost his job at the construction site and with some effort found another, a shoe store that was being remodelled. The pay wasn't as good as the other job had been but it managed to buy food and pay the rent on a small place on the other side of town. It wasn't the best building around, but it was reasonable and they rented to families with children. It took them a week to get used to the noise of the kids playing above them, running through the halls and shouting at stick-ball games in the street.

Jeanette stayed in the apartment all day, sewing baby things for the child on the way and wishing she could be a bigger help to Jacob than she was. With her high school diploma, she could have taken any number of jobs available but with her pregnant body and her constant morning sickness any outside work was impossible. Jacob assured her they would manage, and she wanted to believe him.

Jeanette had been going to a doctor regularly: she wanted to do all the right things for her baby. One afternoon she got off the streetcar and walked the five blocks to their tenement frowning deeply. She tried not to think about what the doctor had told her, to save it for Jacob when he came home. Maybe saying it aloud to him would take some of the shock from it.

'He said *what*? Hell, we can't afford that!' Jacob had barely put down his metal lunch bucket when she had told him, all at once in a stream without breathing, and the nineteen year old father-to-be looked worried. 'It's all we can do to pay for the delivery. A month in there before the kid is born? A month?'

'That's what he told me,' she said and she wanted to cry but she knew she should save her tears for later. 'He said that things didn't look good . . . whatever that means . . . and he thought a month's observation in the hospital would be the best thing.'

'A month!' Jacob rubbed his hand across the stubble growing on his unlined face. 'Does he know how much that's going to cost?'

'He said probably around two hundred dollars.'

'Where the hell am I going to get that kind of money!' He sat down on a kitchen chair. 'That's more than I make in a month. How come the hospital can charge us more than I make?' He looked at her. 'Did he say this was absolutely necessary or just something that he thought should be done?'

'He said it would be the best thing for the baby. Those were his words.'

'This damned baby of yours is costing me an arm and a leg.' He glanced at the kitchen cabinet, got up and walked over to it. He took out a brown glass bottle and poured himself a shot of rye whiskey.

'I wish you wouldn't,' she said, 'it's early yet.'

'Early hell, I just found out I have to come up with two hundred dollars. That sure as hell is time for a drink.' He tossed the shot back, then quickly poured another. He didn't offer her one. Jeanette didn't drink alcohol. He felt better as the brown liquid slid down and warmed his stomach. He stared at her, not speaking, for a couple of minutes. 'Well,' he said finally, 'I guess it's time to eat crow.'

She frowned. 'What are you talking about?'

'Your parents,' he said simply, 'it's time to go see them and be nice to them and ask for the money for the hospital. Maybe we should ask for three hundred dollars just to be on the safe side.'

She felt a sharp pain across her abdomen and didn't know if it was from the baby or his idea. She leaned wearily against the kitchen wall. 'We can't do that,' she said softly. 'Not after everything that's happened.'

'What's happened?' he said. 'Anyway, it's not "we" that are going to ask them, you are. The only way they want to see me, is stretched out in a coffin. But you are the daughter and you, they will help. After all, it's for their blessed grandkid.' He poured another shot. 'Yeah, that's what you'll do. Go over there and ask for three hundred and cry a lot and make them see their obligation to give the money to you.'

She held her position tightly against the wall. She was afraid if she tried to move her legs they would buckle under her. 'Jacob,' she said softly, 'I haven't seen my parents since that night they threw us out. That was almost seven months ago. Seven months!'

There was an ominous silence as Jacob eyed her. 'Ok, Ok, I wrote them a long letter three months ago and gave them this address.' He glared at her. 'I know you told me not to, but I wanted them to know how we

83

were. Anyway, they never answered. I never got the letter back, so I assume the post office delivered it.'

'Well,' he started out of the kitchen toward the tiny bathroom, 'go in person this time. They'll see you. Big and fat as you are, they'll have trouble throwing you off the front porch.' He laughed and slammed the bathroom door behind him.

'Oh Lord,' she said aloud, 'help me make him change his mind. Please Lord. I can't face my folks. Not now.'

The next day Jeanette took the streetcar downtown to her parent's home. She had carefully pressed her blouse and her maternity skirt. She would tell her folks she had no money but she wanted to look as if she had health and happiness in its place. The streetcar ride brought back sights and sounds she had forgotten, things she hadn't realized she missed until she saw them or heard them again. The ride was taking her back to a happier time, an easier time, and she felt like she was on a splendid vacation coming closer and closer to the love and affection of her childhood. Of course, she was going to ask them for money but she would see them again and they would hold her again and everything would be all right.

As she walked up the path to the front door, she noticed that her mother had taken down the hanging plants and the front porch swing. She frowned. Probably the swing was being painted. Her father had been promising for the last three years to paint the thing. She stopped and stared at the heavy lace curtain that hung behind the oval glass in the door. Her mother always had a sheer curtain there. Odd, she thought. She twisted the doorbell handle, patted her hair, smoothed her skirt and tried to calm the little jolts of excitement that coursed through her body. She smiled as the door opened.

'Yes?' the woman said.

'Oh,' Jeanette pulled back a bit. 'I was expecting my

mother to open the door. Would you tell her I'm here, please?'

'Your mother?' the woman asked.

'Yes,' Jeanette stammered, 'my mother. Mrs Prosser.'

'Oh,' the woman smiled, 'they don't live here no more.'

Jeanette reached out and steadied herself against the door frame. 'What . . .?'

'They moved. I bought the house from them'

'They moved?'

'Oh yes, about five months ago. I've been in the house at least four. Yeah, at least four months since I moved in.' She looked at the girl with the swollen belly. 'They didn't tell you? You're their daughter?'

'Yes, I am,' said Jeanette.

'And they didn't tell you they moved?' The woman stared at the girl trying to figure out why those nice people would have moved away without telling their own kin folk. She glanced at Jeanette's left hand. Yes, there was a wedding ring there. So it couldn't have been because of *that*. 'I'm sorry to be the one to tell you but they moved down to live with their daughter in West Virginia. I'm really surprised they didn't tell you. The way I understood it they only had but the one daughter.' She saw the girl's face drain of all colour. 'Here,' she said, 'you just come on in and let me make you a cup of coffee or something. Come on in. I don't know where my manners have been, keeping you standing out here and you with child and all that.'

When it came time for Jeanette to go to the hospital Jacob, of course, still hadn't returned from work. He was sometimes back at the apartment by six but there were days – more and more of them recently – when he didn't come back until almost midnight. He told her where he spent the time: at bars, drinking with his buddies.

She sent one of the tenement kids to the bar and he found Jacob there. The boy told him the baby was coming and he was to get an ambulance and bring it to the apartment building. Jacob had been drinking but not enough that he didn't sober up, slightly, get a horse-drawn ambulance and take Jeanette to the hospital. He had wanted to have a midwife come in so she could have the kid at home and save all that money but Jeanette's doctor was adamant. If he couldn't afford the month's rest she needed, he at least could come up with the money for a hospital delivery.

Jacob handed his wife over to the nurses, then took a hansom cab back home. It was too late and he was too tired to take a streetcar. He flopped, partially dressed, onto the double bed, his head ringing with sounds of horses hooves and a woman crying and nurses chattering. He closed his eyes.

'We're really pleased now!' the voice said loudly.

Jacob sat up, suddenly sober. He listened for it again.

'It's a girl,' the voice said. 'Just as we planned.' There was a laugh. 'A pretty baby girl that will grow into a pretty adult woman. Oh yes, we've been watching her for quite a while now.'

Jacob tried to rise from the bed but something held him down.

'What are you going to do?' Jacob called into the black nothingness of the bedroom. 'She's just a little baby!'

'Oh, we know that. We can wait.' The voice was fading.

'She's my kid!' Jacob yelled.

'Yes, but she's going to be our soul. You'll see.' The voice was fainter now. 'She's ours. You'll see.'

There were eleven babies in the hospital ward along with Mary. (That was what Jeanette had named her: Mary. It was in honour of – and an appeasement to – the Virgin Mary. Possibly Jesus would grant her marriage happiness if the baby was named after His mother.) Of the eleven, Mary was the least trouble, the least noisy and the least to need special attention. She slept most of the three days there, seemed to smile when she was taken in to nurse with her mother and slept even when the other babies were yowling their heads off.

As Jeanette left the hospital for the apartment, a nurse placed the wrapped infant in her arms and said: 'That child is going to be something special. You have truly been blessed.'

Jeanette smiled. She was about to go back to the tenement, back to uncertainty, back to Jacob. It was good to hear from someone that she had something to be thankful for.

Not that she didn't love the baby, because she did. She tried to analyse this love, this affection for a person she didn't even know, a love for a small bundle of skin and hair that had no personality, no past. If it had been a neighbour's baby (and God knows there were enough of *those* where she lived) it would have been just one more life. Yet it was *her* baby and because it was, the baby was a special person.

'A,' Jeanette said and placed the square wooden block in front of her small daughter. She waited while the girl searched the others. 'What comes next?' she asked. Mary scowled, her small hand clutching at different blocks and turning them slowly when she had them in her grasp, then she broke into a grin. She had found the next one. She looked at the mama and laughed aloud. She put the 'B' in place and then sat waiting for the praise that always followed. 'Wonderful! B! That's very good. What a smart three year old you are!' She gave Mary a quick kiss on the cheek. 'I'll bet there isn't another three year old in this town who could do that!' She grinned at her daughter, truly pleased that she was such a bright, exceptional, talented girl. 'You must be the smartest little girl in the entire state,' she said and gave Mary another kiss, smiling happily.

God knows the mama had little else to be happy about. From inside her tiny skull and through her tiny eyes she could see what the mama had to endure with the father. There were the nights when the father came home and fell over chairs and things and finally fell into bed.

Then there were the nights when the father came home and made the mama cry. He would raise his voice to her and sometimes he slapped her and the worst times of all was when he pushed her onto the bed and pulled up her nightdress and got on top of her and while he made strange noises and thrashed about, the mama just lay there with tears in her eyes and muffled cries in her throat. On those nights Mary would roll over onto her side, face the wallpaper pattern and pretend she was asleep. She didn't like it when the mama cried out. She didn't like it when the father shouted, pulled away from the mama, and then was silent as he slept. When the mama finally got out of bed, went to the bathroom and then came back and put on her nightdress she would come over to the crib and Mary would pretend she was asleep. The mama would cover the baby with a blanket, pat the baby's head, blow out the gas light on the wall and get into bed with the father. But the father didn't hear this. He would be making strange noises in his throat and nose, noises that meant he was asleep and far removed from what had just happened in the small bedroom.

Mary would roll over, very quietly, and watch as the mama lay there in the darkness, eyes wide open, silent tears running down her cheeks occasionally raising up on one elbow to look at the father who was sound asleep.

'A,' Jeanette said and placed the square wooden block in front of her small daughter. She waited while the girl searched the others. 'What comes next?' she asked.

Mary scowled, her small hand clutching at different blocks and turning them slowly when she had them in her grasp, then she broke into a grin.

Jeanette had socks to darn and she kept one eye on the child and the other on the wooden darning egg. 'What comes next?' she said again.

Mary's hand went out into the topsy-turvey pile of painted blocks. She grabbed one, studied it, and with a grin of triumph placed it upward on the carpet in front of her.

'That's an "S" Mary, can you say the letter "S" '

Mary didn't reply. Her tiny hand darted into the wooden jumble of square blocks and selected another one. She put it neatly in place beside the first block.

'An "H",' Jeanette said. 'You have an "S" and an "H".' She smiled and continued to darn Jacob's work sock.

Mary's hand shot out again, this time faster and surer and brought out an 'I' and placed it in line. Jeanette smiled and continued to darn.

Then the girl's hand went into the pile, unerringly, and brought out a 'T'. She shoved it into place beside the other letters, sat back and waited for the praise.

'S – H – I – oh, good heavens, Mary! What have you done? Why you poor silly child, look what you've written! How terrible!' and she laughed. 'What a naughty girl!' Jeanette laughed again, reached out with her foot and scattered the four blocks with one kick. 'It wouldn't do to have father see *that*, would it?' she laughed.

Mary looked up at the mama. She frowned. Then she reached out for the blocks. Without a glance at the mama, she rearranged the blocks in front of her. S.H.I.T.

'Mary!' Jeanette screamed delightedly and slid from the sofa onto the floor. 'You can't use that word,' she laughed, 'that's a naughty word! Wherever did you learn it!' She laughed again and her hand broke the line, undid the blocks, erased the word. 'You're such a silly girl,' she said laughingly, 'when you're older you can learn words like that.' She laughed again, thinking how funny it would be to tell her friend and neighbour Rose Carbone about this. It would appeal to Rose's sense of humour.

Mary scrambled for the blocks, silently without a glance at the mama, and started to reassemble the word. The 'S', the 'H', the 'I' when Jeanette reached out again for the blocks.

'Now that's enough of that!' she said loudly. 'I can't have you, at your age, spelling such terrible things! Now you just pick those up and put them in the toy box . . .' her hand went out to the blocks and suddenly she felt a terrible pressure on her wrist. 'Ow!' she cried and looked but there was nothing to be seen on the surface of the skin. She stretched her arm again, and the pressure – the pain – came again. 'Ow! Darn!' She drew back her hand and shook it, then opened and closed her fingers. The ache was still there as if the someone who grasped her wrist refused to let go. 'Ow!' she called again, this time louder.

Mary stared up at her. Not a smile. Not a grin. Not a shred of emotion. The child's tiny hand went out again to the jumble of blocks. The hand went into the pile of painted squares and came out with an 'F'. The hand hovered for a moment and set the block on the carpet. Then the hand went into the pile, came out with a 'U' and set it next to the 'F'.

'No!' Jeanette screamed and she hit the two offending blocks with her hand sending them across the floor. Then she swung out at the rest of the blocks, sending the coloured squares scattering in all directions. Mary looked up sharply at her, not understanding why the mama had done this to the game. The puzzled little girl started to whimper. Then she stopped, suddenly, and watched in fascination.

From the various directions of the room, from across the rug, from under the chair, from behind the table the blocks came out, unaided, by themselves, with a life of their own and as both Mary and Jeanette stared they lined themselves up in front of the child.

Mary raised her gaze at the mama, not an innocent childlike gaze, but one of complete understanding and cunning. 'Mama,' she said and pointed.

The blocks, touched by an unseen hand, grouped themselves into a line, forming a statement. Jeanette put her hands over her eyes not wanting to believe, unable to understand, what was happening.

'F-U-C-K Y-O-U' the blocks spelled. She ran from the room sobbing as the 'J' and the 'E' and then the 'A' and the 'N' 'N' slid into place alongside the terrible message.

On the day of Mary's fourth birthday, Jeanette got her dressed in her best clothes, curled her hair and bought her her first pair of leather high topped shoes. Then she took the streetcar downtown.

'Why don't you sit more to the left, Mrs Lawrence,' the photographer said. 'That's right and smooth your skirt down around your ankles. Perfect! Okay now, little girl . . .'

'Her name is Mary,' Jeanette said.

'Okay, Mary, you stand beside your mother. Yes, there, and put one of your hands up on your mother's arm. No, a little lower. About to the elbow. That's good. Oh, yes, that's real good.' He raised the black cloth hanging down over the back of his large wooden camera and peered in. 'Okay. Little Mary, step just a bit closer to your mother. That's better.' His head came back into view. 'Now when I say "start" I want you both to hold your pose and not move until your hear me say "over". You understand?' Jeanette nodded and so did Mary. After all, Jeanette had been telling her daughter for more than a week how to behave when they had their picture taken.

The picture was to be a surprise for Jacob. Even though it was Mary's birthday she thought Jacob would like to have a gift photo of them both. And, she had told no one of this, she thought she would send another copy of the photo to her parents in West Virginia. They had never seen their granddaughter and maybe when they received the portrait they would see what a lovely little girl she was and how well Jeanette looked and then, maybe, they would write to her and maybe come and see her. Maybe.

The photographer put his head under the cloth. 'Start,' he said. Both mother and daughter held their breaths, didn't make a move. After what seemed like an unnaturally long time, the man called 'Over.' Jeanette and Mary both began to breathe again.

The photos were ready in a week and Jeanette was delighted with them. She had one sitting on the supper table as a surprise when Jacob came home. He washed his hands and sat at his place. He was a couple of hours late, his wife could smell the liquor on his breath.

'What's this?' he said and picked up the photo. He looked at it and then turned it over to see the name of the photo studio and then looked at the picture again. 'When did you get this taken?'

'Last week. On Mary's birthday.'

'First I heard about it.'

'It was to be a surprise,' she said. 'Isn't it a good likeness of both of us?' She watched him. 'It's the first photo I've ever had with my daughter.' He didn't say anything. 'Actually, it's the first photo I've had taken of myself since high school graduation.'

'Where'd you get the money to pay for it?'

'I saved it over the weeks from the food money.'

He grunted. 'I thought things were a little sparse around here.' He put the photo back on the table, image side down. 'Did you iron my blue shirt? I'm going to wear it tonight to the union meeting.'

Jeanette felt angry tears welling up inside her. 'What about the photograph?' she asked.

He stared at her, then shoved a forkful of food into

his mouth. 'What about my shirt?' he mumbled through the potatoes.

For the next few days, Jeanette was down in the entrance hall as soon as she heard the postman's whistle. He placed all the mail for the tenement dwellers on a table just inside the door. She never got any mail, except bills, but now she waited for an answer, a show of appreciation for the photograph, from her folks. They would have to acknowledge the picture. They couldn't look at the image of their pretty little granddaughter and not respond in a positive way.

After two weeks of listening for the whistle, she hurried downstairs and saw the envelope. It was the same envelope she had used to send the photo. The envelope hadn't been opened. It was stamped in red: Refused mail.

Mary started school when she was six. Her first grade teacher was a tall older nun with a crippled arm. She held it down one side of her body, had to pick the bad arm up with the good arm to rest it on her desk, she couldn't hold a book with that arm but Mary (after the initial shock) never noticed. To her, Sister Ann Joseph was the perfect woman. She smiled a lot, and laughed a lot and did more things with one arm to encourage her small students than most parents did with two. The very first week, Sister Ann Joseph started them reading and Mary quickly became one of the best readers in the class. Sister Ann Joseph had a multi-page reading chart. It's leaves were huge, almost as tall as Mary was, and were made of shiny oilcloth. On each large page were big black words like 'CAT' and right beside the word a drawing of a little kitten playing with a ball. One afternoon, just six weeks into the class, Mary stayed a few minutes after school and, as Sister Ann Joseph flipped the large pages with her one good hand, Mary read every word correctly. The Sister wrote a note and told Mary to give it to her parents. Jeanette read it with rightful pride: 'Your little Mary is an extremely bright student. It's a pleasure to have her in my class'. When she showed Jacob the note he only grunted and said something about it not being how smart you were in this life but how much money you had that counted, but Jeanette refused to hear the words: nothing would diminish her admiration for her little daughter.

Jacob went to work on Saturday mornings (most of the time) and after he had gone Jeanette hurried Mary over to the church for her religious instruction. Again, Mary became one of the brightest pupils there. The teacher was Sister Anne Marie and she was a stern taskmaster in spite of her young years. Mary sat entranced, watching this figure in the long black robe, with her face framed by an oval of black material that hid her neck and her ears and a wonderful black bonnet that, in the right light, looked like a large bird in flight. How wonderful to wear such a thing, the girl thought. How wonderful that with just one glance everyone would know what you believed in. Sister Anne Marie had told them she was 'a bride of Christ' and let them examine her wedding ring. Mary had asked her mother why she had married father when she could have married Jesus. Rose was there at the time and she let out a war whoop of laughter. 'At least you'd be living in a church instead of this dump!' and she laughed.

Jeanette grinned and Mary looked puzzled. 'But you knew about being married to Jesus, didn't you, Mama?'

'Sure she did,' Rose snickered. 'Every day she must look at your father and say "Jesus Christ! Look what I married!" ' Again the howls of laughter but this time Jeanette only shook her head. She didn't smile.

Just after wishing a Happy New Year to 1894, the letter came and rested on the hallway table. Jeanette picked it up and read the name and address of the sender. It was from an attorney named Mandenbaum and he had an office in downtown Minneapolis. She shook as she held the letter and walked slowly up the steps to her apartment. It took her a long time to open the envelope and when she did, it simply said that Attorney Mandenbaum would like Mrs Jacob Lawrence to come into his office as he had a matter of interest to discuss with her. She showed the letter to Jacob and he said maybe someone was suing her.

'For what?' she became alarmed.

'I don't know. What have you done?'

She stammered, 'Nothing! I've done nothing. You know that.'

'How can I know what you've done,' he said. 'I'm out of the house most of the time. Whatever you've done, someone's called a lawyer on you.'

She stared at him wondering if he was joking or not. 'But I've not done . . .'

'It's your problem and you'll have to handle it,' he said flatly. 'Go see what he wants.' Jacob finished wiping his hands. 'I'm going out.' He headed toward the front door.

'You'll go with me, won't you?' she pleaded.

He shook his head. 'You don't see my name on that piece of paper. It says Mrs Lawrence, not Mister.'

'But what if it's something bad. How can I go there without you?'

'Whatever it is is your problem and it better not cost me any money.' The door closed behind him.

Jeanette tossed from one side of the bed to the other all night, half sleeping, half in tears. She worried about what the lawyer had against her and wished Jacob would help. But he didn't get back to the apartment until almost four in the morning and he didn't bother coming into the bedroom. He dropped onto the sofa and fell asleep. Jeanette knew there would be no going to work for him the next day.

He was still asleep when she got Mary up and

dressed, packed her lunch box and gave her her breakfast. She walked to school, as usual, with the Carbone kids. Then Jeanette put on what she considered her 'appropriate' dress, neatly arranged her long red hair and took the streetcar downtown.

'Thank you for coming so promptly, Mrs Lawrence,' the lawyer said and he smiled.

Jeanette relaxed when she saw his smile. Maybe things weren't as bad as Jacob had thought they were. 'I got your letter yesterday,' she said.

He motioned her to a chair in front of his desk and as she sat and arranged her full skirt he opened a cardboard file box and took out some papers. 'Your mother took it upon herself to settle your father's estate,' he said, 'and I have here a . . .'

Jeanette felt the shock, then felt the blood rush from her face. 'My father's estate . . .' She shook her head trying to clear it. 'You mean my father is . . .' she couldn't bring herself to say the word.

The lawyer looked up from his papers. 'You mean you didn't know?'

Jeanette sat stunned, unable to speak. There should be tears, she kept thinking, there should be tears.

'I'm terribly sorry,' he said in a softer tone. 'I naturally assumed . . .'

'Of course,' she said and she nodded. 'No one told me.'

The man went to his papers, found the one he was looking for. 'Your father passed away on October 17th of last year. In West Virginia. His body was buried in Logan, wherever that is.'

'My sister owns a farm near there.'

'Apparently there was no will and so your mother inherited everything. Unfortunately, I can't give you an exact figure of the value of your father's estate. It's not in here.'

'That's all right,' she said. Where are the tears, she questioned herself. There should be tears.

'Your mother has a lawyer down in Logan and she instructed him to find you. He somehow chose me and wrote to me and through your daughter's enrolment in public school I managed to get your address. Your mother didn't have it, apparently.'

She wanted to tell him about the refused photograph – the envelope had her address on it – but she decided not to. Why bother? 'No. She doesn't have my address.'

'Anyway, and I'm sorry I was the one to have to tell you of your father's demise, I do have some good news of you. Your mother has instructed the West Virginia attorney to give you the sum of two thousand dollars with the proviso that you use the money to buy yourself a house.' He smiled at her, waiting her reaction. Jeanette, again, went into shock. She just sat and stared at the attorney. Finally he said, 'You do understand what I said, don't you? Your mother will give you two thousand dollars but you *must* use it only to buy a residence.'

Mr Mandenbaum's secretary used one of those new writing machines to peck out a copy of the conditions of her mother's gift. Jeanette sat in the outer lobby watching the woman's fingers as they hit the keys not fully understanding the impact of all this news. It was too much for her. Her father was dead. Her mother obviously still cared for her. She and Jacob were going to own their own home. Yet, where were the tears?

With the papers neatly folded in her handbag, she waited at the streetcar stop. Horses clopped by, pulling carriages, vegetable carts and wagonloads of merchandise. A dog barked at a team-of-four pulling a beer wagon and the streetcar clanked into the stop, the passengers got on and with a jangle of the warning bell the streetcar started up again. Jeanette saw nor heard any of it. She stood there, alone after the streetcar had pulled away, clutching her handbag and staring into space.

Two small boys walked by her, paused and stared. 'Hey lady,' one of them said loudly, 'are you okay?'

The tears started. At last, the tears came from somewhere deep inside and ran down her cheeks.

'Lady, are you okay?'

She looked at them and nodded. The tears had started. 'I'm okay,' she whispered.

'Like hell we are!' Jacob had shouted. 'We're not putting a God damned penny of that money into a house! This place is perfectly okay for us.'

'We can't do it that way,' she said softly.

'Like hell we can't! I'll tell you what we can and what we can't do, Mrs Lawrence!'

'Jacob,' she said wearily. 'I read you the lawyer's papers. We have to spend the money on a house. If we don't, we don't get it. That's how it's been set up.'

'Sure,' he said loudly, 'and the house has to be in your name. I'm your husband. That house should be in my name.'

'That's not how my mother wants it,' she said. 'It's to be in my name.'

'And what about me?' he shouted, his face now close to hers. 'What about me? The *husband*?'

'You can stay in the house as long as you live. You read that. We buy a house, the lawyer pays for it and it's registered in my name but you have the right to live there as long as you live, Mama made that specific.'

'That old bitch!' He started toward the kitchen. Jeanette knew he was going for the whisky bottle. 'She just did this to put me down. I'm supposed to be the husband. Has she taken my *pride* into consideration? Hell no! She gets some cash and rubs my face in it.'

'Jacob,' she raised her voice so he would hear her, 'I'm sure my mother didn't mean anything by it. She just wanted to protect me, that's all. This way we'll always have a roof over our heads. That's all.'

He came back, suddenly, to the living room. 'What

did you say?' He was screaming now. 'A roof over your head? Haven't I always provided you with a roof over your God damned head?' She sighed. 'Well, haven't I?' She nodded. 'Then what's this shit about a roof? Huh?' He grabbed her shoulders and his large work calloused hands hurt. 'She did this just to spite me! That old bitch hates me and now she's trying to make me look like an asshole.' She started to cry as his fingers dug into her flesh. He backed away slightly, looking at her as if for the first time. 'And you,' he said slowly, 'you were probably in on this from the beginning.' He took a step backward. 'I'll bet you and that old bitch have been writing to each other and you set this whole thing up behind my back. You're as much a bitch as she is!' and with a whack! his open palm came up quickly and smacked her alongside her head. Jeanette screamed and staggered backward against the sofa. 'You two bitches think you're real smart, don't you? Two against me. That's how you're gonna play it? Well, I'm going to see about this. I'm going to your fancy-assed lawyer tomorrow and tell him about you bitches and get him to change your plans. I've got my rights! If anybody is going to own that house, it's gonna be *me*!' She watched him tuck his shirttail in and buckle his belt. She knew where he was going. She didn't want to stop him. Let him go. Let him get drunk. She no longer cared. 'Your God damned fat-ass lawyer will hear a few things from me tomorrow! I'm still your husband and there's still law and justice in this country!' She closed her eyes. That way she only heard the door slam, she didn't have to see it, too.

The only thing Jacob succeeded in accomplishing was delaying the process for three months while lawyers wrote back and forth and consulted with Jeanette's mother. In the end, it was Jeanette who picked out the house, Jeanette who signed the papers and Jeanette whose name was on the deed. Jacob refused to have anything to do with it. He even threatened that *maybe* he would stay in the apartment and let Jeanette and the child move into the house alone. Rose thought that was the best idea he'd had in a long time and Jeanette considered the possibility of a life without Jacob. But when the day came to load their belongings into the mover's wagon, Jacob was right there, shouting, supervising and demanding. The Lawrence family was installed in their new home.

The house was all on one floor and rather strangely laid out but Jeanette chose it over the others she had seen mainly because it had no stairs. God, how she had hated those tenement stairs and had vowed if she ever had a home of her own there would be no steps to climb. She had watched drunks (including her husband) stumble up the stairs as well as tumble down the stairs and she had carried baskets of groceries and baskets of laundry and, when the water main had burst in the middle of last winter, buckets of water up those stairs. No, this house was on one level and she loved the idea.

She also chose the house because it was in the same school district where Mary had started first grade. She didn't want to move away from the positive influence of Sister Ann Joseph. Mary had progressed so much during that year it would have been a crime to separate her from her wonderful teacher.

And, St Boniface's Catholic Church was just two streets over, even nearer than from the tenement. It was easier for Mary to get to catechism and easier for them both to go to Mass. Last winter had been especially brutal and they were often frozen to the bone by the time they reached the church. Now it would be easy to get to, no matter what the weather.

The house had a small front yard and a larger back one, room for Mary to play and room for Jeanette to hang the washing. There were even two maple trees, one in the front and the other on the side that shaded the house. They gave Jeanette a sense of permanence. A tree was solid. A tree was tradition. As long as she stayed there she knew the trees would stay there with her. She enjoyed standing with her back pressed against the trunk, feeling the growing energy of the tree through her blouse and the energy of the earth through her shoes.

There was a living room, a large square space, directly in the centre, of the house and it had a 'U' shaped hallway running on three sides of it. The hall, on the left led into the dining room and the kitchen. The hall on the right had doors going into Mary's bedroom and the bedroom Jeanette and Jacob shared. There was a bathroom *inside* the house at the top of the hallway on the right hand side, just a step from the couple's bedroom door. No more going down several flights of stairs, through the darkness and outside in bad weather to go to the toilet like they had to do in the tenement. And, more often than not, when somebody did manage to get outside (in freezing snow or on rainy nights especially) there was already somebody else from the building using the toilet. The man who sold Jeanette this house said the previous owner had installed the toilet himself. He had sacrificed some of the upper hallway space but he had brought the throne in out of the cold.

And there were windows! The tenement, built like a railroad boxcar, had had light coming in the front window of the living room and the back window in the kitchen. Jeanette always kept a lamp lit in the dining area and the bedroom. Now the sun poured into the house at every angle for each room had two windows and, how very luxurious, even the bathroom had a small window up near the ceiling. She marvelled at what money could buy!

The entire two thousand hadn't gone into the house. With all the writing back and forth between attorneys, she got to know Mr Mandenbaum better and convinced him to let her buy a less expensive house and spend the balance on furniture. Her mother had agreed. On paper. For in the entire process, her mother never once communicated directly with her. Jeanette, respecting her mother's wishes (for whatever reason she held them) didn't try to contact her mother personally. The coldness hurt, but the fact that her mother wanted her to have the security of her own home was compensation enough for the lack of any personal contact. Jeanette hadn't told Jacob about the excess being applied to furnishings. She told him the house had come partially furnished and he never questioned it. In fact, he never even asked her how much the house had cost or showed any interest while she picked it out. It was *her* house and it was *her* problem if anything went wrong. The rent money didn't have to come from his salary any more. Good. He'd find other places for it, but he vowed, he'd be damned if he'd give Jeanette one more red cent for expenses than she got in the tenement. He'd have more of his own money in his pocket now. Maybe Jeanette and the old bitch did him a favour by buying this house after all.

Once, about six months after they moved in, Jacob sat up in the middle of the bed, wide-awake. A full moon shone around the edges of the window shade. He had thought he heard something – someone. He searched the blackness, hardly daring to breathe. *They* hadn't followed him here, to the new house. There had been no sign of *them*, whoever *they* were. Jesus, he hoped they didn't know he'd moved to this new place. He didn't want them here. Jeanette had told him, shortly after it had happened, about the blocks Mary had been playing with. He had grown cold as he listened but put on a sceptical grin and asked her if she had been in his whisky cabinet. When she insisted it was true he had shouted at her, telling her she was going crazy. Jeanette had walked from the room and never discussed

102

it with him again. Now he sat, in the dark, as frightened as a rabbit who senses a fox, waiting for something to happen. But nothing did. Finally he lay back down, softly so Jeanette couldn't awake and ask questions, and pulled the blanket over his head. When his heart stopped pounding so loudly, he fell into a troubled sleep.

In the morning Jeanette awoke, dressed, started breakfast and went into Mary's room to call her for school. As she bent over the child she saw a large red rose lying on the pillow, almost touching the little girl's hair. Jeanette picked it up and examined it. The blossom was still moist with dew. 'I wonder where . . .?' she said aloud and then stopped and smiled. How could she ever hope to understand her husband? He obviously had bought the rose from someone who had come into the bar last night and had placed it near his daughter. Jeanette smiled to herself. He was such a strange man sometimes. He would bluster and shout and then do something sweet like this. It was something the *old* Jacob – the man she had fallen in love with – would have done. She decided not to mention the rose, but to let him bring it up.

But Jacob never mentioned it. In fact, had his wife questioned him, he would have told her, truthfully, that he didn't know where the damned thing had come from.

'And when the wise men saw the big star they knew where the baby Jesus would be and they went and . . .' Mary's hand holding the large wooden star swooped down low over the painted figure in the crèche. She smiled up at her father who was sitting on the sofa polishing his shoes. '. . . and there he was! The little baby Jesus was in a manger and so was his mama and his father and some horses and some cows and everything. And the star stayed in the sky and everybody knew the Son of God had been born. Right there. In that

103

place with the straw and the horses. Did you watch me, father? Did you see how the star moved in the sky?'

'Uh huh,' Jacob grunted. 'I saw.'

'And they brought the baby Jesus wonderful presents like money and candy and perfume,' she added.

'No whisky?' Jacob asked. 'A birthday party and nothing to drink?'

'Jacob!' Jeanette looked around the tree as she trimmed it. 'Not for Jesus.'

'Oh, I forgot,' he said. 'They didn't have to bring him any booze, he made his own by turning water into wine. Sorry.'

'No, father, that was later.' Mary stood up and put her hands on her hips, in her lecturing position just like Sister Anne Marie did. 'Jesus was a big man when he did that miracle. He was just a little baby when he was in the manger.'

'It takes a big man to turn water into wine,' Jacob replied rubbing hard at a spot on the shoe. 'Wish to hell I could do it. I'd make a fortune.'

'It wouldn't be around long enough for you to sell,' Rose added from the ladder near the doorway. She had come over to help Jeanette get the house ready for Christmas. 'You'd be your own best customer.'

'Oh, get out of my hair!' Jacob said. 'Just continue with the paper nonsense.'

'Well, it's true,' Rose continued. 'If either you or my Sal could make water turn into wine, you'd both drown in it.' Jeanette just listened. She knew enough not to get involved when Jacob and Rose started picking on each other. They had been in an undeclared state of war with each other long before the move to the new house. Rose wasn't at all intimidated by Jacob and for some reason he let the older woman get away with things that he would never have permitted Jeanette to say.

'If I were Sal and married to you, I'd choose to drown.' he said.

'I don't hear Sal complaining,' she said.

'You don't hear him because your *own* mouth is going a mile a minute, that's why.'

She ignored that. 'Well, he still comes home every night. I give him that much.'

'How much *do* you give him?' he smirked at her.

'Enough that he doesn't have to go elsewhere for it,' she grinned.

'Please, you two. Not in front of the baby,' Jeanette's voice was anxious.

'Yes,' said Mary and picked up the wooden figure of Jesus and waved it at her father. 'What mama says. Not in front of the baby Christ Jesus. We must honour him and respect him for he came here, sent by his father, to save us.' She wagged her Sister Anne Marie finger at him.

'Cut it out,' Jacob said. 'Enough is enough about that baby Jesus of yours.'

'He's not just mine,' the little girl lectured, 'he's yours and yours and yours, too, Mrs Carbone. Jesus is here for ev-ver-rey one.'

'Oh *please*,' said Jacob slipping on his shoe and tying the laces. 'Can't you do anything but parrot what that damned nun tells you?'

'Sister is *not* damned,' the girl's voice rose slightly. 'She is a saint and she is going straight to Heaven when she dies.'

'Too bad she can't go sooner,' he muttered. 'I'm more than a little tired of hearing her catechism lectures delivered second hand. Especially in my house.'

'Your house?' Rose laughed as she tacked a crepe paper streamer over the doorway. '*Your* house? When did Jeanette and Mary die and leave this place to you? You go right ahead, honey,' she said to Mary, 'preach the truth as long as you want to. What's right is right. That's what I always say.'

Jacob was near the doorway, on his way to the coat closet and the front door that would take him to the neighbourhood bar. 'You know, you've got a pretty big mouth,' he said to Rose.

'And you've got a pretty small brain,' she shot back.

'And you've got a helluva nerve!' he yelled and suddenly pushed out with both hands sending the stepladder sideways and sending Rose screaming and sprawling under it.

Jeanette screamed, then put one hand to her mouth to stop any further sound that might come out.

'And you just better watch yourself, too,' Jacob shouted at his wife. 'All this Jesus shit in my house and that kid of yours spouting off like some god-damned priest. It's all gotta stop!' He looked down at Rose who was rubbing her wrist and glaring at him. 'If you're gonna come over here, you treat me with respect or keep your ass in your own house where it belongs.'

Mary put her hands on her hips. 'Father, you shouldn't say words like that! Jesus doesn't want us to say such things. Jesus doesn't like to hear those kind of words!' and she wagged her finger at him.

'Then let him go somewhere where he won't hear them!' Jacob took a couple steps toward his daughter, grabbed the image of the infant Jesus, and ran with it to the bathroom. The three in the living room listened with horror as they heard the toilet flush. Empty handed, Jacob walked past the living room door, put on his jacket and left the house.

It was summer, the year was 1895, and Jeanette awoke early and wondered if there might be a cool breath of air anywhere outside. Last night had been a scorcher and even the slightest touch of Jacob's body next to hers was red hot. She had gotten up, about three a.m., and stretched out on the living room sofa. The two windows at the back of the living room were wide open, in case a wind should spring up and wander into the house. She glanced at the windows now to see if the curtains were moving even slightly. That's when she saw his face.

'Oh God!' she screamed. 'God!' Her voice caught in

the back of her throat as a dozen different possibilities raced through her mind.

The man moved his two hands rapidly and shook his head. 'Please lady,' he said loudly. 'No problem. I want no problem.'

'Go away!' she yelled. 'Go away. You get away from my windows!'

Again he waved his hands, trying to shush her. 'Please lady. No problems. Please.' He didn't try to come through the window, he just stood outside, peering around the lightweight summer curtains. 'I mean no harm,' he said, 'I'm looking for a certain person.'

'Go away!' she insisted. 'Jacob! Jacob come here! Quickly!'

'No harm,' the man repeated with a heavy accent. 'I'm searching for someone, please.'

'Out!' Jeanette yelled. 'Jacob! Get in here!' She had braced herself against the sofa arm, wrapping her arms around her knees which had been pulled up to cover her light cotton nightdress.

'That's who,' the man said and a grin spread across his face. 'That's who! It's Jacob who I'm looking for. He lives here? So I do have the right house?'

Jeanette ceased being terrified long enough to look carefully at the man. There was something familiar about him, yet she was sure she'd never seen him before. 'Are you looking for my husband?' she asked. 'For Jacob Lawrence?'

'Yes!' the man beamed and his aged, white-stubbled face seemed to glow.

'What the hell are you screaming about?' Jacob came hurrying out of the bedroom. 'Sounds like you're being . . .' He stopped and looked in the direction she was pointing. It took a couple of seconds and then his face went ashen. He gagged as if his breath had been knocked suddenly out of him. He was only wearing pyjama bottoms but he seemed to shrink inside of them.

'Jacob!' the old man cried out delightedly.

'Jesus, God-damned Christ!' Jacob said slowly.

'Jacob! You don't recognize me? You don't know your own father?'

Jacob gained enough strength to look over at Jeanette and he shrugged his shoulders. 'That's my . . .'

'Your father? Jacob, is that really your father?' He nodded, still speechless. She jumped from the sofa and ran to the window, not caring she was only in a nightgown. 'Well, for heaven's sake,' she cried loudly, 'for heaven's sake!' She turned back to her husband. 'Oh, Jacob, isn't it wonderful?' Then back to the old man. 'Well, for heaven's sake don't stand out there! Come around the house to the front door. I'll unlock it. Oh how wonderful! Jacob, isn't this something? I mean really something? To have your *father* here? Hurry,' she said to the old man. 'Go around front. Shoo now, go around front and I'll get the door. Oh, I think this is all so . . .' She hastened toward the front door.

'Hadn't you better put something on?' Jacob asked and pointed to her nightgown.

She blushed and started back toward the bedroom, then stopped, shook her head and almost ran to the front door. 'It's all right,' she said quickly. 'He won't mind. After all, he's family. Jacob, isn't it wonderful? We have *family*!'

Jacob, shut in his bedroom, took his time dressing. Jeanette had rushed into the room, changed into a light housedress, scooted into a pair of slippers and was now in the kitchen, making coffee, scrambling eggs, watching the toast and fussing over his father. His *father*! He was sure the old bastard was dead. All these years . . . How many were they? Eleven? That many? That many years had gone by since he hit that old drunk over the head with his own whisky bottle? And there had been blood, lots of it, and he had run out of the house, run out of the old man's life and had come to Minneapolis and started his new life. And always,

108

deep inside his brain and sometimes deep inside his dreams, he relived the scene, the scene where he had murdered his father. Jacob sat on the edge of the bed, only half-dressed, thinking. He had carried that with him all these years, hadn't ever told anyone not even Jeanette. Especially Jeanette. She wouldn't have married a murderer. She would have run from him had she known. He needed her then. *Then*. Did he still need her? Was she important in his life? She had been. But *now*? He got up and took a shirt off a peg on the wall. It was the same shirt he had worn yesterday but it was cool. He looked in the mirror and brushed his hand through his dark hair. It was the same face he had worn eleven years ago back in Milwaukee but it was an older face. There were lines there now, the face needed a shave every day now, there were no more sparkles in the eyes. He sat down and pulled on his socks. He wished he had a bottle in the bedroom rather than in the kitchen. It was early in the morning but, hell, he needed a drink to face the old man. Socks on, he looked in the mirror again. What did the old bastard want? Money? Well, he wouldn't get any here. Did he come to accuse him of attempted murder? Was that it? Was he going to try and extort money from his son because his son had tried to kill him? Just let him try! That old son of a bitch. That drunk. That bastard thinks he can come back now, back into lives that don't want him and don't need him, and start from where it all broke off. Is that what he thinks? Well, it all broke off eleven years ago and it never mended. It ended and it's going to stay that way. Who the hell does he think he is? He took one last glance at himself in the mirror and walked briskly down the hall, across the bedroom and into the kitchen.

'Well,' he said to his father, 'what are your plans?'

'My plans?' Otto shook his head. 'I don't know. I don't have any plans. I'm just here, that's all.'

'Yes,' Jeanette put another sausage on Otto's plate. 'He doesn't have to have any plans,' she said, 'he needs his breakfast and then a rest and then you men can talk plans.' She picked up the coffee pot and refilled his cup. 'He hasn't eaten in two days, Jacob.'

Jacob pulled a chair from the table and sat down. He noted that there was no place set for him, but he didn't comment on it. He'd store it away for future use. 'How did you find me?'

Otto chewed, swallowed, then answered. 'It wasn't easy. I looked everywhere. I even went to the police.'

Jacob stiffened, waiting for what would come.

'But nobody knew where you were. Mrs Baumgartner helped me look. You remember her? Mrs Baumgartner? She lived across the street from the old house.' Jacob nodded. 'She was the one that found me.'

'Found you?' asked Jeanette.

'Three days after it happened,' Otto said and speared a slice of toast from a plate beside him. 'Three days they said I was like that.'

'Like what?' Jeanette had stopped her bustling around the kitchen and was staring at him.

'Unconscious and with the dried blood. I had dried blood all over me and over the sofa and Jacob, they had to throw away that quilt your blessed mother made. You remember it, the one with the blue stars in the middle?' Jacob nodded, still waiting. 'It was ruined. Filled with blood but the doctor said it probably saved my life. It acted like a bandage. When I fell over, it helped stop the blood.'

'What blood?' Jeanette always read the last pages of those dime mystery novels as soon as she bought the book. She hated not knowing the ending of things.

'From the burglar. A burglar came into the house, I was on the sofa, he hit me with a bottle and almost killed me.'

'A burglar?' Jacob's tense body started to relax but only a little. 'How do you know it was burglar?'

'Because the money that was being saved in that

dress upstairs was missing. That's how I know.'

'But that was my money,' Jacob protested. 'I saved that money, not you.'

'I know it was your money, but I knew it was there. I used to count it. You'd put a dollar or two in there a week and I'd count it. I didn't tell him though,' he winked at Jeanette, 'he thought it was a secret.'

Jeanette looked at Jacob. 'You told me your father was dead.' She paused. 'How come you didn't tell me about the burglar? And the blood? Where were you when all this happened?'

Jacob twisted in the kitchen chair and from a special cupboard in his mind, a cupboard that he had prepared years ago in case anyone ever asked him this very question, he brought out his prepared story. 'I ran away. You remember I went to the coal yard to see about why they didn't deliver. You remember?' The old man nodded. 'You had been drinking.' Otto shrugged and grinned at Jeanette. 'And I took longer getting back than I thought and when I did get back to the house there you were. On the sofa and not breathing. I thought you were dead. So I ran.' He paused and looked at his father. He wanted to see if the story he had been saving for just such an emergency all these years would hold up. 'You had been drinking,' he repeated, 'quite a lot. Maybe you don't remember but you had been.'

'I remember,' Otto said. 'I remember there was some problem with the coal company and you going over there, but that's all I remember. I was out for three days at Mrs Bumgartner's. She put me up. She let me stay there until I got better.'

'And Jacob,' Jeanette asked, 'you never tried to find out if your father was alive or dead?' She was still staring at him. 'All these years?'

'I thought he was dead,' Jacob said flatly. 'I mean there was all that blood and he didn't seem to be breathing and so I ran. People had heard us arguing:

111

they might have thought that I'd killed him. I just ran away. I didn't know what else to do. I mean, I was so young.'

'Just a lad,' Otto agreed. 'He was so young then. The baby of the family. Who can blame him? Jeanette, my darling daughter-in-law, maybe just a tad more of that raspberry jam, huh?'

'I really thought I'd killed him,' Jacob said silently and for about the tenth time since the bartender had put the full glass mug in front of him. 'I really did. All those years.' He took a sip and shook his head. 'Living with that guilt all those years.'

'We didn't want you in jail,' he heard a voice say, 'you wouldn't have been any use to us in jail.'

Jacob looked quickly at the man a few stools down at the bar. He was the only other customer in the place. 'What'd you say?' he spoke loudly.

The man looked at him and shook his head. 'Nothin'. I didn't say nothin'.'

Jacob studied him, his large grimy hands, his cotton trousers and work shirt covered in a fine layer of brick dust. Another working slob like himself. 'You sure?'

'Hell, yes. What'd I want to talk to you for?'

'Okay, sorry.' Jacob took another swig from the frosted mug.

'If you were in jail, you wouldn't have been any use to us,' the voice said. It was a low and conversational voice and Jacob whirled around but nobody was behind him. 'You should have gone to jail. You tried to kill your father. That was stupid. You've done a lot of stupid things. But we needed you.'

Jacob didn't glance up this time. He knew that voice.

'We've spent a lot of time getting you out of messes,' the voice said. 'One day you won't be so lucky. One day we won't need you. Then bang! Goodbye you!'

The bartender was just a few feet away, pouring the remains of one whisky bottle into another. He didn't

112

turn around, didn't react to the voice. Jacob knew the man didn't hear it. He, Jacob, was the only one who could hear it.

'Leave me alone,' Jacob thought.

'We will,' the voice said, 'when we're ready. All in good time.'

'Don't bother me!' Jacob thought again. 'Get out of my life!'

'Don't be in such a hurry for us to get out,' the voice said, 'because when we get out of your life, we'll take the life out of you.'

'Is that a threat?' his thoughts answered back.

'No threat. A promise.' There was a pause. 'And, Jacob, we always keep our promises.'

'He's been here a week now and it's time he left. Moved on.' Jacob looked at Jeanette as she washed the supper dishes. He, of course, just stood there, doing nothing to help her with the chore.

'Shhh,' she said quickly, 'he'll hear you.'

'I don't care if he does. He's been here long enough.'

'Jacob, he's your *father*!'

'He's an old drunk and a pain in the ass and I want him out of here. Are you going to tell him or am I?'

'You'd think,' she said, 'that now you know he's alive you'd be so relieved and happy you'd want him here with us always.'

'I am relieved to know he's alive. Believe me, very much relieved. How much, no one will ever know but I don't want him here any longer. Not in this house.'

She was going to remind him it was *her* house but she held it back. 'He doesn't have any place to go,' she said. 'It took him months to find us. It was just pure luck that our name was in the new city directory. If we hadn't bought this house, that librarian in Milwaukee would never have discovered us. Otto said the lady in the library searched several city directories and couldn't find us. Then one day when the new Minneapolis directory arrived in the mail she recalled our name and there we were. He said he was so excited when she told him about it. Oh, Jacob, let him stay. He *is* your father.'

'Look, when I ran away from him, I ran away from everything in my past. Everything. Him. My two worthless lying brothers. My mother's ghost. The goddamned church. Everything. And I'm not going to let the past come crashing back – uninvited – into my present. I won't have it!'

'Don't raise your voice. He'll hear you.' Jacob shrugged. 'He doesn't have any money to go anywhere.'

'He never has any money. He drinks it all up as fast as he gets it.'

'And if he did, where would he go?'

'Back to Mrs Bumgartner.'

'She's dead. He told me that. He has nobody back in Milwaukee.'

'That's not my fault.'

'We have room for him. Mary has been happy sleeping on the sofa. We can manage for a little while longer. I gave him that picture of me and Mary, you know the one my folks refused and he was so happy to get it, he started . . .'

'He leaves next week!'

'Jacob . . .' she sighed. 'He's *family*. He's found you, his son. He's found Mary. He didn't even know he had a granddaughter and you see how much she likes him. He tells her stories and she hangs on to every word.' She dried her hands and came closer to her husband. 'Be nice, Jacob. He's an old man and all alone. Let him stay a little while longer.'

'In your "while longer" he'll be an even older man and will still be all alone. No. I've made up my mind. He's getting his worthless hide out of here.'

She took a deep breath. 'Jacob. This house is in *my* name. You seem to forget that. The house is mine and *I* want him to stay.'

114

'And you seem to forget that you are my wife!' He swung his arm back so unexpectedly she didn't have time to duck the open palm that roughly slapped across her face. 'You can shove your house up your ass,' he shouted at her, 'but you are my wife and you are supposed to obey me. You've got awful uppity since you had a house. You're still nothing but a god-damned woman and don't forget it.'

She rubbed the numbness of her cheek knowing that in a moment or two she would start to feel the pain. 'I feel sorry for you,' she said. 'You really are a miserable creature.' She ran out of the kitchen and almost bumped into Otto who was standing just outside the kitchen door. She didn't have to ask the old man if he had heard. She knew he had.

In the morning, there was a crudely written note on a page from Mary's school tablet lying on the kitchen table. '*Jeanette my daughter i think it is time i went someplace. Someplace else where i am wanted. Do not know where that could be but i will look. Maybe in California i might find my 2 other sons because i don't have no son here anymore. I love my little angel Mary and you. Not to worry i will do o.k. I will remember you in kindness for the kindness you gave me. i love you, papa Otto.*'

A railroad guard at the St Louis switching yard found the body. The man had obviously tried to jump aboard a moving boxcar just as it rounded the curve and he was caught by the wide load on the flatcar coming the other direction. The wheels had cut him in two. It happened liked that sometimes. There was no identification on the body so relatives couldn't be notified. That was common, too, these days. The only thing he carried (there was no money in his pockets) was a photograph of a neatly dressed young woman and a little girl standing beside her.

It was difficult to pinpoint when it exactly happened, but Jeanette started to feel weak shortly after Otto had gone. At first she put it down to disappointment in her husband's attitude and discouragement with the realization that he would never change. Then she attributed the lassitude and the frequent headaches to possibly being pregnant again, but the doctor told her that was not the case. Then she thought it might be because winter was coming and she didn't like cleaning sidewalks and carrying coal buckets and bringing in clothes that had frozen into strange shapes. All she knew was that she was tired. She took some pills the pharmacist gave her and started taking a daily tablespoon of an 'iron tonic especially for women' that Rose recommended, but the tiredness didn't go away. Like everything else in her life, she learned to live with it.

In May of 1896, Mary became a fully-fledged member of the Roman Catholic Church. She went through her First Communion and Jeanette was so proud.

The Saturday before the formal service, Sister Anne Marie lined up all her charges from the catechism class and made them sit patiently in the front row of the church while, one by one, they made their first confession.

'What the hell does a nine year old kid have to confess?' Jacob had demanded as Mary dressed to go to church. 'She didn't shoot anybody or get pregnant or rob a bank. What a lot of shit your church dumps on people to keep them in line.'

'They don't really expect the children to *confess* anything,' Jeanette tried to explain, 'it's to instill in them the idea of confession for the rest of their lives. Today, it'll be more the ritual of how to do it than what they say. And tomorrow she'll take her First Communion. You always go to confession before taking communion.'

'Who says so?'

'The Church. It's part of the rules. You can't partake of the communion cup if you still have sins on your soul.'

'And telling your sins to some damned priest is gonna

make you all crispy clean?' he laughed. 'The priest has probably been screwing all the nuns he can get his peter into and yet he can take away sins. Please, Jeanette, grow up someday, will you?'

'Priests and nuns have a special relationship,' Jeanette replied heatedly. 'They don't think like you do. Their minds are not below the belt buckle like yours always is.'

'They're human beings and human beings like to screw.'

'They've taken their vows!'

'Saying some Latin nonsense ain't gonna remove the urge between their legs. The only thing that can do that is a knife. When they start cutting off priests' balls, then maybe I'll believe some of that goody-goody malarkey.'

'You're impossible,' she said and started walking from the room.

'Yeah, and you're ignorant. You're a stupid fool to believe that bullshit they're dumping on you. And I don't like the idea that Mary swallows all of it, too.'

She turned in the doorway and looked at him. 'Look. Today and tomorrow are very special days for Mary. Don't do anything to spoil them for her. Okay?'

'Okay. I'm not planning on going to the ceremony tomorrow.'

'That's fine. Neither of us expected you to. In fact, neither of us *wanted* you to.'

The first row had finished their confessions and Mary was sitting at the beginning of the second row. Sister Anne Marie motioned her to rise and to go to the confessional booth. Mary knelt, as she had been taught, and made the sign of the cross.

'Bless me, Father, for I have sinned,' she said in her small voice.

'What did you do, my child?' the priest asked.

'I thought bad thoughts about Molly Prescott. I didn't

like how she got to light the candles in catechism last week and I didn't.'

The priest waited. 'What did you do, my child?' he repeated.

'And the other night when my father didn't come home, I was glad because when he does come home there are usually fights and yelling.'

'What did you do, my child?' he repeated again, much louder. 'Please speak up, I can't hear you and I can't see you either. You'll have to learn to speak up.'

'And I have wished that Grandpapa Otto would come back even though I know my father doesn't want him in the house.'

'Will you please speak up!' the priest said loudly. 'I can't hear you.'

'And once I took a taste of the whisky in my father's bottle but I didn't like it.'

'I cannot give you absolution unless I can hear you,' he said. Why didn't these children learn to speak up? If he was saying Mass, these kids would probably yammer all the way through it.

Mary closed her eyes and a slight tremor ran down her body. It lasted only a second. 'And one day when we are stronger,' Mary said, 'we will take large worthless buildings like this one and raze it to the dirt. And scum like you,' she lifted closed eyelids at the curtained window of the confessional, 'will be drawn and quartered and your bodies let broil in the sun for the vultures to pull apart.'

'Really, my child,' the priest sighed. 'I can't hear a word you're saying.'

'And these stupid painted statues will all come off the walls and they'll be ground into dust and that dust will be shoved down the gullets of those pious-mouthed old ladies who come here to spin their beads and light their stupid little candles. Our time is not yet, but it will be soon. Oh yes, Reverend Father, our time will soon be here.'

The priest sighed wearily. If this little girl wasn't going to talk loud enough for him to hear her, he'd have to move on to the next child. There seemed to be a wagonload of kids waiting for him.

'Ego te absolvo a pecates tuis,' he said quickly. 'God bless you. Go in peace. And for heaven's sake, speak up the next time you make your confession. The church likes to hear what you're saying, you know.'

Christmas that year was more subdued than Mary would have liked. Almost all the excitement of the season took place in school or at church because at home her mother was hardly able to do anything. Jeanette made an effort to keep the house clean and to have supper ready for Jacob but it was an effort that left her exhausted by sundown. Mary, in the third grade, came straight home after school to help with things like ironing sheets and pillowcases (it didn't matter if they had a few wrinkles in them), peeling potatoes and sweeping the sidewalks. Jacob spent longer and longer each evening at the saloon and Jeanette was glad for the peace and quiet. Jacob had brought in a single bed and mattress, pushing their double bed against the wall to make room for it. Jeanette slept in the smaller bed. She complained that Jacob's restless rolling and tossing kept her awake and drained her of energy she didn't have. At this point in their relationship, Jacob was more than happy to have the sick, complaining woman out of his bed. When Jeanette heard the church bells usher in the new year of 1897, it was all she could do to smile at her daughter and hope that this would be a better year for both of them.

School had been out for summer vacation only three days when Mary looked from her bedroom window and saw the lady getting out of the horse-drawn cab. Then she watched as the driver unloaded two large suitcases and watched as he struggled with the cases up the front

walk and onto Mary's front porch. She waited until the
lady twisted the bell before she opened the door.

'Well! You must be Mary!' the woman's voice was
loud and harsh. 'You don't look a thing like I thought
you would. I thought you'd look more like Jeanette.'

Mary stood there, staring at the woman, taking in
her bright pink skirt and the matching jacket and the
yellow blouse with all the red garnet beads (see copy)
sewn on it. The woman's hat had three large pink
feathers on it. The woman reminded Mary of the
posters in front of the vaudeville house.

'Well, aren't you going to invite me in?' the woman
said as she pushed her way past the girl. 'Where's your
mother? Hmm, nice room this. Hey hon, where's
Jeanette?' Mary pointed to the open bedroom. 'Can't
wait to see her. Hey! Jeanette. You in there?' The
woman walked into the bedroom and saw Jeanette
lying on the single bed. 'Honey! What are you doin' in
bed at this hour of the day? C'mon, get up. I've been
travelling for three days to see you!'

Jeanette stared at the woman, then a broad grin
stretched across her emaciated face. 'My heavens, I
don't believe it,' she was almost crying. 'Minna! For
God's sake, it's Minna!'

Jeanette sat at the kitchen table, wearing an old house-
coat, while Minna bustled around the room making
coffee and a light breakfast. Jeanette guessed Jacob
was at work. Last night had been another night when
he hadn't come home.

'I'm on my way to San Francisco,' Minna said as she
watched the omelette thicken in the frying pan,
'always wanted to see it and now that I can, I will.'

'Was mother in much pain?' Jeanette asked.

'At first she was but the doctor gave her some sort of
tea to drink and that seemed to help. She spent a lot of
time in her bedroom and I tried to make sure she was
comfortable.'

'I'll bet you did,' Jeanette tried to smile, still shaken by the news of her mother's death. Yet, somehow, as soon as she saw her older sister, she had *known* her mother was dead. 'It was kind of you to take care of both of them in the last years,' Jeanette said.

'Well, I had that big old house and all those bedrooms and all that land, I really didn't feel they were in the way. They didn't eat too much, either one of them,' she laughed. 'My three kids ate for a dozen, they did! Lord, I used to spend half my days in the kitchen just putting food on those kids' plates.'

Jeanette glanced at Mary, happy to know that her daughter was so well and alive. 'It must have been a great sorrow for you,' Jeanette said.

'Well, it all happened so fast. One week they was all healthy and noisy and the next week I was lowering them into the ground. That's how diptheria works, you know. It just comes suddenly and so swift and there's nothing you can do about it and it takes who it wants to take and,' she sighed as she lifted out the omelette, 'it took my three little ones.'

'Did you have a Mass said for their souls?' Mary wanted to comfort this strange sweet-smelling lady, this stranger who was to be called 'Aunt Minna'.

'A Mass? You mean like in a church?' Mary nodded. 'No. Didn't do that. I don't have much truck with the church anymore. I had my fill of it when we were forced to go every Sunday up here. And besides, there ain't no Catholic Church for miles around where my farm is.' She laughed. 'I mean *was*. I keep forgetting I sold the damned thing.'

'No church?' asked Mary. Minna shook her head. 'How awful!'

Minna looked at her sister. 'I guess you've been keeping up the family religion.' Jeanette nodded. 'Well, you always were one for praying and saying the Rosary and all that. I guess you need it. Some people do. I don't.'

121

'I had my First Communion last year, Aunt Minna. Do you want to see my picture?'

'Sure, hon. Let's see it.' Mary hurried to her bedroom. 'Seems like a sweet kid.'

'She is,' Jeanette said. 'I'm very proud of her.'

'What time do you think your husband will be home? I've gotten curious to meet him. Especially after everything the folks said about him.' She laughed. 'He never won any medals from mom and dad.'

Jeanette smiled. 'No he didn't. In fact, I think he deliberately went out of his way to antagonize them.'

'But you know dad,' Minna said. 'Stubborn as batshit on a barn wall. Once he made up his mind, that was it.'

'And he made up his mind that Jacob was no good.'

'Well, that and the fact they both hoped you would see the light one day, leave Jacob and come back to the family.'

'I could never do that,' Jeanette replied softly. 'Jacob and Mary are my life. Jacob is my husband. I couldn't break up my family.'

'Do you love him?' Minna asked, looking her sister directly in the eyes.

'I think I do,' Jeanette replied slowly. 'In the beginning, when we first were married, I knew I did but things have altered over the years. I love him but ... he's just not the man I was in love with. This is the first time I've ever said that out loud. Does that make any sense?'

'Complete sense,' Minna said. 'I loved my old man, too, until he started to change. I probably would have left him but he decided to die on me. Saved me the trouble of packing my bags.'

Mary hurried back into the kitchen. 'Here, Aunt Minna. Look at this photograph. It's me at my First Holy Communion.'

Minna took the larger-than-postcard-size cardboard photo and examined it. There was Mary, wearing a

122

white lace bridal gown. The material was cotton with dozens of white embroidered eyelets. The dress came down to the floor and the white train swirled around her feet. The bridal veil had been lifted for the photo even though it was taken when Mary was not yet 'a wife of Christ'.

'That's real pretty,' Minna said handing the picture back to the girl. 'Are those real white roses you're carrying or silk ones?' Mary assured her they were real. 'You make a lovely little bride,' she said and glanced quickly at Jeanette. 'Let's hope that when you become a *real* bride you have better luck than the two of us did.'

'But this is a real bride,' Mary insisted.

'I mean in the *real* world, kid. Not the church world. You'll grow up soon enough and will find out the difference. You can't spend twenty four hours a day at Mass. Sooner or later you have to go outside into the daylight and *that* world is a God-damned pisser.'

'Is this the first time you've been back to Minneapolis since you left?' Jacob sat across from Minna in the living room. Jeanette and Mary were in the kitchen preparing dinner. Minna had wanted to help but her sister had insisted she was strong enough to do it alone and, besides, Minna was 'company'.

Jacob had poured them both a beer and Minna had a shot of whisky along with it. 'Yep,' she nodded. 'When work got bad here, Frank and I said the hell with it and went down to his daddy's place in West Virginia. Probably the best move I ever made. Going down there was good for me. I ended up by eventually owning the whole ball game.'

'How long were you there till the old man died?'

'Frank's father? About a year and a half. He was weak and sickly. And just between us,' she sipped her whisky and smiled at him, 'he was a pain in the ass. Nothing anybody did could please him. Try as hard as you might and he still found something to bitch about.'

'So you didn't shed many tears when he died?'

She grinned. 'Not a helluva lot.'

'And your husband?' Jacob asked. 'How long after his father died did he die?'

''Bout another year. Real sudden it was. One day he was out in the fields behind the plough and the next day he was laid out in a box in the parlour. At least he didn't suffer.'

'Did you?' Jacob looked at her.

'Did I suffer? Me?' She frowned. 'Oh, now I got 'ya. No, I'm not the suffering kind. I ain't got any wiltin' flower blood in me. I'm strong. I've had to be.'

He smiled and deliberately let her see his slow gaze run up and then back down her body. 'You *look* pretty strong,' he said.

'Honey, you better believe it. All those deaths happening around me, one after the other was tough, they made me a free woman but I *always* did what I wanted to do and when I wanted to do it. There are no flies on me. I don't jump through anybody's hoop.'

'You don't jump?' his eyes were on hers. 'Not all all?' His smile had turned to a smirk.

'I get your drift,' she said, 'but why bother to jump when it's so much more fun just to lie back and enjoy it?'

The strength that seemed to rally Jeanette when her sister had first arrived had diminished and it was all she could do to get up and go to the bathroom. The summer heat filled every corner of the small frame house, crawling into the bed linen, soaking into the overstuffed furniture and settling under arms and around hairlines. Minna had only intended to stay a week but as her visit stretched into a month she didn't talk about going to California as much. Her concern, as she told anyone who would listen, was the health of her dear sister. She'd stay as long as Jeanette needed her. After all, they were family and the last survivors of the

124

family at that. They had always been close (she told Rose when she visited) and the only reason they hadn't communicated over the years was that Minna didn't like to write letters. She preferred 'talking to faces in person'. The fact that it was difficult for her to read or write was never mentioned.

Jeanette considered her sister an angel sent from heaven. Minna was beside her sickbed day and night. She brought fresh towels and made sure the bowl of water beside the bed always had ice chunks in it. Jeanette could wipe her heated face and arms with cold water as often as she needed. Minna, herself, kept cool with cold beer from the icebox and a paper fan from the Logan Funeral Home. Mary was pressed into service for every meal. She went to the market, pared potatoes, shelled peas, set the table and washed the dishes. She did it all at Minna's request, but she would have done it anyway. It helped her mother and that was important. At times, Mary resented her aunt taking over the running of her mother's house and once, after Minna had slapped the girl's hands when she dropped a pitcher of iced tea, Mary complained about her to Jeanette. Her mother admonished her, saying that Minna was a blessing for them all. Why, whatever would they do without her around to help? Mary was also a little resentful that Minna had taken over her bedroom. When the woman was only going to stay a week, Mary hadn't minded sleeping out on the living room sofa but now, after a month, Minna had moved Mary's things into boxes that were stacked in the hallway and when she needed something to wear to school she had to look through the boxes and iron out the wrinkles before she could wear it. Minna's clothes, and she had two suitcases crammed full of them, were all hung in Mary's closet.

One night, Mary lay awake listening for her father to come into the house. He had left right after supper telling Minna he was going to have a beer. Hours later, when everyone was asleep, he had returned and had sat on the front steps for a long time. His footsteps had wakened her. Finally she heard the door handle turn and she watched as he tiptoed across the living room. He stopped at the sofa, peering down at his daughter. She pretended she was asleep. It was always better that way when her father was drunk and tonight she could smell the alcohol as he leaned over her. He swayed lightly, then headed for his bedroom. With one hand on the doorknob he paused, thought for a moment, then turned around and went to the door leading to Mary's bedroom. He twisted the knob and opened the door. Then he went into the room and closed the door after him. Mary lay on the sofa, trying to suppress the giggles at what was about to happen when her father discovered his mistake and how funny it would be when he came flying out of the room. Mary waited and waited but her father didn't come out of Aunt Minna's room all night.

Minna was hanging clothes to dry on the backyard line. Jacob had his arm around her and his other hand was caressing her breast. 'You cut that out now,' the woman ordered. 'She might see us and then what?'

'She's in bed. She ain't gonna see nothing. Here, let me get a better feel of that.' He worked his hand between the buttons of her blouse and sought out the warm mound of flesh under the brassiere.

'Stop that!' she laughed and pulled away. 'I declare you are the most anxious banty rooster I've ever seen!' Again she laughed. 'The neighbours might look over here and see us. Then what?'

'Then we'll fall onto the ground and I'll jump on top of you and really give the old busy-bodies something to talk about.' His hand tried to get under her blouse again.

'Your own wife is lying in there, more sick than well, and you can't control yourself,' she said. 'Shame.'

'I couldn't control myself from the first moment I saw you,' he replied. 'You know that.'

'I only know what the bulge in your trousers told me,' and she laughed. 'Good thing your peter isn't on your face. The whole world would have seen it then!'

'Don't make fun of the way I feel,' he said.

'Honey, I don't make fun of any man with a peter like yours!'

Mary lit the candle and after pausing silently for a few minutes, got off her knees and went and sat on one of the pews. She had stopped at the church on her way home from school. It was getting more and more difficult for her to pay attention in class knowing that her mother was so ill. She knew her grades were suffering but there was little she could do. Her mother was constantly on her mind. 'Please Blessed Jesus,' she said silently, 'make my mother well. Make her healthy and happy as she was before. Please.' A tear started down her cheek. 'She doesn't like being in bed all day any more than I like her being there. Give her back her strength and then we can have a normal family again.' Her gaze went up to the big plaster Jesus that hung on the wall behind the altar. He must have arms three feet long, she thought. She tried not to look at the horrible hands, with the nail holes and all that bright, red blood. Even though his head hung down at an angle and blood streamed from under his crown of thorns, even though his eyes were closed, she knew he was listening to her and she knew he would grant her prayer. 'And Aunt Minna, isn't there anything you can do with her? She is getting awfully bossy and she doesn't even try to keep the house clean or anything. At first, I liked her but now I don't.' She blushed and made the sign of the cross. 'I'm sorry,' she said quickly, 'I shouldn't say bad things about people, especially to you and Aunt Minna has been a big help taking care of Mama and being there during the day when I'm at school, but Jesus,' (she wondered how she could phrase it without seeming to be complaining), 'if you would make Mama better then Aunt Minna wouldn't have to stay and she could continue on with her trip to California. So you see, Lord,' she studied the blood-streaked face hanging way up there, 'if Mama got better it would be wonderful for all of us. Not just me. Wonderful for Mama and wonderful for Aunt Minna, too.' The statue said nothing. 'Don't you agree that would be the very best thing that could happen? For all of us?' She wondered if she should mention her aunt's drinking. The woman and her father drained a bottle between them almost every night. And, almost every night, her father slept in Aunt Minna's bedroom. 'Really it's my bedroom,' she said to the statue. 'I don't say anything about it to Mama. Aunt Minna said it was best this way because it gave Mama a better rest at night, not having Father in the same room coughing and things while Mama was trying to sleep. Aunt Minna also told me not to mention it to Mama because Mama didn't like to be reminded that her sickness was putting Father out of his very own bedroom.' Mary, at first, thought it was odd that her mother never objected to the new sleeping arrangements but when Aunt Minna showed her the special sleeping tea she gave her sister every night after supper Mary understood. Mama was falling asleep earlier and earlier and waking up later and later. Aunt Minna assured Mary it was okay. It was the special tea.

On the second Friday in October, a cold snap hit the city and the old furnace at Mary's school – which should have been replaced years ago – cracked from the sudden raise in coal heat and threatened a fire hazard to the building. None of the students were surprised when after sitting through a chilly morning they were told to go home and not come back until Monday. The furnace would be fixed by then, they were assured.

Mary, her uneaten sandwiches still in her lunchbox, opened the door to the house and walked down the hallway to the kitchen. She set the lunch pail on the counter, then took off her coat and scarf and hung them on a peg behind the door. She had taken that space for her things when she had been moved from her own room. She glanced at the stove, there was nothing cooking on it, but it was too early for supper anyway. She walked back down the hallway and was starting across the living room when she saw them. Her father and her aunt. On the sofa. Her aunt was lying on her back, her skirts and petticoats up under her chin, her stockinged legs wrapped around her father's middle. Her father only had his socks on. The sight of his naked skin and the sounds of his grunting mixed with her aunt's moaning shocked her into complete rigidity. She stood there staring. She wanted to turn but her body wouldn't budge. She wanted to run from the room but her legs wouldn't obey. So she stood there, like a statue, and watched until her father, his naked rear end pumping furiously, let out a loud groan and fell weak and silent onto her aunt. When neither of them moved, Mary somehow was able to turn and run from the room.

'So I came over here,' she said to Rose Carbone. 'I didn't think you'd mind. I couldn't think of any place else to go.'

The woman still held the girl, her head cradled against her shoulder, even though she had stopped crying. Mary had burst into her flat, silent and red-faced. When Rose, quite surprised to see the girl, asked her what was wrong, Mary broke into violent sobs that took Rose several minutes to calm. 'I thought when you first came in here that something had happened to your mother,' the woman said.

Mary shook her head. 'I don't know if she's okay or not. I didn't stop to check. I just grabbed my coat and ran out the back door. Oh, Rose, it was horrible! Just horrible!'

'And with your mother lying on her sickbed right in the very next room,' she said.

'That's what's so terrible,' Mary said. 'Suppose she came out and *saw*? Suppose she heard them and couldn't get up but had to lie there and *listen*? Oh, Rose, how awful for Mama!'

'You're not going to tell her, are you?'

Mary shook her head. 'No. What good would it do? It would only cause trouble and Mama would feel worse. No, I can't tell anybody. Only you.'

'How about the priest. Are you going to tell him?'

'I don't know. I don't think so. It isn't something I have to confess. It's something *they* have to confess.'

'But they don't go to church.'

'Then it'll have to remain a sin on their souls. Both their souls.'

When she finally came back to the house, it was at her usual arrival time from school. She pretended nothing had happened. She went to see her mother, who was half-awake, half-asleep at that early hour, then she helped Aunt Minna prepare supper. It was almost impossible to swallow as she sat at the table with the two sinners. She ate almost nothing. Her aunt didn't notice and her father didn't care.

A week or so later, Mary awoke from her sofa in the living room and listened to the voices coming from the kitchen. Her father and aunt had gone out early in the evening and had been back home only a short while. The clock on the wall showed it was almost two a.m. She knew they were both drunk, their slurred voices told her that.

'. . . can't just up and do it that way.' That was her aunt.

'. . . too much damned trouble way she is.' That was her father.

'. . . time will take care of it.' Her aunt.

'. . . don't have time.' Her father.

'. . . get blamed for it.' Her aunt.

'. . . nobody would find out.' Her father.

'. . . suspicious in West Virginia.' Her aunt.

'. . . was down there. This is up here.' Her father.

'. . . she's my own sister.' Her aunt.

'. . . didn't stop you with your *own* kids.' Her father.

'. . . you bastard!' Her aunt.

They came out of the kitchen and tiptoed to Minna's bedroom. Just in case they looked at her, Mary closed her eyes and pretended to be asleep. The conversation continued a little while longer but Mary couldn't make out any of the words with the bedroom door closed.

Two days later, while Mary was at school and Jacob went to work, Minna prepared a cup of her special herb tea. It was the same herb tea that she had prepared for her husband and father-in-law, the same tea she had prepared for her mother and father and the same tea she had given her three diptheria-ravaged children.

'Here darling,' she said and handed the cup to Jeanette.

She had arranged the pillows and raised Jeanette up against them into a sitting position. Jeanette's trembling hands could barely hold the cup. 'You are so good to me,' she said to Minna. 'I really don't know what any of us would do without you.'

'Nonsense,' Minna replied, 'I'm just doing what any sister would do.'

'No,' Jeanette shook her head. 'You're very special. I'm so glad you came back into our lives.'

Minna guided her sister's shaking hands up to her mouth. 'Take some tea,' she said, 'careful not to spill it. It's got all kinds of special things in it. That's right. Now isn't that good? Now take another sip. Don't want to let it get cold. Uh huh, just like that. Good, isn't it? Now another sip and you'll have half the cup down. Okay . . . let me wipe your mouth for a second. Again now, another little bit. Uh huh. And another. Just one more sip. That's it. Perfect. All gone. Now that wasn't difficult, was it?'

Jeanette smiled and shook her head.

'Now let me help you lie back down.' She lowered Jeanette onto the bed and pulled the blankets up around her. 'Now you just stay that way,' she said, and left the room.

*   *   *

That afternoon when Mary returned from school she found her mother stiff and dead – exactly as Minna had left her.

Part Two

'Of course, this must be a decision based on the love of Jesus, not just on your desire to do good.' Sister Amelia looked at Mary. 'You must love Jesus more than you love life itself,' she said, 'you must love Him above all else and above all others. If not, you should not enter into marriage with Him. You should not seek His blessed love as a means of avoiding wordly responsibilities. You do understand that, don't you?'

Mary nodded. 'I've given it a lot of thought, Sister, really I have and I want to become a nun. Really, it's all I've ever wanted.'

'The call to the sisterhood is not one that is given to everyone, you know.'

'I know, Sister. I understand that. I've been reading and praying a lot and the answer always seems to be the same: Become a nun.'

'This answer, as you call it,' spoke up Father Paul, 'how does it come to you?'

'How?'

'Yes. How? In a dream? Like a voice in your head? Just an understanding or a feeling that you are doing the right thing? Tell me. I need to know.' Mary was silent for a moment. The young priest smiled at her. 'I've observed you in church, Mary,' he said. 'I've watched you during Mass. You do all the right things. You kneel at the right times, you cross yourself at the right times, you go to confession at the right times, so I know you have the mechanics of Catholicism down pat. What worries me are your motives and where your urgings to join the convent really come from.'

Mary's eyes widened. 'You don't think my urgings come from the Devil, do you, Father?'

He laughed. 'No,' he smiled at the black-robed Sister, 'not from *that* source. But I need to find out why you feel your young life is committed already to the church. It will be a long and difficult role once you renounce your secular life for the religious. There's no going back, you know. A decision to give your life to God is a decision you must stay with until the day you die. It's not a childish decision.'

'I am not a child any longer, Father,' Mary said solemnly. 'I am fourteen years old, almost fifteen. In three years, I will be out of high school. In three years, I'll be the same age as my mother was when she married my father. I'll be an adult in body but I feel that now, at almost fifteen, I already am an adult in mind. Aren't I, Sister? Aren't I more grown up than most of the others in my class?'

The Sister nodded. 'She is quite grown up, Father. In fact, I often let Mary lead the class in prayer or let her choose the Bible story for discussion. And she is the President of the Mother Mary Society for the young people of the parish.'

'I call the meetings to order and I make sure the meetings proceed normally and there are even older kids than I am in the club but *I* am the President of it. I give the orders and the older kids take them.' She turned to the Sister. 'Isn't that right? Do you think I do a good job?' The woman nodded. 'So I would do a good job if I were teaching school. If I were a Sister, then I could teach little children and they could learn about Jesus and the Holy Mother and about the saints. I could teach them.' She took a deep breath. 'I could help them. But,' and she looked from the priest to the nun and back again, 'I can't be a teacher unless I become a Sister. And I want to teach. I *want* to become a nun.' She put her fingers, automatically, to the cross and chain that hung around her neck. 'In a few more weeks, I'll be fifteen and fifteen is when I should start with the special studies. If I know in advance that I might be accepted, then I can make arrangements and spend more time at church and more time on studying the special things I'll need to know before I go into the convent.'

'You only have your father, don't you?' The priest asked. Mary nodded, seeing her father's face for a brief moment and then blotting it out of her consciousness. 'What will he think about your becoming a nun? Will he approve? We will need his approval, you know.'

Mary took a deep breath. 'I don't know what he'll say,' she answered slowly, 'He's not a very religious man.' She watched their faces. 'I mean, he *is* a Catholic but he doesn't go to church . . . a lot.'

'Why not?' this from Father Paul. 'Is he ill?'

Mary saw an image of her father sprawled out on the bathroom floor. That's the way she had discovered him just this past Sunday when she awoke to get ready for Mass. He had thrown up and then had fallen asleep in his own vomit. 'Yes,' she said softly. 'There are times when he is ill. Times when he can't make it to church.'

'And your mother,' the priest asked, 'was she a good Catholic?'

'Oh yes!' Mary's face lit up. 'We used to go to church all the time, my mother and I did. We heard Mass, we went to the Novenas, we said the Rosary together every day. Right up till the time she got sick, she and I would come to church. Mrs Carbone always stopped by for us and we would all come together. You know Mrs Carbone? Rose Carbone?' The priest nodded, not at all sure he knew who this woman was. 'For a couple years Mother made things for the bazaar. One year she knitted a cover and another year she embroidered two pillowcases. They had blue humming birds on them.

137

Blue humming birds and tiny red flowers. Some lady from over at the Holy Rosary bought them just minutes after the bazaar opened.' She beamed. 'I embroidered hankies that year. I made twenty-five of them during the winter and stitched a letter of the alphabet on each one, like initials, except I didn't make one with the initial X because I didn't think anybody had a name that started with X and they all sold except for the D. Nobody bought the D. Mother laughed that I had made it for the Devil and she said *he* never pays anybody for anything. On yes,' she paused, 'Mother was a good Catholic. She really was.'

'How long has she been gone?' the priest wanted to know.

'Almost five years now,' Mary said and stopped to listen to her own answer. Lord, had it been five years *already*?

'And you live alone with your father?' Father Paul still questioned. Mary nodded a yes. 'He never remarried?'

Suddenly Aunt Minna's face was in her mind's eye. Aunt Minna with the bloated features and the lipstick and rouge and the smell of stale booze on her breath. 'No, he never remarried.'

'How old is your father?' the Sister asked.

'Thirty-three,' Mary said quickly. 'I remember that because at his last birthday he said he was as old as Christ and if he could live through one more year, there wasn't any danger of his being crucified.' The Father scowled and so did the Sister. 'But I didn't think that was funny,' she added quickly. 'I told him there were some things a body didn't joke about.'

'How old was your mother when she passed over to Jesus?' Father Paul asked.

'Twenty-eight,' Mary said softly. She looked up at the priest. 'That's very young, isn't it?' He nodded. 'Mrs Carbone said she will always be a young angel and that's how I should think of her. As a young angel. I

138

do sometimes. I see her in a white dress and with large white wings. I try to remember her when she was well and moving around the house but I guess the last weeks of her life made such a memory for me that it's difficult to see her that way with a real clear picture. I try real hard to remember her as being alive but sometimes when I shut my eyes at night I see her the way I found her.' Tears started to form and she didn't want them to be there. 'She was cold and so silent. I think that's what I recall the strongest: how silent she was. Not a breath. Not a sound.'

'Mary found her mother's body when she got home from school,' Sister Amelia explained. 'It was quite a shock to her.'

'I guess I kind of went a little crazy,' Mary said and smiled at the priest. 'I said a lot of things I didn't mean to say, especially to my father and to an aunt that was staying with us at the time. I confessed it all, of course,' she added quickly. 'As soon as I could get to confession, I got it off my soul.' It was difficult to get rid of, she wanted to say, difficult to forgive her father and Minna for keeping her sedated for three days after her mother's death. Difficult to forgive them for not having a funeral for her mother. When whatever Aunt Minna had given her finally wore off, her mother had been taken from the house, buried and forgotten. She hadn't had a Catholic funeral so she couldn't be buried in a consecrated cemetery. Instead, her body lay in a city-owned graveyard and there wasn't even a stone to mark the spot. Her father refused to buy one. When Mary had insisted her mother have a headstone, he had shouted at her: 'She can't move! What the hell's she need a stone to weigh her down for?'

Minna had left town right after the burial. Neither Jacob nor Mary had heard from her since.

Mary was aware of the silence as the two church figures looked at her. She wondered if possibly, unaware, she had voiced her thoughts. Could they read her mind as to how she *really* felt toward her father and her aunt? If she were a truly good Christian, she would tell them everything but, on the other hand, if they could hear what she had in her heart for her father and her aunt, they might not approve her entry into a convent.

'I really don't see,' said Father Paul, Mary stiffened, 'why we cannot consider you for the religious life.' Mary visibly relaxed. 'But I am sure Sister agrees with me, it would be better for you to finish your education.' The Sister nodded. 'To get your high school diploma. It would make studying easier at the convent. It would make you a better teacher if you completed your schooling. Certainly, Jesus would be more understanding of someone who had completed her secular life before entering her religious life. Don't you agree?' The Sister nodded again. So did Mary.

'It will mean,' Sister Amelia said, 'that you will shortly start to study things about the Church and the Holy Fathers that other girls your age will not have to learn. It will also mean a constant vigilance on your own thoughts and your own reasons for wanting to become a nun. Your must never stop analysing your reasons and never stop asking yourself *why* you have chosen this most difficult of all paths. And you must listen to your answers and your answers must please yourself and they certainly must please the authorities of the Church. As Holy St Peter was *the* rock upon which the Lord built his Church, so, too, must each novice member of the Church be as firm as a rock herself. Only with strength upon strength can we keep the foundations of our Church solid and indestructible.'

'I understand,' said Mary. 'I really do understand.'

For once, Jacob came home from work at the right time. Mary had dinner waiting, as she always did, but this time it was his favourite things: pot roast with noodles and creamed peas and fried cabbage. Usually she fixed a lighter supper, something that could be warmed up by putting it back on the stove-top or back into the oven but tonight was different. Tonight, she was going to tell him about the papers she wanted him to sign. She'd had them for three days, ever since her fifteenth birthday, and she was waiting for the right time to tell him about them. She calculated tonight would be the night.

'This is really good,' he said as he shovelled another spoonful of noodles into his mouth. 'What's the occasion?'

'None,' she said and smiled. 'Just thought you'd like to have it. The butcher got the beef in this morning and he assured me it was tender.' He nodded in agreement. 'Rose made the noodles. I stopped there after school and she gave them to me.' He nodded again. No matter what his personal opinion was of Rose, he had to admit she was a good cook. 'I was going to make a pie but I knew you wouln't have any room for dessert.'

'Don't need no pie with all this stuff,' he said with a mouthful.

'You want some more coffee? There's lots in the pot.' He shook his head and she remained seated. As he heaped his stomach full, she looked at him. There were more lines on his face than there had been when her mother was alive. And there was a tremble, at times, to his hands that hadn't been there before. Mary remembered how smooth and lean his face had been. Now it was unshaven and puffy. He put a razor to his cheeks once or twice a week. Rose said it was the booze that made his features puff up, that gave him the bags under his eyes and the creases around the corners of his mouth. She thought about his being thirty-three and wondered if Christ looked as old and worn as her father did. Thirty-three wasn't ancient. Mary actually knew a girl who had a grandfather who had had his seventy-fifth birthday. Now *that* was old. She looked at his rough hands and the dirt that was always present

141

under his fingernails. 'I've made up my mind about something,' she said slowly. He glanced at her, then back to his plate. 'It's about what I want to do with my life.' She paused. 'When I grow up, I mean.'

'Oh?' His eyes checked the quantity of noodles still left in the serving bowl.

'You know how I have always liked to study? And read things?' She waited but there was no response. 'Well, I've been thinking – looking around – and seeing what I could do with my life that would have books and learning and things like that in it and I think I know what I want to do.'

'Nobody knows what they want to do.'

'I do.' Her voice rose just a tiny bit. 'I want to be a teacher. Like Mama wanted to be.' She paused waiting for his blessing or his explosion.

'Good idea,' he said without looking at her. 'A woman can always get a job as a teacher.'

'I like children. I'm good with children. At school, sometimes, I sit in with the younger kids and help them when their teacher asks me to. I like to see people learn things and I feel good when I know I've helped a child understand things.' He nodded and his jaw continued to chew, his eyes on the wall behind Mary, not seeing his daughter at all. 'And so I thought that being a teacher would be the very best thing possible. Don't you?'

'I already said I thought it would be a good idea.' he said. 'It's respectable, at least. Doesn't pay a lot of money but doctors and lawyers marry teachers. Those rich guys like smart wives.' He laughed. 'Sure. Become a teacher and grab a rich husband. Why not?'

Mary paused and pushed a creamed pea from one side of her plate to the other. 'Well, it probably won't be like that *exactly*,' she said. How could she tell him that she wanted to become a teaching nun? 'I didn't really plan on the husband part. Only on the teaching part.'

He wiped his mouth with the cloth napkin. 'Nothing

wrong with thinking big,' he said. 'You gotta think big if you wanna get anywhere in this world. Especially you being a woman.'

'Well, the kind of teaching I want to do doesn't really lead to a rich husband.' She felt herself getting bolder. 'As long as you don't object . . .'

'I don't object. Why should I?'

'As long as you don't object, then, I have a paper that you have to sign so I can take it tomorrow.' She held her breath.

He had been pushing his chair away from the table. He stopped. 'Paper? What kind of paper?'

'So that I can be a teacher. A paper saying you approve of me being a teacher.' Again, she held her breath.

'A *paper*? What kind of nonsense is this? You gotta finish your high school first and then you can be any God-damned thing you want. You don't have to have any God-damned paper.'

'I do. It's a paper that I have to return.'

'Return? To who?'

'To . . .' It was now or never. 'To Father Paul.' God, she wished she didn't have to tell him *everything*.

'Father Paul? What the hell does he have to do with your wanting to be a teacher? Jesus Christ, he's just a God-damned priest, he ain't no school superintendent so what kind of paper does he think . . .' Jacob broke off his sentence in mid-air. He frowned as he listened to the information that was forming just behind his forehead. 'Being a teacher,' he said slowly. 'Are you talking about being a teacher in a *Catholic* school?'

She nodded, knowing what was coming.

'In a God-damned *Catholic* school?' Again she nodded, barely moving her head. 'You gotta be a God-damned *nun* to be a teacher in a God-damned Catholic school! What the hell's the matter with you? Is that what you're trying to tell me? Is that it?' He reached quickly across the table and put his hand under her chin, tilting her face so she was forced to look directly at him. 'Is that what all this bullshit is about being a 'teacher'? You wanna become a God-damned nun?' She nodded as best she could in his grip. 'A God-damned nun! Well, Jesus Christ! I thought you were smarter than that! A fucking God-damned nun!' She felt his fingers tighten around her chin. 'I thought you had some brains. I gave you a helluva lot more credit than *that*!' She started to whimper and he released his grip and shoved her face away from him. 'You're just a kid and a Goddamned *stupid* kid at that. You're too young to know what the hell you want. Well, I ain't. I'm your old man and I don't want you to become a nun and that's that. So get the idea out of your head. Now! No kid of mine is going to spend the rest of her life living with that mumbo-jumbo. You're gonna get your high school diploma and you're gonna get a job and bring some money into this house and someday meet a guy and get married and have kids! And someday, you and those kids will take care of *me* when I get too old to take care of myself. That's what kids are for, to take care of their parents. I took care of you all your life, now you better plan on taking care of me when *I* need it.' He grabbed her hair and yanked her head sideways. 'You hear me? You understand me? You're gonna have a *normal* life. Here. With me. In this house. And I don't want to hear anymore of this nun crap or I'll beat the shit out of you and then beat the shit out of that son of a bitch Father Paul!' He yanked her hair and she cried out in pain. 'You hear me?' He yanked again. 'Answer me. You hear what I just told you?' She nodded and mumbled the word 'yes'. 'That's better.' He relaxed his grip. 'Now get these dishes taken care of and this kitchen rid up and I don't wanna hear anymore shit about being a nun. Ever!'

She had told Sister Amelia how her father had reacted to the idea of her becoming a Catholic teacher and the Sister had sympathized with her saying that maybe her father would change his mind. Mary said she didn't think he would. The Sister had said that people *do* change their minds sometimes and suggested she go into the church and pray about it.

'And that's the only thing I really want,' she told the statue of the Virgin. 'That's the only thing I've *ever* wanted. As long as I can remember. To be a teacher and to be a nun and serve you and your blessed son Jesus.' She said these words aloud. It didn't matter, there was no one else in church to hear her. It was a one on one conversation between herself and the Mother of God. 'Please make my father change his mind. Please! I don't know what I'll do if he doesn't change his mind. That's what it'll take. For him to change his mind. Sister Amelia says I can't start the studies without his approval and could never enter the convent without his signing that paper. The only way I could get in without him would be if he would die and then I'd be an orphan and then I could do it.' She looked down at the floor. 'I thought about that, too. I committed a sin and thought about my father dying and I didn't cry or even care. That is a terrible sin, I know it is and I *am* going to confess it the next time but I wanted to confess it to you right now to show you how desperate I really am. Of course, I don't want him to die but it would be so much easier if he wasn't around.' She glanced up quickly at the beautiful lady in blue with the silver crown. 'Another sin. I know. I'm sorry. Last night, in bed, I did think of ways around him. I thought about having someone else sign the papers, someone who could write like my father and make it look like his signature. I even got out of bed and tried to copy his signature myself. But if I did that, if I turned a paper over to the church that had a sinful signature on it, how would that look? I mean, what would Father Paul say if he found out about it? What would you say if I did such a thing?' She got up off her knees and sat back in the pew. 'So now I don't know what to do. I've told him what I want and he won't let me do it. I've told *you* I won't try to do it in a sinful way. I promise you it'll be done in the right way. But I need your help, Blessed Mother. I must have your help. I can't change my father's mind all by myself. You *must* help me!' She crossed herself. 'I'm sorry. I didn't mean to say "must". Sister always says we should never tell you or any of the saints what you "must" do. She says that's a sin. You people up there know what you should do and all we can do is ask you to do it. We can't *tell* you to do it.' She crossed herself again. 'I'm sorry I said "must". Forgive me but I'm desperate.' She got back down on her knees. 'Please, Mother Mary, I *do* love you and I *do* believe in you and I *do* believe in your son Jesus and I worship you and I love you and I venerate you and adore you so won't you please, just this once, see what you can do with my father? Just this once and I'll be forever grateful and won't ever ask you for a special favour again.' She got up and took one last look at the painted smile on the painted plaster face. 'Please.'

Mary genuflected in the aisle and walked to the rear of the church. She dipped her fingers into the font of Holy Water that was on the entrance pillar, crossed herself again, genuflected again, turned and walked through the large wooden doors.

Nobody was there to see the Holy Water suddenly foam up, turn yellow and boil over, splattering onto the stone slabs of the floor.

For the first time since his marriage, there was no Christmas tree that year in Jacob's home. Mary wanting to be a nun had both angered and frightened him. The Catholic Church had never kept any of its promises to him, he reasoned, and he was damned if he would let it take his only daughter. He needed the child – in reality, a rapidly maturing young woman – and while he couldn't admit he *loved* her she was all the family he had left. He needed her for other reasons, too: washing his clothes, cleaning his house, preparing his meals and just *being* there. Even when he came home drunk, he knew she would be there. The older he got the more he hated being alone. *They* had not been around lately. *They* had not awakened him, had not played tricks on him, had not frightened him. Perhaps *They* had gone away. For good. Perhaps *They* were bothering somebody else. If so, fine. Just as long as *They* didn't bother him, didn't lie in wait for him, didn't try and take his daughter. He remembered, with stomach-wrenching vividness he remembered, how *they* had called Mary *their* soul when she was born. The voice had said: 'She's ours. You'll see.' But *they* hadn't done anything recently. Not for years as far as he could tell. Maybe *they* had forgotten. Maybe *they* were just a bunch of unearthly jokers who loved to upset human beings and never kept their threats. Maybe *they* didn't have the power, the energy, to carry out their threats. Maybe *they* were even bigger bullshitters than the priests and nuns were. That would take some doing, he had to admit, some doing to spread more shit on the sidewalk than the Church did. And that's why there was no tree that year. No baby Jesuses under it. No crosses and angels hanging from it. No red and green paper shit draped from wall to wall. No candle shit lit in the windows. 'That's kid stuff,' he had told his daughter. 'You're too old to believe that nonsense.'

On Christmas Eve, she went over to Rose's place and stayed the night. Jacob didn't care. He and three other drinking buddies spent the night sitting in his kitchen playing cards. When Mary came home Christmas afternoon, she had to clean up the mess before she could start supper.

Mary wore black to the Mass of the Presanctified that Good Friday in 1903. The service was early in the morning, just after dawn, but the girl didn't mind the sacrifice. After all, it was a time of mourning. The Lord had been humiliated, beaten, forced through narrow streets carrying His own cross and then nailed to that cross. He had died. It had been a horrible day for Him. A horrible day for all Christians and the least a good Catholic girl could do would be to get up early and wear black.

There were very few parishioners there that morning. It was just too early, at least that was Rose's excuse for not going with her. Mary sat, a whole pew to herself, and hoped the chill would go away. The old church was especially drafty that morning. Spring was on the way but winter had crept into the walls of the church and wouldn't leave until the summer sun chased it.

Even though she knew what they would do to the statues, she was shocked to see them draped in purple cloth. The Virgin stood there on the wall – her Blessed Virgin – looking like a mound of raspberry pudding. The other saints also wore the purple draperies, from halo to toe, obscuring their identities, making them even more mysterious and remote. Mary knew the statues were in mourning, just as she was. It had been a terrible thing what had happened to the Lord. She stared at the large figure of Jesus that hung on the wall behind the altar. The purple cloth hid Him as well. Even though He was covered she knew He was still suffering under there, that His hands and feet still throbbed in pain and the blood from the thorns clouded His eyes.

Father Paul appeared up front as did the altar boys but, for this special service, they were dressed in black. There would be no Mass, no normal service, at this time of sorrow and pain. There would be communion, but only for the priest. The host had been sanctified yesterday and the priest would partake of it today. The parishioners would not be permitted to taste the body of the Lord, one more reason for sorrow.

The priest read from the scriptures. Mary wasn't

sure what he was saying but she sat solemnly and listened because she knew it had to be important. Every now and then his voice would rise almost in song, then drop back to the flat humming of the Latin.

Then Father Paul, his back turned to the scattered few, genuflected three times in a row, and reached for the silver cross that always sat in the centre of the altar. Today the cross was draped in purple just like the enormous Jesus hanging on the wall. The priest said something in Latin and pulled back the cloth, revealing the right arm of the cross. The he said something else and revealed the left arm. Then he pulled the cloth from the top of the cross and then, finally with more words and humming, took the cloth away completely. The silver cross sparkled in it's new-found freedom. Then he lifted the cross, kissed it's base and carried it forward down to the communion rail. There he set it, most carefully and reverently, on a gold fringed purple pillow. The altar boys scurried to remove their shoes and, barefoot on the cold carpeting, they took a few steps, genuflected, took a few more steps, genuflected, a few more to finally reach the cross, genuflected again and then each, in turn, kissed the base of the cross.

The priest signalled to the only full pew of worshippers there that morning; a row of nuns. They rose and filed up to the silver cross and the pillow. One by one, they kissed the base of the cross and moved silently away. Then the priest signalled again and the few sitting around the nave rose and moved into the aisle, forming a line, awaiting their turn, to kiss the cross themselves. Mary was toward the end.

Father Paul smiled at her as she got nearer the object of devotion. He had smiled at everyone in the line but he made an extra effort for Mary. He had heard her story, he knew how difficult her home life was and how much she wanted to join the church to escape it. He made the sign of the cross in the air over

149

her head as she neared the silver cross.

She jerked her head up at him, looking him straight in the eyes. 'I don't need that!' she said in a loud voice.

Father Paul took a backward step, stunned by the girl's outburst. Those who had gone silently before her turned and looked. Those who were behind her craned to see.

'Keep your hand signals for those who want 'em,' her voice said, 'I don't!'

The priest tried to speak but the words stuck in his throat.

'And I don't need to kiss this cheap piece of metal, either!' she continued. 'And neither do you people,' she shouted at no one in particular. 'You'll keep breathing whether you show up at this place or not!'

'Mary! The idea!' Sister Amelia ran down the aisle and grabbed Mary by the shoulders and shook her. 'What a terrible thing to . . .' She stopped, for as she looked the girl's eyes turned upward. The pupils slid out of view leaving only the whites. Then Mary exhaled, letting out a long audible gasp of air that filled the front of the church with a stench like burning chemicals. Mary collapsed. Sister Amelia held on. 'Father Paul,' she screamed, 'we must do something!'

They put it down to exhaustion, the early hour, the emotion of her family life, the fact she was going through puberty. Neither Father Paul nor Sister Amelia personally blamed Mary for the outburst. The fact that she had fainted was enough to convince them it had been a case of frayed nerves. Mary didn't tell Rose about this and certainly not her father. There wasn't too much she could have told him even if she had wanted to. She tried to remember the sequence of events. She had been standing in line to venerate the cross, then she had opened her eyes in Father Paul's study. She had been lying on a sofa and Sister Amelia had been rubbing her wrists. She had no memory whatsoever of anything between those two events. They had told her what she had said and how she looked and she had cried and begged their forgiveness but she felt as if she was asking them to forgive someone else, another person who had offended the Church. It hadn't been her. She tried to convince herself that she had done those things but it was impossible. She would never say what they said she said. The good Father and the sweet Sister wouldn't lie, of course, but something in Mary's mind told her, most emphatically, that it wasn't her who had said those things. The Sister had suggested she rest at home for a few days and read several pages from St Teresa of Avila. She read the passages but went to school as usual. Jacob was on one of his between-jobs-drinking-bouts and at school she would be assured of at least eight hours of peace away from him.

In October of that year, Mary went to Church with Rose while the woman had a special Mass said for the soul of her grandfather who had just passed away in Italy. Rose had always liked the old man so kept her teary face in a handkerchief most of the time they knelt before the burning candles. She didn't see the basket of flowers by the side altar tip over by itself. There was no one near it, yet it fell and scattered blossoms across the carpeted floor. Mary caught the movement and drew in her breath when she saw it topple over. She closed her eyes and said her own prayer for the dead man way over in Italy while making a mental note to set the basket up again before she left the church. When she opened her eyes and looked again, the basket was in place. No flowers or water touched the floor. Mary blinked her eyes, looked again, but there it was.

The two left the pew, walked toward the door, with Rose still sniffling for a grandfather she hadn't seen in over forty years; suddenly the basket of flowers slid from the side altar platform, bumped down the two steps onto the floor and moved smoothly up the aisle behind them. If they had not closed the door when they did, the basket probably would have followed them out into the street.

'Go on,' urged Sister Amelia, 'open it. It's just a small gift.'

'From you and Father Paul?' Mary didn't know what to say.

'From both of us,' the Sister said, smiling. 'We don't usually do these things but we think you're kind of special. So "Happy Birthday",' she said, shoving the small package with the gold foil paper at the girl.

'I recall when I was sixteen,' said the priest. 'I thought I was all grown up,' He laughed. 'You know I did most of my growing up *after* that date!' He looked at the small size young girl before him. Both he and the Sister wished they could do more for her, but it was impossible. 'Open it. It won't bite.'

Mary had tears in her eyes. The Sister had told her the Father wanted Mary to stop at his study after school but she didn't tell her why. Mary never suspected it had anything to do with her birthday. She had almost forgotten about it herself and she knew her father wouldn't remember it. The last person, at home, to celebrate her birthday had been her mother and that was six years ago. 'You shouldn't have,' she muttered and her fingers tore at one edge of the paper.

'We know we shouldn't have,' Sister Amelia said, 'but we did.'

'We did because we wanted to,' said Father Paul. 'And we don't do it for everybody.'

'I know,' Mary smiled at him and opened the red plush box that had been under the fancy paper. She lifted the lid and gasped. 'Oh! It's beautiful!' She stared at the contents. 'It really is! And I've always wanted one!' she sniffled. 'I'm going to cry.'

'Not on my rug, you're not,' Father Paul admonished. 'Keep my study dry, young lady.'

Mary's fingers caressed the chain that held the delicate gold crucifix. 'It really is so beautiful,' she said softly. 'I . . . I don't deserve it.'

'You let us be the judge of that,' Sister Amelia said. 'Here, let me help you put it on.' The woman took the box and in a few seconds, she had unfastened the chain from the box and had unclasped it. She went behind Mary and deftly placed the chain around the girl's neck, closing the clasp behind her. 'There,' she said, 'now isn't that pretty?'

'It's been blessed by the Bishop,' Father Paul said. 'I had him do it myself.'

Mary's fingers went to the figure on the cross. 'It feels so good,' she said. 'I really don't know how to thank you. It's such a surprise. Such a nice surprise.'

'You deserve it,' the priest said. 'There, behind that door, look at yourself in the mirror. See how good it looks on you.'

Mary walked to the dark stained oak door and pulled it open. The full length mirror that Father Paul always used just before going 'out on stage' as he called it swung around and Mary saw herself reflected in it. Her dark brown eyes sparkled as she stared at the crucifix. Her reddish hair hanging fashionably down to her shoulders was the perfect frame for the gold figure on her breast. 'It really is so lovely!' she said with a smile. 'I never expected anything like this when Sister told me you wanted to see me. I thought maybe I had done something wrong and you were going to tell me. . . .'

She broke off her sentence suddenly, then stared at the image in the mirror, as she started to scream. 'Oh! It's hot! It's burning! Oh dear God, it's burning me! Please! Take it off me! It's burning me!' She ran from the closet to the two adults. 'Please,' she was crying now and they could see the fabric of her blouse begin to

153

char as tiny wisps of smoke rose from it. 'Please take it off me!'

Father Paul grabbed the crucifix and yanked, breaking the thin gold chain. He opened his hand and they looked at the small image resting in his palm. 'It's not hot,' he said. 'I don't feel any heat.'

Sister Amelia stuck one trembling finger quickly onto the metal. 'I don't either,' she said. 'It's not hot.'

'But look what it did to my blouse,' Mary said, 'there's a hole burned into it.'

And indeed there was.

Mary didn't try to wear the crucifix after that. She had carried it home, in the red plush box, and had put it in her dresser drawer. Both Father Paul and Sister Amelia thought the burning must have come from some reaction between the composition of the metal, the cloth of the blouse and the rays of the sun coming in the study's stained glass window. They assured her if she would wear another garment, a wool sweater for instance, there wouldn't be a problem. Mary decided she would put the gift on only for special occasions because, after all, it had been given to her by special people for a special occasion. That Easter, however, when she wanted to wear it to Sunrise Service, she discovered the box was empty. She knew she hadn't lost it, because she had never worn it. Jacob must have taken it and sold it, she figured. There had been a few weeks that spring when there was no work. A gold chain and crucifix would have been worth a couple of dollars at the pawnbrokers. She knew it would do no good to ask her father, he would just deny it. Anyway, she didn't have the courage to accuse him of it.

If Mary had had the courage, she would have been surprised at Jacob's truthful answer: he hadn't taken the crucifix. He never even knew she had it.

The ringing of the doorbell was incessant. Mary was in the kitchen, on her knees, scrubbing the floor. Jacob's new job was digging a hospital basement and every night his muddy boots tromped brown gritty smears through the house. The bell rang again. 'Just a moment,' she called. 'I'm coming.'

She got up, wiped her hands on her apron, stepped over the bucket of water and hurried down the hall. The bell kept ringing. 'All right!' she shouted. 'For Heaven's sake, I'm coming!' She yanked open the door prepared to face a salesman or a neighbourhood child asking for something.

'Happy Fourth of July, kid!' The woman shouted and grabbed Mary around the waist, pulling her close for a hug, then a kiss on the cheek. 'Great to see you!'

'Aunt Minna!' Mary was horrified.

'The very same, little darlin'. All the way from California to wish you a Happy Fourth of July!' She turned and yelled at the cab driver who had parked his horse and wagon at the curb. 'Okay. You can bring in the bags. There's someone home.'

Mary felt faint and wished she could lean against the doorway for support. 'It's a . . . a . . . surprise to see you, Aunt Minna,' she finally managed to say.

'I know it is, kid. I'm a surprise even to myself. Now don't bang those suitcases, mister! Got things in there that'll break. Well,' she said to Mary, 'aren't you going to invite me in?'

'Oh. I'm sorry,' and she tried to smile. 'Of course. Please come in Aunt Minna. Don't mind my manners, it's just that I didn't expect you. That's all.'

'Nobody ever does,' the woman laughed. 'Catch 'em off guard and hit 'em hard and then leave 'em again. That's my motto,' she laughed again. 'Okay if I put the bags in my old room?' she asked. 'Here,' she said to the driver, 'follow me. I'll show you where you can set the bags. Oh, don't make a face. I'll tip ya'. I got money on me. That's one of the troubles of the world, kid,' she continued talking as she walked toward Mary's bedroom, 'nobody will do nothin' if they don't get their palm greased. There,' she pointed, 'that door there, the one that's open.' The driver put the bags inside the room, came back, Minna put a few coins in his hand, he looked surprised, then grinned, took off his cap, said 'thank you, lady' and went out the door closing it behind him. 'Where's your old man?' Minna asked. 'Workin' I hope.'

Mary nodded. 'He should be home around sundown. For supper.'

'Supper! That sounds great! I'm so hungry I could eat a boiled cat. What you having tonight anyway?'

'I was going to make a meatloaf,' the girl said.

'Oh hell kid, don't celebrate my arriving back here with a *meatloaf*. Take this,' her hand went quickly into her purse, 'buy us some steaks. Some nice T-Bone steaks. And stop and bring back some beer from that place down on the corner. Let's have a party. We got two things to celebrate. Tomorrow's the Fourth of July and today your Aunt Minna is back in town. Back in town to *stay*.'

Sister Margaret stared at her. Mary stood by the teacher's desk, downcast eyes looking at nothing in particular. 'I really am concerned about you,' the woman said, 'and I think you should be also.'

'Yes, Sister.'

'I asked you two questions in class today, two simple questions, and you didn't have the answers. Even Joey Pavelnik knew the answers! Shows you how simple they were! Anyway, you who *used* to be my prize pupil didn't even know what I was talking about.'

'I *did* know what you were talking about,' Mary defended herself, 'it's just that when you asked, I couldn't say the answers. I tried but I couldn't make the answers come.'

Sister Margaret got up from her chair and put her

arm around Mary's shoulders. 'What's wrong?' she said softly. 'Are you ill?' Mary shook her head. 'Am I not explaining things properly?' Again, the girl shook her head. 'Is it at home? Is something happening at home?'

How could Mary tell this nice elderly sister what was happening at home, what had been going on ever since Minna showed up on the third of July? Her father had been delighted to see Minna. How Mary felt about having the woman stay there was never taken into consideration. The very first night, Minna waltzed into Jacob's bedroom and stayed there. Mary tried to feel scandalized but she had expected it. Minna remained in the bedroom all night and nothing was said about it the next day, the Fourth. The three had gone down to the river bank that night to watch the fireworks and as one long rocket zoomed into the air, quivered a moment and then exploded, Minna let out a laugh and said loud enough for half the crowd to hear: 'Now that one reminded me of your old man, kid!' Jacob just grinned. Mary wanted to dissolve into the earth.

At least she was able to keep her bedroom for herself. Minna hung her things in the closet where Jeanette's once hung and used the dresser drawers that Jeanette once used. On the fifth of July, Minna went to town and came back with a pink bedspread and almost matching pink and dotted swiss curtains for the bedroom windows. 'Get this depressing damned thing out of here,' she told Mary as she tossed the dark blue bedspread that Jeanette had bought onto the hall floor. 'And these curtains, you might as well burn them. I wouldn't put these up in a dog house let alone somewhere where people live.' Mary had wanted to tell her that Jeanette had made those curtains, cut them and fixed them from a second hand pair she had found at a household auction. She remembered what pride her mother had in her face when she hung the curtains. Jacob had refused to give her any money for the house that spring. He said, even though he continued to frequent the corner bar, that he didn't have any money for nonsense after buying food and clothes for the two of them. Jeanette confessed once to Rose, but Mary overheard, that she would go through Jacob's pockets when he came home drunk and take whatever was in there. When Rose said that could be dangerous, Jeanette told her Jacob was always so drunk he never remembered how much he had in his pockets by the time he got home.

'Did father give you the money for the bedspread?' she had asked her aunt.

'No, I bought the spread. He paid me for the curtains.'

Mary felt a new emotion, that of bitterness, rush through her brain. '*He* paid for the curtains?'

'Right,' Minna stepped back to admire them now that they were hung. 'Your father's an old sweetie. He really is.' She started to ask Mary what she thought about buying new towels for over the tub but the girl had left the room.

Sister Margaret was still talking. 'You only have two more years of school, Mary, and they are important years. The last two years are the culmination of all the other years that have gone before. You're going to have to get yourself under control if you expect to graduate with honours. Are you sure you're not ill?'

Mary shook her head and remembered lying in bed last night listening to the sounds that came from their bedroom into her space. The sounds started almost as soon as the two of them shut the bedroom door. There was the laughter. Then the silence. Then the squeaking of the springs. Sometimes more laughter but more often than not just mutterings and moanings. Then the springs would squeak more rapidly, the moans would change to loud groans, the mattress would rustle madly, then her father would shout, her aunt would cry out and then would come the silence. The first few times Mary had lain there, in the dark, and imagined pictures to go with the sounds. But after the first few weeks, she tried to blot out the noises by putting cotton in her ears. She knew even if she burnt out her ears with a hot poker, she would still hear them on the other side of the wall.

It was difficult to do homework in that house anymore. Minna liked big suppers and Mary was expected to help her prepare them. Minna was one of those cooks who dirtied every pot in the kitchen and expected Mary to wash them and put them away. After the meal, Minna and Jacob would either go and snuggle in the living room or go and drink in the corner bar. Minna simply pushed herself away from the dirty table and went to enjoy herself. Once the kitchen was in order, Mary could do her homework. It was better when the couple went to the saloon, that way Mary's studies weren't disturbed by having to listen to the conversation coming from the living room sofa. It was getting harder and harder to concentrate on her homework and harder and harder to remain awake in class when she got so little sleep at night.

'You have to apply yourself more, Mary,' Sister Margaret was saying. 'Idle hands make idle minds.'

'Yes ma'am.'

'Now I don't mean this as a form of punishment,' the Sister said, 'but while I told the rest of the class their homework assignment was the first ten questions at the end of the chapter, I want you to do the first twenty. I want all twenty written out and handed in to me tomorrow. I don't want to seem mean but you must start applying yourself. There can be no smooth future without a rock strewn path.'

'Yes ma'am.'

Mary stopped at the church on her way home that afternoon. Maybe if she sat and became silent within herself things would get better. 'Look inside for the truth,' was what Father Paul had told her in confession the last time. She had told him of Minna's disrupting influence but stopped far short of her aunt's sexual acrobatics with her father. What they were doing was their own business, she told herself. It was *their* sin, not hers. She didn't like it but it was not her sin to confess. Anyway, she was not about to tell Father Paul such scandalous things. He was a priest, after all, and priests led a sheltered life. There was no way she would tell him what was going on in her house. Why, being a priest, a holy man, he very probably had never even *heard* about what her father and her aunt were doing. Then, maybe, *she* would have to explain sex to Father Paul and, Lord, how embarrassing *that* would be! No, telling anyone about it (except Rose) would be a mistake. This was something she would keep to herself and, who knows, maybe it would go away. Maybe Aunt Minna would go away. Now wouldn't *that* be nice?

An elderly lady, all in black, walked in front of Mary and picked up one of the wax tapers in front of the burning vigil lights. There were six rows of candles, each in their own small amber glass pot, tucked into a six-branched metal holder. Mary had been at church when all the candles had been lit, creating a bonfire of light in the darkness near the side altar but today there were only a few of them candles burning in the holders. It was early and a weekday at that. The lips of the lady in black moved in private prayer as she lit the end of the slim, wax taper and touched one of the candles. It didn't light. She moved the taper over to another candle but it didn't take either. She shook her head and tried to light another one but with the same result. Finally she muttered a word aloud, a word Mary was positive wasn't a holy word, and jabbed the taper at another candle. It didn't light either. 'Are these damned things wet?' she called out. Mary snickered aloud and the woman turned to her. 'Well, are they? I can't get any of them to light.'

'Why don't you blow on them, you old bitch.' Mary said. 'Your breath would burn down an outhouse!'

'What?' the woman screamed. 'What did you say to me?' She started for Mary, the taper still smouldering in her hand. 'How dare you talk to me like that!'

Mary jumped up, stuck out her tongue at the woman, and ran up the aisle and out of the church. As she was halfway down the steps the cool, fall air startled her. She shook her head, blinked her eyes and looked around. 'What . . .?' she said aloud and her mind raced with questions: What was she doing outside? How did she get there? Why did she leave the church? Why didn't she remember leaving the church?

Christmas of 1904, Minna and Jacob went to St Louis to spend the holidays with a couple Minna had met when she was in California. Mary, not really wanting to go, wasn't invited anyway. She stayed home alone, except for Christmas Eve which she spent with Rose, and for Christmas Day when she went to Mass. She didn't bother to decorate the house. What was the use of it? When they came back, neither of them asked her how she had spent Christmas and New Years. Neither of them cared.

It was the first Sunday after Ash Wednesday, a cold February morning, and Mary went to Mass by herself. Rose had stopped attending regularly, ever since one of her children had taken ill and had died very quickly. Rose had prayed for the little girl's life and when the Virgin Mary didn't save her, Rose had been angry. She had taken it personally and decided to show the Virgin what she thought of her by staying away from Mass for a few weeks.

Mary sat bundled from the cold outside, not wanting the cold inside to creep through her clothing. Father Paul was saying Mass that morning. She liked his Masses. Because she had a personal relationship with him, she felt as a consequence she had a more personal relationship with Jesus at Mass time. And the young Father was more than a priest, he had become her friend. He was her confessor and she wished she could also make him her confidant. She wanted to tell him about conditions at home but just could not get up the courage.

The second step of the Mass was being said. Once the introductory prayers of the Missa Catchumenorum were finished, Father Paul prepared for the Missa Fidelium, the Mass of the Faithful. He kissed the altar, turned to the congregation and said 'Dominus vobiscum.'

'Et cum spiritu tuo,' Mary and the others replied aloud.

'Oremus,' said the priest. Then, as the choir sang, the ushers went up and down the aisles collecting the wooden plates of coins, and the occasional piece of paper money which the parishioners gave the church. Mary smiled and waited for the offering of bread and wine, one of her favourite parts of the service.

The priest took the host, placed it on a footed silver plate, made a prayer and offered it to the statue hanging on the wall. Then he placed it on the altar. '*Suscipe, sancte Pater, omnipotens aeterne Deus, hanc immaculatam hostiam, quam ego indigni famuli tuus offero . . .*'

'Indignus!' Mary shouted out. 'It's "indignus" not "indigni" or whatever you said!'

Father Paul stopped suddenly, his hands hovering over the altar, his eyes searching out the cause of the interruption.

'And it's not "famuli" either,' Mary continued, 'it's "famulus". It means "unworthy servant" and that's exactly what you are! An indignus famulus!' She rose from her seat and turned to look at the others in the congregation. Those close by could see she had her eyes shut. 'I don't know why you idiots think you've

162

gotta be here every Sunday morning. You think by hearing some mumbling in a language you can't understand that you're going to get out of burning in Hell? Well, let me tell you . . .'

Father Paul didn't move but Father Cipriano and Father Carlo did. They ran to her, pushed past those cringing away from her, and grabbed her.

'Vade Satana!' Father Cipriano shouted. 'Begone Satan!' and he made the sign of the cross on her forehead.

Mary screamed, her body crumpled onto the pew, and they carried her, unconscious into Father Paul's study.

The priest, still shaken from the first interruption he had ever experienced while saying Mass, made the sign of the cross to the congregation, then over the table where the host and the wine sat waiting. '. . . *indignus famulus tuus offero tibi Deo meo vivo et vero* . . .' he continued to intone but in a noticeably shaky voice.

Jacob got down from the plank that straddled the two stepladders and, wiping the drying plaster dust from his hands onto his overalls, approached the priest. When the foreman told him a priest wanted to see him, he immediately thought that something had happened to Minna. Maybe she had been hit by a trolley car and taken to the hospital. He hoped it wasn't that. What would he do without Minna in his life?

'Jacob Lawrence?' the priest asked. Jacob nodded. 'I'm Father Paul.' Jacob waited. 'I'm the pastor where Mary goes to church.'

'Mary?' Jacob said, the relief apparent in his voice.

'Yes, Mary,' Father Paul said, trying to hide the anger in his voice. He remembered enough of what the girl had told him to be prepared not to like this man; and he didn't. 'It's your daughter. I'm concerned about her. She had a spell in church yesterday. Did she tell you about it?'

Jacob shook his head. 'In church?' His breath made a cloud in the cold morning air. 'She doesn't tell me about church.'

'She became ill in church yesterday. During the Mass.'

'She looked okay to me yesterday.'

'She disrupted the Mass by standing and shouting blasphemies.'

Jacob grinned. 'She did, huh?'

'It was a most unusual occurrence for her. And for me, I might add. We're not used to interruptions during Mass.'

'Too bad,' said Jacob.

'She was taken into my study afterwards and was unconscious for almost an hour. She was hardly breathing at all. Several times we had to put a mirror under her nose to see if she *was* breathing. It gave us all a scare.' He watched the expression on Jacob's face. 'But she didn't tell you any of this, did she?'

'No. I guess she thought it wasn't important,' Jacob said. 'But she looked okay when she got home. Of course,' and he grinned again and ran his hand through his thick brown hair, 'I didn't get up too early yesterday. Sunday is my day to sleep in. I probably got up around noon. She was okay then.' Actually it was almost two o'clock by the time Minna and Jacob felt their hangovers would let them get out of bed. 'She didn't say anything to me,' he continued. 'Course, Mary doesn't talk much.'

Father Paul stared at the man and wished he could verbalize what he was feeling toward him. 'We are concerned about her health,' he said. 'Has she been having any spells at home?'

'Spells?'

'Yes, faintings or sudden outbursts or any unusual behaviour?'

Jacob shook his head. 'Not that I've noticed. She seems fine to me.' He paused. 'She's not in the hospital or anything, is she?'

The priest shook his head. 'No. I don't think she needs medical attention. It might be more ...' he paused, '... how can I phrase this ... more *mental* attention she needs. Just possibly your daughter should see a mental doctor. Maybe she should discuss things with him.'

'Things? What things?'

'Things she's bottling up inside, things she can't tell you ... or me.'

Jacob scowled. 'There isn't anything she can't tell me. She tells me things, everything. She don't have any reason not to. After all, I'm her father.'

'And I'm her priest and I'm concerned.'

'Well, don't be. Mary is fine and healthy and sure in hell doesn't need a mental doctor. She's a school kid. She's going through some growing problems, that's all.'

'But you do admit she has problems,' Father Paul said quickly.

'Everybody's got problems,' Jacob replied. 'I got 'em and you got 'em and Mary's got 'em. That makes her normal. It doesn't make her crazy and needing a brain doctor. I know my own daughter for Christ's sake.'

'You're sure?' Father Paul wanted to punch this man, to knock him off his feet and onto the snowy, muddy ground. 'You're sure you know your daughter?'

'Look, I don't know what you are after with all this,' Jacob said slowly. 'If this is all some sort of bullshit to get me to sign a paper so she can become a nun, forget it. I already told her she ain't becoming no nun and now I'm telling you. I didn't raise her to wear black and live with a bunch of frustrated old women.'

'This has nothing to do with her becoming a nun,' Father Paul said rather loudly, 'it has to do with her health.'

'Look, don't come bothering me with ideas about my daughter's health. Her health is *my* responsibility and Mary is in good health. She's never felt better. Your responsibility is her *religious* health. Not her mental not her physical but her religious health. And that's Mary's idea, not mine. It's a carry over from her mother. If I wanted to be a real bastard, I'd forbid her to go to your church at all, but I *ain't* a bastard. I'm a good father and a good provider. And I'll be the one to judge if she needs a head doctor or not.'

'Well, we at the church think she does.'

'Well, you had better keep your noses out of it. I'll take care of my daughter, thank you.'

'You had better do it quickly.'

'Don't tell me what to do.'

'Somebody should.'

'Father, go to Hell!'

'So what kind of shit have you been doing?' Jacob stood, hands on his hips, staring at Mary as she stirred a pot on the stove. 'Some damned priest came to the site today and said you'd been acting crazy in church! What the hell's going on?'

'Father Paul?' Mary asked. 'Did Father Paul tell you what happened? How did he know where to find you?'

'How the hell should I know? He was there, and he told me you had acted like an idiot, shouting things and playing sick at Mass. So what's this all about? I gotta right to know.'

Mary sat down, heavily, on a kitchen chair. 'Father Paul said *that*? He said I was acting like a *crazy* person, like an *idiot*? He *said that*?'

'More or less. Yes, that's the way he put it and I want to know what the hell you think you were doing? Jesus Christ, do you know how embarrassing that is, to have a Goddamned *priest* come looking for you at work? Do you know how that made me feel?'

'I'm sorry.'

'Oh, sure you are. Sorry. Well, I don't have to go through stuff like that just because you don't have any

166

more brains than to start screaming during a Mass. Goddamned kid. You've done some stupid things in your lifetime but that was about the stupidist. Can you imagine what your mother would have said if she'd known about this?' He paused waiting for the effect. He didn't often mention his dead wife but when he did it was always for special effect. 'Your own mother would have disowned you if she had known.'

Mary started to cry. 'I don't know what came over me,' she said. 'I don't remember saying what they said I did. I don't remember any of it! Please,' she looked at her father through tear-filled eyes. 'Believe me, I don't recall saying those things.'

'So the priests are liars? Is that it? You are Miss Goody Two Shoes and the priests are lying?' He came very near to her. 'Do you know how it looked down at work having a damned Catholic priest come to see me? Do you?' She was sobbing now. 'You better get your Goddamned self under control or I'll smack the shit out of you!' He grabbed her hair and pulled her face upward. 'You see this hand? I'll split your Goddamned lip if *ever* this happens again! You hear?' He gave another yank on her hair. 'Do you hear me?'

'Yes,' she choked on her own tears, 'yes, I hear you.'

'And don't forget it!'

Minna came into the kitchen. 'What's all the yelling about?'

'This Goddamned kid of mine acted like a fool in church the other day and the fuckin' priest came to bawl me out about it.'

'Bawl *you* out?' the woman said.

'Yeah. Can you imagine? She goes nutty and *I* catch hell from that black-suited son of a bitch! Don't that beat all?'

'What'd you do?' Minna asked Mary.

'Nothing,' the girl replied. 'I didn't do anything. It just happened.'

'Sure,' Jacob said loudly, 'you didn't do nothing and

the priest came to see me because of nothing. She expects me to believe that,' he said to Minna.

'I didn't do anything,' Mary sobbed, 'it just happened.'

'Things don't just happen,' Minna said.

'Remember,' Jacob warned as he gave one more yank to her hair, 'one more time and you get a split lip. Now get off your ass and let's get some supper on the table.'

'She's at that age, hon,' Minna said to Jacob, 'that age when they start lyin' . . . and other things.'

'What other things?' Jacob demanded.

'You know,' Minna winked. '*Other* things girls do that they don't want their folks to find out about. She's at that age. Look at those bumps under her sweater. Those aren't oranges in there, hon. She's at that age.'

'Is that what you've been doin'?' Jacob screamed at Mary. 'Is that what Father Paul was warning me about? Is it?'

At this Mary began to cry even harder, putting her forehead on the tabletop and sobbing.

'You gotta keep your eye out, hon,' Minna advised, 'she don't tell everything she knows and neither do those Goddamned priests.'

'I ain't gonna have no tramp for a daughter,' Jacob said 'and no crazy girl either. You better start walkin' the straight and narrow and if I hear or even suspect you of anything wrong, you'll get it from me. Now stop that blubberin' and get this kitchen back to normal.'

Minna walked out behind him. 'Imagine the nerve,' she laughed and then mimicked Mary's tearful voice: 'It just happened, daddy. Really, it just happened.' She laughed.

'It *did*,' Mary whispered to herself. 'I don't know how or why any of this happens. It just *happens*!'

A year had gone by and nothing had changed. Minna was still in the house, still giving orders, still acting like Mary's mother during the day and like Jacob's wife at night.

Jacob was working steadily now. The job that had started out as a basement excavation turned into helping pour the cement, then helping with the walls. Jacob and the boss got along very well – drinking together almost every night after work – so when his hangovers made him late (or caused him not to show up at all) the boss didn't object. The boss had met Minna, too, and along with his girlfriend the four used to get together for long drinking sessions. Mary worried about the safety of that hospital building: excavated and built by drunks.

The girl had managed to get through another year at school. She had passed all her junior year classes, but just barely. She had fallen from her 'A' average as a freshman, to a 'B' average as a sophomore, to getting mostly 'C's' as a junior. Her teachers, tired of having to lecture her and tired of blaming themselves for her decline let her alone. 'She's a big girl now,' Sister Margaret said more than once to the others on the staff, 'and if she wants to throw away her life, there's just so much we can do.' The others nodded their wimpled heads in agreement.

She still attended Mass regularly. Father Paul kept an eye on her, watching her comportment in church, listening carefully to her confessions but everything seemed normal. There had been no outbursts during services, no faintings and no outward signs that Mary was being tormented. She told no one of the torments. There was no one to tell.

They had started shortly after the fainting spell in church. They had started slowly and became more terrifying as time went on.

She had been in bed, asleep, when the first one came. It was the lightest, and as she recalled them, the tenderest. It was merely the sensation of fingertips caressing her face. She had been dreaming of school and taking tests and when the sensation was felt, the dream instantly turned into one with her mother. Her mother was standing over her and caressing her skin. Mary smiled and opened her eyes as the pressure mounted. There was no one there. She rubbed her cheek and tried to bring back the tender sensation. Recalling the image of her mother, she smiled, shut her eyes and drifted back into sleep.

The next time the fingertips caressed her, she smiled in her sleep, and turned over onto her side. The fingertips slid from her face down along her neck, then moved onto her shoulder. They brushed her warm skin for a few moments and then slid deeper under her nightgown, coming to rest atop her breast. She awoke with a start as the sharp pain of a pinch on her nipple stabbed through to her conscious mind. She sat up and rubbed her breast. It was aching. She wondered how she could have caught her breast in such a way that it pinched amid the soft bed clothing. She managed to get back to sleep.

The next time the fingers came she was just drifting into sleep and as they moved down her cheek and onto her shoulder she opened her eyes and stared into the darkness. As the hand crossed her breast, she screamed. Then she jumped out of bed and fumbled for the lamp wick, turning it up and seeing for herself that there was no one in the room. She yanked the blankets down and patted around trying to find the insect or – horrors – the mouse that had walked across her. The bed was empty. Jacob and Minna hadn't heard her scream, they weren't back from the saloon as yet.

A month later, a full month after she had forgotten the other incidents, she again felt the fingertips. This time she awoke and tried to analyse where they came from. She rolled over and turned up the lamp wick, she didn't fuss, didn't try to get out of bed. As she lay there the hand passed over her breasts, kneaded them and then started down her belly. When she felt it getting closer to that private part between her legs, she rolled out of bed, almost falling on the floor in her haste. She

170

ran from the room, taking the lamp with her. She sat for several hours on the living room sofa, trembling and afraid to get back into that bed.

The next day in school, as she sat on the toilet in the girls' restroom, the hand glided across her belly, her naked belly where her underpants usually were. Mary let out a yell and jumped up, continuing to pee down her leg and onto the floor. Because the commode cabinet partitions began a foot from the floor, the other girls could see her shaking her long skirts and see the puddle of urine she had created. Mary hurried out of the cubicle, stared at all the amused faces and said 'I need to get the mop.' The school janitor, a male, waited until the next class started before going in and cleaning up the puddle.

'Did you hear about Mary Lawrence?'

'What?'

'She peed herself!'

'No!'

'Yes she did. In the girls' restroom. She soaked the hem of her skirt and made water on the floor.'

'Maybe she's sick.'

'More like she's just stupid!'

'She really did? She peed herself?'

'Really! Everybody knows about it. Even the Sisters. I mean *everybody*!'

Mary wanted to tell someone about the fingertips. But who? Who would believe her? Who would not think she was going crazy?

And there were times when she, herself, doubted her own sanity.

'I got this letter today.' Minna held up a long envelope and waved it as Mary came through the front door. 'It's from your school. They're about ready to throw your ass out of there. You know that?'

'You got the letter?' Mary had been warned such a letter would be coming. 'They sent the letter to you?'

171

'Well, it was addressed to your old man, but I opened it.' Minna wasn't smiling. 'Christ, kid, why are you almost failing? I mean, well, Jesus, I thought you had some brains.'

Mary glared at her. 'I'm *not* almost failing. I've got a "C" average. Anyway, that letter's for my father. Not for you.'

'Don't get uppity with me, kid. The letter came to this house – *my* house – so I had the right to open it. What the hell's the matter with you at school? They say you're not paying attention, that you don't have your homework, that you do "strange" things during school hours, that your parents should have a talk with you.'

'You are not my parent.' Mary didn't know where this new-found strength came from suddenly. 'I only have one parent. My father. Not you.'

'Look, you little bitch, don't get your ass out of line with me. You know as well as I do that I'm almost like your mother.'

'Almost like my mother? My God!' Mary felt something rise up in her throat. 'You are *nothing* like my mother! My mother was a saint!'

'And what am I?' Minna demanded.

'You are like a . . . a . . .' The word 'whore' was on the tip of Mary's tongue but she shook her head and refused to say it. 'Never mind,' she sighed. 'I'll discuss this letter with my father.'

'You'll discuss it with me,' Minna shouted. 'I'm part of this family, too!'

'Not as far as I'm concerned,' Mary answered.

'Don't you be insolent!'

'And don't you be telling me what to do.' Mary walked closer to the woman, her breath coming in short bursts, her eyes closed. 'Don't you *ever* tell her what to do, you slut! Don't think because you're screwing her father that you can rule her life! Just be careful of how far you push, because we can push harder than you've ever imagined!'

172

'I'm going to tell your dad on you!' Minna screamed. 'You have no right!'

'And you have no right to live! Don't fuck with us lady! You're not in our plans!' Mary reached out an arm and shoved Minna back a few steps. 'You are nobody! And we eliminate nobodies easily.'

'I'm telling your dad!'

'If necessary, we can eliminate him, too!' Mary pushed past the wide-eyed woman. 'Now get out of her way. This girl's got homework to do.'

'I will!' Minna screamed. 'I'm telling your dad! When he gets home, you'll see! You don't talk to me like that, young lady! I have some say – so in this house! I'm telling your dad!'

Mary turned at her bedroom door and stared at Minna, stared through closed eyes. 'Tell Jesus Christ himself if you want to.' She slammed the door behind her.

'And she said these terrible things to me, Jacob. I mean she really treated me terrible! Like I was street garbage!'

Mary stood in the middle of the living room, head hanging.

'Did you do that?' Jacob shouted. There was whisky on his breath.

'Of course she did!' Minna said loudly. 'I just told you she did.'

'Why?' Jacob's face was just inches away from his daughter's. 'Why?'

'I don't recall why,' Mary said softly.

'I don't recall why,' Minna mimicked. 'Well, I recall very well that you did. I recall what you said. You called me a slut! Imagine, Jacob. My very own niece called me a slut!' She started to cry waiting for him to start slapping Mary across the face. 'Well? Aren't you going to do something? She called me a slut.'

'I didn't,' Mary said quietly.

173

'So you're telling your father that I'm a liar? Is that what you're telling him?'

'I'm trying to tell you that I don't remember calling you anything at all.'

'Huh!'

'I came into the house, you had a letter from the school and you started yelling at me and then the next thing I remember I was in my room. I don't recall anything in between.'

'Very convenient,' Minna said.

'It's the truth,' Mary said.

'You let *me* decide what the truth is,' Jacob said.

'I'm telling you I don't recall saying those things to Minna.' She looked her father full in the face. 'It's like those times in church. When they said I said things that I didn't remember. It's just like those times.' She started to cry. 'Maybe Father Paul is right. Maybe I do need a mind doctor. Maybe I am going crazy.'

'Very convenient,' Minna said again. 'Do things and then claim not to remember them. That way you think you can get away with murder. Well, not with me, young lady. You owe me an apology and I want it now.' Mary didn't even blink. 'Jacob,' Minna turned to him, 'tell her to apologize to me. Make her apologize to me.' Jacob just looked from one woman to the other. 'Well, all right then,' Minna said, 'if you won't do something, *I* will!' She rushed over to Mary, swung her right hand back as far as it would go and sent it crashing toward Mary's face. Just before her fingers made contact with the girl's skin, her arm stopped. Then her fingers twisted, her wrist was wrenched downward and she fell onto the floor writhing in pain. Minna gasped for breath through the sudden rush of tears. 'Oh God! My God! Look at my arm! Jacob, did you see what she did to me? Jacob, did you see?'

Jacob, who had watched the scene, shook his head. Mary hadn't moved. Minna had fallen to the floor on her own account. Mary hadn't done a thing.

174

'Did you see what she did?' Minna shouted again.

'No,' said Jacob softly, 'in truth, I didn't see a thing.'

'So they are back,' Jacob said aloud and kicked his muddy boot at a mound of dry leaves that had fallen on the sidewalk. He had left the two women in the living room, left them glaring at each other and had gone for a walk. By himself. So, he mused, they have come back and this time they've come for Mary. He shook his head. He wondered why they hadn't been bothering him. Wondered where they had gone. Wondered when they would make a reappearance. Now he knew. Mary. It was Mary they wanted. They had waited until she was almost grown up and they had come back for her. It wasn't his daughter who had said those things in the church. It was them. It wasn't Mary who had sassed his beloved Minna. It was them. A cold wind blew around the corner and he fastened the top button of his dirty work coat. They had told him, the very day the girl had been born, that they wanted her. He had feared them, then doubted them, then finally ignored and forgot them. Now they were back. And they probably would take Mary with them when they left.

'Hey! Watch where you're going!' A man shouted at Jacob who had stepped from the curb right in the path of his horse and wagon.

'Sorry,' Jacob mumbled and waved the driver on. So what was he supposed to do now? Minna wanted Mary punished for the insults she had received. How could he explain to Minna that it wasn't Mary who had sassed her, but rather some 'ghost', some 'demon', some 'energy' he had no control over. No, no control. He stopped and stared in a shop window, seeing his daughter's tear-stained image in the glass. He had no control over them, whoever they were, but they had control over him. They had control over all three of them. Even Minna who was impossible to control. They had grabbed her arm, twisted it and forced her onto

175

the floor before she could harm Mary. He shook his head with the memory of it. He had seen the whole thing, yet who would believe him? Minna's hand had stopped just inches from the girl's face, then she had been wrenched and had fallen to the floor. Who the hell would believe it? Now Minna would want Mary punished for physically attacking her. He was sure of that. That would be the next thing. Minna wanted the girl chastised first for the insults and now for the physical abuse.

A stray dog came up to Jacob and he growled at it. The animal slunk away. If he didn't punish Mary, what would Minna do? What would her reaction be? He stopped, ran his hand over the stubble on his face, and felt something pain him suddenly in his stomach. Suppose Minna went away? Suppose if he didn't punish the girl, Minna left him? Oh God! What would he do if Minna left him? What kind of loneliness would he face without Minna? *His* Minna. Maybe he could tell Minna about the ghosts who were doing all this. Maybe she would understand if he sat down with her and patiently explained, explained everything, from the beginning. Maybe she would see things in a different light. Maybe it would make her a better friend of Mary's. He stopped suddenly and a woman with a grocery bag almost bumped into him. No, that would only make things worse. Minna would probably not believe him. Who would? She wouldn't believe him and she would think he was making it all up just to excuse his daughter. She'd accuse him of taking sides and then she would leave him. If he took *Mary's* side, she would leave him. And if she *did* believe him, then she would be so frightened about ghosts being in the house she wouldn't spend another night under that roof. She was terrified of ghosts. She told him that. So she would leave him. Either way, she would leave him. No, there was only one thing to do. He knew it was the wrong thing but it was the *only* thing.

He turned a corner and started back toward home. He walked quickly to his house, up the steps onto the front porch and pushed open the door. He tried not to think about what he had to do. All he thought about was not having his Minna beside him. Maybe later he would explain himself to Mary. Maybe later the girl would understand. Minna was sitting on the sofa, flipping the pages of a magazine. She glanced up at him, then back at the magazine. He knew he had to make himself look brave and commanding in her eyes. Too much was at stake if he didn't carry it off.

'Mary!' he shouted through the closed bedroom door. 'Mary! Come out here!' He turned the doorknob and the door opened. The girl was lying on the bed, her face swollen from crying. 'Mary,' he said loudly, loud enough for Minna to hear. 'There's something I have to do. You know it as well as I do. We can't have this insolence in the house.' His trembling hands unfastened his belt buckle and Mary shut her eyes hearing the swishing sound of the black leather just before it came down across her shoulders.

Sister Bertoletta pointed with pride to the photograph on the classroom wall. She was smiling even if the big boned man in the picture wasn't. 'Our Pope, our Holy Father Pius the Tenth, has only been on the throne for three years but already we have seen wonderful advances. Haven't we?' She looked at the faces looking back at her. 'Who can give me an example of what our Holy Father has done so far?' Hands shot up. 'Yes, Daniel?'

'He has been helping the poor people in Italy,' the boy said.

Sister nodded. 'Anybody else? Yes, Margaret Ann?'

'He has been trying to keep the original traditions of the Church and not permit modern thought to influence it.' The girl smiled, obviously she had listened to last week's Sunday School lesson.

'Right,' said Sister, 'the Holy Father doesn't want the ideas of modern thinkers modifying the original doctrines. After all, those ideas were set down by Jesus himself along with Saint Peter. We have traditions that must be preserved,' and she smoothed the long dark skirt she was wearing. 'Yes, you, Mary Lawrence. You have something to add?'

'Yes ma'am,' Mary said, 'just one thing. The Pope is an ass.'

Sister Bertoletta almost lost her balance against the blackboard. The students, after a collective moment of stunned silence, began to gasp and raise their voices in protest.

'An ass!' Mary repeated. 'That old fool thinks he can cover up all the crimes of the Vatican by handing out baskets of food to the starving. It won't work. People aren't that simple minded.' Mary stared at the Sister who was clutching at her large pectoral cross and trying to decide if she should faint or not. 'All that money in the Vatican?' Mary's voice was harsh, almost masculine. 'All that gold that ignorant people have given the church?' The Sister saw Mary's eyes were closed. 'The Pope is sitting on all that wealth and what does he do?' Mary turned and the others heard her voice but stared in amazement: Mary's lips weren't moving! 'Can you imagine how many pennies, given by the poor and by people who can't afford it, are sent to Rome every Sunday after Mass? How many people sacrifice so he can wear a crown of gold?' She stood up and eyes still closed and lips not open, shook a finger at the nearly hysterical Sister Bertoletta. 'And you foster this crap! You stand up here and tell these innocent children to give to the Church, to believe the Church, to never doubt the Church! That's bullshit! Pure and simple bullshit!'

'Mary Lawrence!' Sister Bertoletta managed to find her voice. 'You shut up! You shut up this instant!'

'It's pure and simple bullshit and you, a so-called

teacher, are a simple frustrated old virgin who doesn't know – but should know – better.' Mary turned and started for the door. 'I'm getting out of here before my boot tops get covered with all the shit on the floor.'

'You stop, Mary Lawrence!' the Sister screamed. 'Don't you leave this room!' Mary continued toward the door, her eyes shut tight, yet not bumping into a thing. 'Stop her!' the Sister screamed and two boys jumped up and grabbed Mary. The girl roared like a wounded bear and flailed out with her arms, sending the boys over backwards across the desks. 'Oh, Blessed Holy Mother of God!' the Sister cried. Mary turned, raised one hand, then raised one finger on that hand and made an upward motion into the air. It was that gesture that forced Sister Bertoletta to decide if she was going to faint or not. She did.

Jacob shifted uncomfortably in the chair in front of the desk. He had taken the morning off from work, had put on his 'good' clothes and had been prepared to argue with the priest on every point. But he and the young Father were not alone. Sister Amelia was there along with Sister Bertoletta and so was Father Cipriano. They had arranged themselves on the side of the room where Father Paul was sitting. Jacob sat by himself, alone and feeling like a criminal on the witness stand.

'So you see why it's impossible for us to let her continue at school,' Father Paul said. 'We've studied her case, we've gone over each incident, each detail, and have all come to the same conclusion. Your daughter, Mary, is dangerous. Dangerous to herself and dangerous to others around her.'

'And dangerous to the Church, it sounds like,' Jacob said.

'Nobody is dangerous to the Church,' Father Cipriano spoke quickly. 'The Church is solid and shall prevail. One lone girl is not a threat to the Mother Church.'

'Then why are you being so rough on her?' Jacob asked. 'Let her finish out this year. Let her graduate. She's only got a few months to go. After all, she's put in almost twelve years with you people.'

'As much as we love Mary,' Sister Amelia said, 'we cannot subject the other children to her dangerous physical outbursts.'

'Nor her impiety,' added Sister Bertoletta.

'The parents of our students have entrusted their children to us for an education, both secular and religious. Someone like Mary only destroys what the parents desire, destroys what the good Sisters teach. It's not fair to the other children.' Father Paul stared at Jacob, hoping this rude bricklayer would understand their point of view.

'So Mary opens her mouth, disagrees with you and gets tossed out. Is that it?'

'No, that's not "it", as you call it,' said Sister Amelia, 'we are asking her to leave because she is not normal. She cannot be counted on to have the normal reactions that other girls her age have.'

'In other words,' said Jacob, 'disagreeing with your dogma is not normal. The "normal" kid swallows the bait and the hook.'

'It sounds,' said Father Paul, 'that Mary received her anti-Catholic beliefs at home. Mr Lawrence, weren't you born and raised a member of the Church?'

Jacob nodded. 'I sure was but I'm not anymore.'

'Why?' Father Paul asked.

'Because,' Jacob said slowly, 'the Church demands everything and then doesn't keep its promises. You've got a million rules that must be obeyed yet when one lone Catholic asks for a favour, it's denied him.'

'I don't understand,' said Father Cipriano.

'You wouldn't,' Jacob replied.

'What favour were you refused?' Father Paul asked. 'Where did the Church fail you?'

'I had a mother and I had a wife and both those

women were sainted women. I know that now. They were saints and they were devout Catholics and they had families they loved and families that needed them. I was told, by people like you,' he pointed toward the Sisters, 'that if a person prayed and had faith and believed then both these women would be spared. I prayed for my mother and she died. Mary prayed for her mother and she died. Have faith in the Church. Blessed Jesus will never fail you. Horse shit.'

The Sisters coloured under their wimples. 'So you taught Mary to blaspheme the Church,' Father Cipriano said. 'You took an innocent child and twisted her mind around to your way of thinking? Is that why Mary is where she is today?'

Jacob shook his head. 'No. It's not my fault. Mary had gone to Mass and to Church and to this damned parochial school because she wanted to go. I never wanted her to be so religious, but she wanted it. It was her idea. She never listens to me about anything, anyway. If she got up in class and said things . . .'

'Terrible blasphemies!' Sister Bertoletta interrupted.

'. . . said things that upset you old biddies and upset your church, it was all her own doing. I had nothing to do with it. Hell,' and he squirmed in the chair, 'I want her to graduate from high school as much as she does. Then she can get a job and bring some money home for a change. She wanted to be a nun, remember?' he asked Father Paul.

'I remember,' the priest said, 'but that's impossible now.'

'Even if I sign the papers?'

'Impossible even if you sign the papers.'

Jacob rose. His hat had been respectfully in his hand, now he put it defiantly on his head. 'So where does that leave Mary?'

'Out of school!' Sister Bertoletta said quickly.

Father Paul shot her a stern glance. 'Yes, out of

school but hopefully, Mr Lawrence, you'll try to get help for your daughter.'

'What kind of help?'

'Mental help.'

'You think Mary's crazy?'

'I don't know what to think,' the priest replied truthfully. 'I don't think Mary does these things deliberately and I don't think she is a "bad" girl. It's almost as if what happens to her is not her own fault. Back in my country, in Ireland, when a person is bad without any reason to be bad we say: "The devil rocked her cradle." I think that's what happened to your daughter. I don't have any answers.' He looked Jacob steadily in the eyes. 'Do you? Do you have any answers? She's your daughter. You should know what's happening to her.'

Jacob let his gaze slide toward the floor. 'Yes,' he said in a softer voice, 'I know what's happening to her, but I doubt if there is anything I can do about it.'

'You *do*?' Sister Bertoletta said loudly. 'What is the problem, if you know.'

'It wouldn't do me any good to tell you,' Jacob said as he walked toward the door, 'because none of you would believe me.'

'But perhaps we can help,' said Father Paul.

Jacob shook his head. 'There's nothing you can do. There's nothing *anybody* can do.'

'It's a size five,' the woman said with a smile.

'The measurement says size six,' Mary said.

'Those measurements are always wrong,' the woman replied impatiently. 'I take a size five shoe. I always have.'

'Yes, ma'am.' Mary got up from the kneeling position in front of her customer and went into the back room for the size five, in black, the woman had asked to see. She took one shoe out of the box, checked the size and then looked at it. She didn't know how she was going to get that small shoe on that big foot. She sighed and came through the curtains and back onto the floor.

She had been at Greenbaum's Quality Shoes for almost two weeks and supposed she liked it. She wasn't sure. She would rather have been in school but that was now an impossibility. Part of her past that she could never recall. Both Sister Amelia and Father Paul had told her how sorry they were and hoped she understood their position. She understood. It would do no good to tell them it wasn't *her* that had said those terrible things against the Pope and the Church. Sister Bertoletta and all the kids in the class had heard her say them . . . yet it wasn't *her*. How could she explain? She had tried, after the incident in church, but wasn't able to convince anybody of her point of view. Her body was there, a voice came out of it but it wasn't *her*. Sister Amelia had listened to her explanations, then asked: 'Then who was it?' Mary had been unable to answer that question. She didn't know who it was, just that it wasn't her.

Surprisingly, her father took her side on this. When he returned from the meeting at school he had told her, in simple no-nonsense words, that she had been expelled. That she would not go to school anymore. She had reached out to him, he had taken her and held her and after she finished crying she told him she was sorry for what she had done. And he, amazingly, had looked into her face and said: 'You don't have anything to apologize for. I know you didn't do anything.' Mary had almost fainted with relief when she heard those words. She wondered later what he knew and *how* he knew, but she didn't ask. You didn't ask her father to explain things. If he wanted you to know, he'd tell you. If he didn't, then forget it. Later, Mary heard her father tell Minna that she had been expelled from school. Minna's answer: 'I'm not at all surprised. Now she can get a job.' And she did get a job, at Greenbaum's, selling shoes.

'Are you sure this is a five?' the woman tried to squeeze her foot into the shoe as Mary held it.

'Yes, ma'am. It says so right inside and on the box, too.'

'Well, They must have made a mistake at the factory. They mis-marked it. That's what they've done. It's not a five at all. Probably more like a four. Feels like a four.'

'Would you like to see this in a larger size?' Mary asked. Possibly a six?'

'A six? No. I don't wear a six. I told you that. A six would just flop all over my feet. No, go back there and get another five. They probably got the boxes mixed up.'

Mary went into the storeroom and took down another box marked '5'. She looked at the shoe the lady couldn't get on and compared it with the one in the new box. The same size. She shoved the new box back on the shelf and took out a box marked '6'. Then she came back onto the sales floor and over to the customer. 'Here,' she said, 'try this one on.'

The woman's foot slid easily and comfortably into this shoe. 'Oh, that's much better,' she said. 'I told you they got the boxes mixed up. I always take a five, don't you see?' She smiled and then looked down at the shoebox on the floor. She could see the numeral '6' from where she was sitting. 'Well, really young woman! You gave me a six! That's why it's so loose. I told you I took a five! Really, I don't know where Mr Greenbaum gets his help nowadays. Incompetent. Absolutely incompetent! There he is! Mr Greenbaum. Over here. Could you come over here? I'm having simply terrible trouble trying to get a pair of shoes.' The other customers stared at her and Greenbaum rushed in her direction to quiet her down. 'I told this girl here,' she said to him, 'that I wore a five and she gave me one wrong size to put on and then brought me another wrong size and I have things I have to do. I

184

mean, I just can't sit here all day while this child, this incompetent girl, learns the business. I mean, really, didn't you teach her anything? Is good help so hard to get anymore?' She put her own shoe back on, the signal that there would be no sale for Greenbaum's Quality Shoes that day. Mr Greenbaum was muttering apologies at the woman and glaring at Mary and motioning another sales girl over to him.

'Her feet are not size five,' Mary said. 'You measure them.'

'My feet have always been size five! Ever since I was a young girl, they've been size five! Don't you try and tell me how to buy shoes, young lady.'

'The only thing I'd like to tell you,' said Mary, 'is how you can go straight to hell!'

'What?' the lady gasped. Greenbaum gasped right along with her.

'Straight to hell with your big feet. Maybe the flames would melt them down and you'd be able to wear a size five after all.'

'Miss Lawrence!' Mr Greenbaum shouted. 'That will be enough!'

'No,' Mary said and she had her eyes closed as she looked at the man, 'I had enough putting up with her big mouth and smelling her big feet.'

The woman screamed as Mr Greenbaum shouted: 'You're fired!'

Mary walked slowly toward the door, all eyes on her. 'We don't need this job,' she said without moving her lips. 'We were only marking time.' And she pushed over a multi-tiered rack of children's shoes as she went out the door.

Her father was angry she had been fired, but said he 'understood'.

'Well I sure as hell don't!' Minna had exclaimed. 'That was a damned easy job. Any idiot could have stuck it out.'

'Things happen,' Jacob replied.

'Well she had better start pulling her weight around here or out she goes.'

Mary flared at her aunt. 'Wait a minute,' she shouted. 'This is my house! My mother had it set up that when she died I became the owner of this place! Don't you tell me I'll have to get out.'

'I don't give a damn what is says on some piece of paper,' Minna yelled, 'if you cannot support yourself you get the hell out!'

'Maybe you should get the hell out!' Mary shouted in return.

'Me?' Minna's eyes opened wide and she stared at Jacob. 'Me? Did you hear that Jacob? Did you hear? Your daughter is throwing me out.'

Jacob hung his head and said nothing.

'Is that what you want?' Minna yelled at Jacob. 'Do you want me out of here?' No answer. 'Well, do you? All you have to do is say the word and I'll leave. I'll be more than happy to leave!'

Finally Jacob spoke, in a soft voice. 'I don't want you to leave. Nobody's throwing you out.'

'Mary is. Mary says she wants me to get out.'

'She doesn't mean it,' he sighed. 'You just got her upset. That's all.'

'She tells me to get out and you tell me I got her upset? What the hell is that supposed to mean? This stupid kid who can't even keep a dumb shoe-selling job insults me and you take her part. You say I upset her? Your poor little half-crazy daughter? Who the hell is she to tell me these things? Is that what you want too?' She grabbed Jacob by the arm. 'Whose side are you on? Mine or hers?'

'Do I have to be on anybody's side?'

'You're goddamned right you do.'

'Then,' he sighed, 'Mary, apologize to your aunt. Tell her you didn't mean it.'

'Apologize?' Mary said loudly. 'She threatens to throw me out of my own house and I have to apologize to her?'

'Apologize,' her father said, 'it's easier.'

'On who?' the girl demanded.

'On all of us,' he said.

Mary glared at him, then at her aunt. 'Okay,' she said through clenched teeth, 'I apologize.' She turned to her father. 'Okay?'

'Okay.'

'Well it's not okay with me!' Minna said loudly. 'She may say she's sorry but she doesn't mean it. I've put up with a lot of shit in this house and I don't have to stay where I'm not wanted.'

'She apologized,' said Jacob, 'now let it be.'

'I can have my bags together and be out of here in an hour!' Minna shouted.

'Good,' Mary shouted back. 'I'll help you pack!'

'You brat!' Minna screamed and ran into the bedroom and slammed the door behind her. Jacob stood for a moment not knowing whether to punish his daughter or run after his mistress. Finally he decided, glared at Mary and went into the bedroom to console a loudly wailing Minna.

'It's my house,' Mary said aloud to the empty living room. 'My mama gave it to me. I can have whoever I wish living here. And if I don't wish,' she said louder, 'I can throw them out. My mama said so.'

Another six months passed, with a Christmas that went uncelebrated in the house, with a New Year that was celebrated in the corner saloon and an early spring that brought signs of new life and new beginnings. During those six months Mary had taken a part-time job, over the holidays, at a candy store but lost it when she insulted an overweight customer who wanted her to 'pick out the ones that are least fattening'. Then she took another job, briefly, at the newspaper office typing out bills. When a stack of due-notices suddenly burst into flame atop her desk, she was fired. She didn't bother to protest. Then came a job in a dairy but when some of the bottles of fresh milk she touched turned sour, she was out of that place too. She worked for a florist until the water in her sprinkling can became boiling hot and killed a row of prize geraniums. Finally she found a job in the hospital. On her knees, scrubbing floors from midnight to dawn. She quit that one, after just one week, on her own accord.

She was sitting on the front porch steps, it was too hot in the house even though the sun had been down for hours. The past-midnight air was still heavy with the heat that had soaked into the earth during the daylight hours. She had a thin cotton dress on, and had been waiting for darkness to take off her shoes and stockings and let down her hair. In the dark, the neighbours could not see. She fanned herself with a piece of folded newspaper and tried not to think of anything in particular. It was too hot to think.

Minna and Jacob appeared under the street light, walking arm in arm out of affection but also out of a need to keep each other from falling down. They were singing a song they had heard at the saloon: something about a sailor and a talking parrot. Jacob wore a short-sleeved white shirt and white linen trousers. Mary could see the stains of ketchup and spilled booze on them from where she sat. She sighed. They had been clean when he'd put them on, now she'd have to boil them, again. Minna wore a long thin skirt of some dark crinkled material she claimed was cool and very expensive. Mary thought she looked like a lamp shade in it. Her pale pink blouse had, sometime that evening, come up out of her skirt and the tails tied in a knot under her breasts. Mary was amazed that she would show her naked belly on the street that way. Minna had undone her hair, never her most attractive feature, and fastened it atop her head with many bobbypins pushed any old way. It might be cooler, Mary thought to herself as they approached the porch, but it makes her look like a manure pile.

'You still up?' Jacob slurred his words.

'Too hot to sleep,' Mary answered. 'It's cooler out here.'

Minna stepped around the girl with slightly drunken daintiness. She tried not to acknowledge Mary's presence. She was still not speaking to her, after an argument that had erupted at the breakfast table over who was supposed to beat the hallway rug. Minna had become offended when Mary accused her of dirtying everything and cleaning nothing. The girl voiced her opinions to Minna whenever necessary for she knew she couldn't count on her father being on her side or even seeing her side. Minna, meanwhile, had decided just that morning that since she was a lady she would refuse to let the idiot-child get under her skin. She could put up with whatever the girl dished out because it was only a matter of time before Jacob would throw the young tramp out.

'It is too hot,' Jacob agreed and he sat down heavily on the step beside his daughter.

'Jacob!' Minna called from the doorway. 'Don't stay out there. Come on in here. With me. I'll get the bottle and a couple of glasses.'

'Just wanna sit out here,' he said. 'For a while.'

'Jacob,' Minna's voice was coy and whining now, 'come on in and let's have a drink together. Just the *two* of us.'

Mary caught the word 'two' and smiled in the darkness.

Jacob shook his head. 'That's okay. You go ahead if you want to. I'll be in in a bit.'

'Jacob,' now the voice was petulant and childish, 'we could play games. It's not too hot to play games, is it?' He didn't answer. 'Betcha you'd like to play a game. Wouldn't you?'

Jacob turned and looked at her and shouted 'Hey! Don't do that! Not in the front door.'

189

Now Mary turned to look as well and gasped loudly as she saw Minna standing in the open doorway, the light from the hallway candles flickering across her naked breasts. She waved her blouse at Jacob. 'C'mon. You like this game.'

Jacob glanced quickly at Mary. The girl turned her head and stared into the blackness of the neighbour's yard.

'I'd better get her inside,' he mumbled.

'Yes,' Mary said softly, 'you'd better.'

It seemed to Mary, as she sat on the steps and listened to the sounds coming from the darkened living room, that the heat had grown more oppressive. What had been merely a hot summer's night now became like sitting in a furnace where wave after wave of embarrassed emotion washed thickly over her exposed skin. She hoped none of the neighbours had seen the image in the doorway. She could never explain it away. The heat stuck to her cheeks and forehead. But why should she explain it to anyone? It wasn't *her* doing. It wasn't her that had exposed her breasts. But it had taken place on *her* front porch, in *her* neighbourhood. And, it was *her* father that permitted this woman to stay there. How could she explain *that* away? And why had he put his own daughter in this embarrassing position? Why? Why couldn't he see what that awful woman was doing to him? And to his only daughter? If he didn't care about his daughter, that was okay. That was understandable. But not to care enough about *himself*? To let that woman, that adultress, lead him around by the nose. Granted her father wasn't the smartest of men, he didn't have a high school education and couldn't read very well but he *had* to be smart enough to see how Minna was ruining his life.

She felt something touch her shoulder.

'Why'nt you come in too?' Minna's voice was low and her words reeked with booze.

Mary sat speechless.

190

'C'mon. You're old enough. You can play the game with us too.' She smiled and ran her hand down Mary's arm. 'C'mon,' she urged. 'C'mon in.' The hand moved up across Mary's breasts. 'You'll like it. You'll see.'

Mary jumped from the steps and screamed: 'Get away from me!'

'C'mon,' Minna pleaded. 'Just a game. Just the three of us.'

'You're drunk!' Mary shouted.

'Just you, me and your daddy,' Minna said softly. 'C'mon.' She motioned toward the house with her hand. 'Give it a try. You're a big girl now.' The woman staggered down the front steps and over to Mary who was standing on the grass, speechless. 'Too hot to do anything else,' the woman said. 'Just this once. Okay?'

Mary found her senses, gave her aunt one strong push and the woman went over backward onto the lawn. Minna was completely naked and the glow from the streetlight moved quickly up both legs.

'Oh my God, I don't believe this!' Mary said. She stared at Minna who was trying to rise up off the grass, and then ran around her body, up the steps, across the porch and into the house.

'Gotch'ya!' Jacob shouted and grabbed his daughter around the waist.

Mary screamed and tried to dig his hands away.

'I gotch'ya now!' Jacob said loudly. 'Now we gotch'ya. Now we'll have some fun. Won't we? Won't we have some fun?'

Mary managed to spin out of his grasp and as she turned to shout at him she saw he was also naked. His half erect penis pointed at her. 'Oh my God!' she gasped.

He advanced toward her. 'Just you and me and Minna, kid. That's all. Just the three of us. You're old enough to do it. We won't tell anybody.' He reached out and stroked her hair. 'We'll go real easy. Minna says the first time should be real easy.'

191

'Real easy kid.' Minna stood in the doorway, her eyes glazed, pieces of grass sticking to her legs and in her hair.

'Look at these,' Jacob said and his hand caressed Mary's breasts. 'They're ready. They're big enough. Bet I could make 'em both stand up if I put 'em in my mouth.'

Minna started lifting Mary's skirt. 'C'mon. Let's see what you've got hiding under here.'

Mary twisted away from both of them, her breath coming in harsh spurts that burnt her throat. 'Leave me alone!' she managed to shout. Jacob's hands were touching her, again. Minna had come closer and was trying to kiss her on the lips. She could smell the woman's booze and her heavy perfume. Mary twisted her face away and pushed at her father's hands. She started running across the living room, hoping to make it to her bedroom where she could find safety behind a closed door. Then she fell. There was something in the darkness, something out of place, and Mary collided with it and went sprawling onto the floor. In an instant both her father and her aunt were on her, pulling at her clothes, rubbing their hands between her legs, trying to stick their tongues in her mouth.

'C'mon baby,' her father was saying. 'Open up. Don't be like that.'

'No!' Mary screamed and with some newly discovered strength pushed both of them aside and grabbed the arm of the sofa, managing to stand up. She left both of them sprawled on the carpet as she ran into the kitchen and out into the blackness of the backyard. She stood alone, unmoving like a statue, drawing in deep breath after breath. In a few minutes there would be tears, but not now. The shock was still too great.

'Mary!' Jacob stood on the back porch, shouting into the darkness. 'Mary! You come in here!'

She stopped breathing, terrified that by inhaling she would reveal herself.

'Mary! I'm warning you! Get back in this house!'

She didn't answer.

This time it was Minna's voice in the blackness. 'You think you're too good, don't you? Too good for us. You think you're somebody special, don't you?'

She still didn't answer.

'Goddammit Mary,' Jacob shouted, 'you get back in here and stop causing a scandal.'

'You're just a goddamned tramp!' Minna called. 'A tramp!'

She still didn't answer.

Jacob peered, bleary eyed, through the backyard darkness. 'That's the way you're gonna be? Is that the way?' He waited but no answer came. 'Then you can go straight to hell! You hear me? Straight to hell! And you know what else? You know what else?' Still no answer. 'I'm glad your devils are after you! I'm glad they want you! You hear me? I'm glad they want you! And they can have you! They can take you and do whatever they want with you! I give you to them! You hear me? They can take you and they can screw you and they can make your life miserable! You deserve it!'

'Jacob,' Minna said loudly, 'what the hell are you talking about?'

'Her devils,' he shouted, 'her demons! Those things on the other side that want to take her. Those bastards hanging around me, wanting me to give in so they can have her! Well, fuck you daughter! They can have you! You hear me? They can have you, little Miss High and Mighty! You with your Jesus and your church and your fucking virginity! You know what a curse is, you bitch?'

'Jacob,' Minna tugged at his arm. 'That's enough. Come inside.'

'You know what a curse is? With all your church learning you should know. Well I'm cursing you and I'm telling those sons of bitches on the other side that they can have you! You can't treat me this way! You think

193

your shit don't stink! I've had enough of you and your ways!' He grabbed the backporch railing and leaned drunkenly out into the blackness. 'They can have you! You hear me you bastards? There's my daughter! There's Mary! Take her!'

'Jacob,' Minna tugged at him. 'C'mon.'

'Find her out there in the night, you slimy bastards, and take her and keep her and good riddance. Yeah!' He laughed loudly. 'Good riddance to all of you!' He put his arm heavily around Minna's bare shoulder and the two staggered back into the house.

The girl stood in the night, alone. The silence had descended. She could feel moisture start to build in her eyes, then brim over her lids and then run hotly down her cheeks.

Then she felt the writhing in her insides. The churning of her stomach. Felt the contractions in her abdomen and the sudden intake of gasped air to her lungs.

Then she felt the stuff moving up her throat and into her mouth. She opened her lips and gagged repeatedly as the wet slimy balls of feathers, small bones and fur poured out of her, splashing onto her bare feet and staining the green grass a dark brown. Some of the disgusting stuff was absorbed into the warm earth but other, larger chunks of it wriggled away into the shadows as if, transformed by the hot air, they had suddenly assumed a life of their own.

Part Three

The elderly nun looked up from her clenched hands and her worried expression turned into a smile. 'Father Paul? Is that you?'

The tall, thin man stopped and stared down at the woman all in black. 'Yes,' he said slowly, trying to place the face in his memory. 'Why,' he said cautiously and then delightedly, 'Sister Amelia! Well for heaven's sake! How nice to see you again.' He went over to the nun and took both her hands. 'I didn't expect to see you here,' he said.

'Nor I you,' she smiled. 'I see you have some grey in your hair now.'

'Yes.' He returned the smile. 'Some grey and more than just some wrinkles. It's been a few years.'

'You left Minneapolis about five years before I retired,' she said.

'Yes. In 1910. I've been in Toledo and then Indianapolis and now I'm in Chicago. At the seminary there.'

'Permanently?' she asked.

'As permanent as any other position in our profession,' he laughed. 'And you? I heard you'd retired. Where did they send you?'

'To the convent in Appleton. It's very nice there. They call it a retirement home but we are constantly busy with things all the time. You know how it is.'

'Indeed I do,' he smiled. 'Its now 1928; if I left in 1910 that means I haven't seen you in eighteen years. How times flies!'

She nodded and he saw she had many more wrinkles now than when she was his head teacher at the parochial school. 'Those eighteen years went by so quickly,' she sighed.

'But you hardly notice them,' he said, 'especially when there is something new happening almost every day. I haven't been bored, have you?'

She laughed. 'Bored? Who has time to get bored? I thought that when I joined the order I'd sit around and meditate. Heavens, I haven't had a moment to "meditate", whatever that is. It's been a good life, serving the Lord.' She sighed. 'A really good life.'

He sat down beside her and lowered his voice. 'Do you know why we're here?' he asked.

She looked sharply at him. 'Don't you?' He shook his head. 'I was hoping you would,' she said. 'I got a letter from the Bishop asking me to report here, to his office, today and at this time.'

'So did I,' he nodded, 'But that's all my letter said.'

'Mine too,' she shrugged. 'All the way over here on the train I kept trying to figure out what His Lordship wanted of me. I went over all my sins,' she laughed, 'and couldn't come up with one of them that merited chastisement by the Bishop.'

'Maybe he's going to make you a Mother Superior,' he grinned.

'Not before he makes you Pope!' and she laughed.

The door to the inner office opened and a young priest came out. 'Father. Sister. The Bishop will see you now.'

Father Paul waited for the elderly woman to rise from her chair, then he followed her into the office. The Right Reverend Paul R. Rhode, the Bishop of Green Bay Diocese, smiled at them from behind his large and cluttered desk then waved them to be seated. They sat, each with a worried glance at the other.

The Bishop, a large man with ruddy complexion and snow-white hair, cleared his throat and then opened a

198

manila file folder. He took out one sheet of paper, his amethyst ring glinting in the flare of the newly installed electric light, and pushed the paper across his desk. First to Father Paul. 'Do you know this person?' he asked.

Father Paul read the one name written in the centre of the paper, scowled, creased the little lines at the edge of his eyes, then after a moment nodded. 'Yes, Your Lordship,' he said.

'And you Sister. Do you know this person?'

Sister Amelia hunted in her small black leather purse for her glasses, found them and hurriedly slipped them on. 'Oh yes,' she said quickly. 'Mary Lawrence. She was a student of mine.' She looked at the Bishop. 'Why?'

'Yes,' Father Paul wondered aloud, 'why?'

The Bishop ignored their questions by asking another of his own. 'What can you, either of you, tell me about her, this Lawrence person?'

Sister Amelia glanced at Father Paul waiting for him to speak first. When he didn't she said: 'She was a girl in my school in Minneapolis. She was a good student as I recall. She wanted to join the religious life but was unable to. She got into trouble in her last year, as I recall, and I don't think she graduated.'

'She didn't,' the Bishop replied. 'What kind of trouble?'

'Well, she couldn't control herself, if memory serves me, and she caused problems in the classrooms. Did things and said things . . . you know.' Sister Amelia looked to Father Paul for support.

'What kind of things?' asked the Bishop.

'She was disruptive,' the priest finally said. 'Disruptive and blasphemous. She claimed it wasn't her fault. She claimed she didn't remember doing the things she did.'

'Who did she say did them, if it wasn't her herself?'

'Ahh, well . . .' Father Paul tried to remember. 'I

199

don't think she blamed it on anyone else, anyone in particular, if you know what I mean. She didn't, did she?' This to the Sister, who shook her head. 'She just said it wasn't herself who did them.'

The Bishop looked from one to the other. Finally he said: 'Did she ever put the blame for these outbursts on Satan?'

'Satan?' Father Paul said loudly as Sister Amelia crossed herself. 'You mean the Devil?'

'Exactly,' the bishop replied.

The priest shook his head. 'No, I don't think so.' He thought a moment. 'No, I'm sure she didn't. She caused a commotion in church once, I was saying Mass and she interrupted me. We took her into my study but she had fainted by that time and didn't remember any of it.'

'Once we gave her a cross and chain as a present,' the Sister volunteered, 'but she couldn't wear it.'

'Why?'

'It made her blouse catch on fire.'

'On fire?'

'Yes, Your Lordship, we put it around her neck and the thing started to burn a hole in the material. Of course we took it off immediately. It was the strangest thing. You recall that, don't you Father Paul?'

The priest nodded. 'We tried to get help to her but it became impossible. As Sister has stated, the girl wanted to become a nun but her actions and her poor school record forbid it.'

'And her father,' put in the black-robed Sister, 'don't forget her father.'

'Oh, right. She had a father who was a real reprobate. Absolutely worthless, financially and morally. He must have been a terrible influence on her even though she denied it. I met the man a couple of times hoping I could understand his daughter better but he was impossible. I don't know what happened to him.'

'He's dead,' said the Bishop.

'Oh, the pity of it.' Sister Amelia crossed herself again.

'No great loss,' the Bishop said flatly, 'Not if what you and others have told me is true. He was worthless, Father, you're absolutely right. He died,' and he opened the file and looked at another paper, 'in a hospital in Arizona in 1914. Seems he had cancer.'

'That's terrible!' said Sister Amelia. 'I recall him quite well now. He was a loud ruffian but I'm sorry he died with that terrible disease.'

'Well, at least it gave Mary some peace,' Father Paul put in. 'As I recall, the house she and her father lived in belonged to the girl. Her mother had made it a proviso in her will.'

'Mary was not living in the house,' said the Bishop. 'She hasn't been in that house since she was twenty years old. Her father threw her out of it. Ordered her out of it.'

'But it was *her* house!' the priest protested.

The Bishop shrugged. 'Be that as it may but her father threw her out. He moved from Minneapolis shortly after that and sold the house.'

'But Mary owned the house.' the priest repeated.

'But her father somehow got it in his name and sold it. Mary got nothing.'

'But that's not *fair*,' said Sister Amelia, 'I knew her mother and she . . .'

'Mary got nothing,' the Bishop said. 'Just a kick in the pants out onto the street.'

There was a brief interruption when the Bishop's secretary came into the office and had him sign a letter. The priest and the nun exchanged puzzled glances during this time, then when the secretary left the room, Father Paul asked: 'Your Lordship, I'm afraid that neither Sister Amelia nor myself understands what this is all about. I mean, why have you asked us to come here? To discuss Mary Lawrence?'

'Because she is under investigation,' the man replied.

201

'By the police?' Sister Amelia's voice rose.

'No. By the church.' He paused, staring at them. 'It's a most unusual investigation,' he said, 'and I must ask for and receive complete confidentiality in the matter.' He got up from behind his desk and walked around to where they were sitting. His long grey robe rustled against the carpeted floor. 'The Holy Mother Church is in trouble. If all the reports are true, Satan is amongst us on earth once more.'

There was a long silence. 'Satan?' Sister Amelia finally said.

'The Devil, Lucifer, Mephistopheles, the Prince of Darkness . . . whatever name you want to call him, seems to be back.' He paused looking at them. 'And in carnate form.'

'Carnate?' Father Paul raised his voice. 'You don't mean in . . .'

'Yes. Yes I do.'

'In . . . in . . .' Sister Amelia found it almost impossible to say, '. . . in *Mary*?'

The Bishop nodded.

'Oh, that's absurd,' Father Paul said quickly, then coloured just as quickly, 'I didn't mean, Your Lordship, that *you* were absurd, it's just that the idea of someone as innocent as Mary could possibly be thought . . .'

'It's more than just a thought,' the older man said. 'It's almost been proven.' He glanced at the door to see if anyone was listening. It was a nervous gesture. He had had many nervous gestures lately. This business of the possessed woman was starting to wear on him. 'I don't care whether you believe me or not,' he said. 'I would hope that you would, however, listen to what I have to tell you and that you keep privy *everything* you hear from me today. It cannot, it must not, go any farther than this room.

'But Mary Lawrence?' the Sister said softly. 'She's just a girl.'

'She's a woman now,' the Bishop said. 'You last saw

her as a school girl. This is 1928. Mary Lawrence just had her fortieth birthday.'

'Forty?' the Sister let the word roll around her tongue. 'Yes,' she said nodding her head, 'yes, I suppose Mary would be about that age now. My, how time does fly. Little Mary is forty.'

'It is hard to think of her as a grown woman,' Father Paul added, 'she was such a small and dainty child.'

'She's still small and dainty,' Bishop Rhode said. 'Still about five foot three and can't weigh more than ninety-five pounds or so.'

'You've met her?' the priest asked.

'I've seen her,' the Bishop replied. 'I watched her one afternoon when she didn't know I was there.'

'In church?' the Sister asked.

'In a mental hospital' the Bishop replied.

Sister Amelia's aged hands fluttered inside her purse for her rosary. 'Mary is in a mental hospital? Our Mary is crazy?'

The Bishop shook his head. 'Apparently not. She's been examined by some of the best mental doctors and they can't come to any conclusion. Most of them don't know what causes the things around her. Most of them don't think she's doing it. They think something *outside* herself is doing it. Most of them think Mary should be allowed to go free. To live a normal life outside the hospital.'

'What hospital is she in?' Sister Amelia asked. 'I could go and visit her.'

'I'm afraid I can't tell you that. She's not even registered in her own name. We thought it best. We don't want any publicity. Newspapers. The weeklies. You know. Trash of that ilk. If they found out about her they'd make her life even more miserable than it is.'

'What's she doing in a mental hospital if she's not crazy? I mean,' said Father Paul, 'isn't that rather harsh?'

'She was put in there to protect her from herself.

She's in a padded cell and no sharp objects are permitted in there with her. She was arrested four months ago in . . .' he consulted the manila file folder again '. . . in Milwaukee. She was attending services in a church there when she became angry, violent actually, and after disrupting the Mass she ran up the aisle and tore the font of holy water out of the wall. It had been put in there with long metal screws years ago, but she yanked it out, screamed curses at the congregation and threw the font across the sacristy and hit a stained glass window. Several men in the congregation grabbed her and held her down until the police could get there. I guess it was quite a tussle, they say she exhibited the strength of ten men. When the police did get there she had fainted and they took her to jail. They asked the parish priest if he wanted to press charges and he referred them to the Bishop of Milwaukee. He told them to keep her in jail until he could get in touch with me.' He walked over to his bookcase and removed two large volumes with spines decorated in gold. He brought the books back to his desk. 'I thought this might help at this point,' he said. He opened one book and took out a bottle of sherry. Then from the other book he took three small crystal glasses that nestled in red velvet. 'A gift on my ordination,' he said and handed a full glass to each of his guests. Then one for himself. 'You see, I had been hearing about this Mary person for quite a while. I'd get reports from priests and other bishops of how she would disrupt things. At first I thought she was some crazy woman, or even *worse*, a Protestant. She had asked for exorcism several years ago when she was in Minneapolis, but nothing was done for her. I guess they were all afraid of her. But they took notes on her and watched her . . .'

'Like we did back in my church,' Father Paul interrupted.

'Right,' the Bishop said. 'I have your notes on her. The ones you wrote when she started all this crazy business. Well, it got so that there wasn't a church around that didn't keep an eye out for "Crazy Mary" and many of them, when they saw her come in, quickly threw her out.'

'Threw her out of the church?' Sister Amelia exclaimed. 'They denied her the Blessed Sacrament?'

'They did. It was either deny her the sanctity of the Church or watch her reduce the Church to rubble. They had no choice.'

'But she had no place else to go!'

'Right, Sister. The one place she craved, the Church, was denied to her. We denied it. I'm not proud of that.' He poured himself another sherry. 'It is not easy to deny the solace of Jesus Christ to a suffering human being, but we did it. It was either that or watch things disrupted and destroyed.'

'Well,' put in Father Paul, 'how did she live after her father threw her out? I mean, she didn't have to resort to sinful street ways, did she?'

'Not that we know if,' the Bishop said. 'Her father threw her out because she refused to engage in sexual orgies with him and a wicked sister-in-law that lived with them.'

'Her own *father*?' this from the aged Sister.

'Her own father. She refused and he threw her into the streets. Didn't even let her pack a bag. So she went to stay with a friend, a Mrs . . . I've got the name here in the file, a Mrs Rose Carbone, and she stayed there with her for over two years. Then the Carbones inherited some land in Italy and went back there and Mary was on the streets again. That was around 1911. So she managed to get a job in a grocery store but that only lasted a few months and so she moved from the furnished room she was in to another place, a cheaper place along the river and there she just existed, I suppose existed is the only word, for a few years working as a part-time scrubbing lady and a restaurant dishwasher and whatever she could get that would pay anything. Then around 1915, if these notes are correct, she was arrested for vagrancy and sentenced to six months in the county jail. At that time she had one of her fits . . .'

'Fits?'

'Or whatever you want to call them, and was unconscious for about three days. Didn't eat or drink and almost didn't even breathe. The sheriff thought she was dead but when they took her to the morgue she jumped up and screamed and laughed and ran outside and down the street naked as the day she was born, so after they caught her they took her to the mental ward of the local hospital and that's when they started compiling this folder on her.'

'And her father sold the house and didn't give her a dime,' Sister Amelia was indignant.

'Not a dime,' the Bishop replied. 'They could only keep her in the hospital so long, then they had to let her go. When she was lucid she was perfectly normal. I mean there was not one hint that there was anything wrong with the lady. She would go for months and nothing would happen, then suddenly bam!' He clapped his hands together and Sister Amelia jumped in her chair. 'Then came the time when the statue fell at the Church of the Holy Cross. Brand new it was. Had just been installed a few weeks prior. This woman, Mary, had gone inside when it was quiet and had started praying. Then she had started acting crazy and screamed at the statue and called it all sorts of names. Then I'll be damned if the statue didn't fall straight off the wall, as if it was trying to crush her. It shattered into a million fragments on the marble floor below. She was the only one in there at the time, a priest heard the ruckus and he called the police. Once more she was arrested for vandalism and sent to a cell, then sent to a mental hospital. It was beginning to be a pattern with her. Church, jail, crazy house. And this file kept getting bigger.'

'Poor child, all alone and on the streets,' Sister Amelia's voice was choked with emotion. 'We all knew she had problems, but never suspected anything like . . .' she trailed off.

'Nobody could have suspected it,' the bishop said. 'In this modern day and age none of us thinks of demonic possession as a factor in someone's behaviour. It's all blamed on their parents, their upbringing, little sparks that go haywire in their brains but never possession. Never the work of the devil.'

'Why are we here?' the priest asked. 'What can we do to help?'

The Bishop sighed and took out another sheet of paper. 'Your names, both your names, appear quite often in the reports. You were important influences in her life, influences for the good I might add, and she has talked of you often to counsellors, other priests and medical men. When she looks into her past, into her childhood, you two are the ones she mentions most.'

'And we abandoned her,' Father Paul said softly. 'When she most needed us we expelled her from school. I don't think I can quite forgive myself for that.'

'Well, you'll have to,' Bishop Rhode said crisply. 'You were unaware, at the time, what was really happening. You had a school and a church to maintain, to serve as pastor. You can't blame yourself if one student was misunderstood.'

Father Paul said quickly: '*What man of you, having a hundred sheep, if he lose one of them, doth not leave the ninety and nine in the wilderness, and go after that which is lost, until he find it?* St Luke, chapter fifteen, verse four.'

'Ah, yes of course,' said the Bishop, embarrassed.

'But what can we do?' the Sister insisted. 'You have us here now, we've both travelled great distances to be here. Surely you didn't call us here just to tell us your theories about little Mary. Surely there must be a *reason* we are here.'

'I was getting to that point Sister,' the Bishop replied unsmilingly. 'I needed to know that what she had told us, about her childhood and religious training, was true. I needed to meet you and get your personal reactions about her personality and her sickness. I needed to really believe that she was once the normal young girl she says she was. And I also thought – perhaps hoped is a better word – that you two would be able to help her out of this. Whatever it is.'

'Help her out?' this from Father Paul.

'Yes,' the older man said. 'Maybe the sight of you two would trigger something deep inside her.'

'You want us to see Mary?' the priest asked. 'To exorcise her? Your Lordship, I'm not an exorcist. I don't know the first thing about it. I'm just a priest and a teacher, nothing more.'

'No. I wasn't counting on either of you getting rid of whatever she has. I just wanted to see how she would react to seeing you again. You were both such positive influences in her past that possibly, just possibly, seeing you two would trigger something; something positive maybe.'

'I'd be happy to do anything I could for little Mary,' the Sister replied.

'So would I, of course,' added Father Paul.

The Bishop walked toward the door. 'Good. I was hoping that would be your reaction. Come with me.'

'Come with you?' Father Paul said. 'Are we going to see Mary now?'

'Yes. I had her brought here, from the hospital. She doesn't know you are coming. I wanted this meeting to be as much of a surprise as possible. Father Vincent, do you have it?'

The young priest who acted as secretary to the Bishop nodded. 'In here, Your Lordship.' He held up a gilded flask.

They walked down a long hall lined with pictures of the saints and popes, the Bishop leading the way. He came to a door, opened it and reached up to grab a chain of small metal beads. Immediately the staircase, leading down, was illuminated. 'Great thing, electricity,' he said. 'Much better for your cassock than dripping candles.' He started down the steps, Father Paul behind him, a nervous Sister Amelia behind him and finally the long-robed secretary. 'The doctors thought it was best to have her put down here where her noises wouldn't disturb people. We have a storage room we've not used in years. They put a bed in there for her. It's only for a couple of days.'

The staircase wound down past one level, then there was a platform and another door. The Bishop opened this door, pulled another chain and a new staircase was illuminated. They headed down these steps, each of them lifting the hem of their long skirts.

'It's chilly down here,' the Sister said.

'It gets very cold in the winter,' the Bishop said. 'That's why we don't use this level very much. Mary's room isn't cold though. We've had a steam pipe placed in it.'

'But there's no sunlight down here either,' Sister Amelia stepped carefully. 'It must be dark all the time.'

'She says she prefers the darkness,' the young priest behind her spoke up. 'At the hospital they keep the shutters closed, even in the daytime. She says the light hurts her eyes.'

The brick floor under their feet, now that they had reached the bottom level, was cold and slightly sticky as if someone, years ago, had broken a barrel of molasses and it had dried. 'Are there rats down here?' the Sister asked hesitantly.

'You don't want to know,' said the Bishop and he laughed.

'But this is like keeping an animal,' Father Paul protested. 'Is all this really necessary?'

The Bishop turned and looked him straight in the eyes. 'You'll see,' was all he said.

They continued along the brick floor, their steps echoing strangely off the side walls. As they rounded a bend they could see a lamp light. 'That's Sister Ann Fabian,' said the secretary. 'She is keeping watch.'

The Sister rose from her chair and put the book she was reading on the small table with the oil lamp. 'The electric wire doesn't go this far,' she said, pointing at the lamp.

'Is the woman awake?' the Bishop asked.

'I think so.'

'Have there been any untoward outbursts?'

'No, Your Lordship.'

'Well then I suppose we can go in. Will you unlock the door, Sister?'

The nun took a large key that was hanging from a cord around her waist. She couldn't find the keyhole and brought the lamp closer to the lock. Then she jabbed the key inside, twisted it and they all heard the latch inside the door slide back. Sister Ann Fabian, the oil lamp still in one hand, took hold of the door handle and tugged. The door opened slowly.

'Hold the light high, Sister,' the Bishop ordered.

They stood crowded in the doorway, none of them really wanting to be the first to step inside.

'Holy Mother of God!' was all Sister Amelia was able to gasp.

'Is he here yet?'

'No, Your Lordship,' Father Vincent said, looking up from his desk. 'I'll show him in as soon as he gets here.'

'Yes,' Bishop Rhode ran a hand through his short white hair. 'Do that. Yes, do that please. Show him right in.' He glanced at the large clock on his study wall. 'He's late, you know.'

'He is getting on in years, Your Lordship.'

'He's only sixty,' the Bishop replied quickly. 'That's not old anymore.'

'Yes, Your Lordship,' the young Father replied.

The Bishop looked at the clock once more as if it might be wrong. 'Well, show him right in as soon as he comes. I want to get this thing over with.'

'Yes, Your Lordship.'

Bishop Rhode went back into his office and closed the door. He walked behind his desk, idly fingered a few letters that had to be answered, glanced out the window, headed toward the book with the sherry in it, thought better of it, went back to his desk, then over to a large leather sofa that was in a far corner, lifted his long cassock skirt, stretched out with his head resting on the leather arm and closed his eyes.

It was the same image. Ever since he had taken that priest and that nun to see the possessed woman it had been the same image whenever he closed his eyes. The small frame, the grey-streaked, uncombed hair. The cornered animal look in her eyes. The smell and smear of her excrement. The smell and smear of something else, something nameless, in the room with her. How she smiled when she recognized the two old friends. How she howled when they made the sign of the cross over her. How she cried when the Sister reminded her of her early school days. How the Sister screamed when the woman dug her dirty fingernails in the Sister's face. How she had raged at him and how she cursed him first in English and then in Latin. Grammatically perfect Latin. Then when they were about to leave, how she had cried and begged to kiss Father Paul's ring and as he extended his hand how she bent down and bit the Father's fingers, and how delighted she had been at the blood running on the floor. That's when the Bishop had ordered his secretary to open the vial of Holy Water and splash it on her and as she pulled away in terror against the wall they had made their getaway. Later Sister Ann Fabian had told him how the woman had cried all night long, whimpering like a lost puppy, asking for the Father and the Sister to return, asking for forgiveness, asking to be set free.

211

He opened his eyes and swung his stout legs off the sofa and back on the floor. No, she wasn't just sick. She was possessed all right. The doctors had been correct. This wasn't an ordinary case of nerves or craziness. There was no pill she could take or operation she could have that would free her of what ailed her.

He had read all the reports. Severals years of reports. Doctors and experts all over the area had examined her. One group of Protestant physicians had written in their conclusion: 'Even though we do not believe in the medieval idea of demonic possession we can only state that all her symptoms are similar to those of cases reported at that time.' Another group of learned medical men had written: 'Our thorough examinations resulted in the unanimous conclusion that the patient in question does not betray the least sign of nervousness, that she is normal in the fullest sense. There is not the slightest indication suggesting physical illness. Her undeniable and unusual experiences cannot, physically, be accounted for.'

'Physically!' the Bishop said the word aloud. Of course there is nothing physically wrong with her body. And nothing wrong with her mind either. She had held conversations with others, clerics as well as laymen, in languages she could not possibly have studied. She spoke fluent Chinese with one man, then switched to Arabic when a missionary from Morocco was called in. Once, a priest had handed her a book written in Hungarian and asked her to read what was on a certain numbered page. Without opening the book she rattled off an entire paragraph. When he checked the page he found she was absolutely correct.

The Bishop glanced into a mirror that sat on a bookshelf. He examined the bags under his eyes, stretching them at the edges to verify for himself how they had developed ever since he had heard this woman was in his prelacy. More than once he asked himself, 'Why me, God? Why me?'

He had remembered, more than once recently, the words he always pronounced when he conferred the Order of Exorcist on young men who were candidates for the priesthood. Granted it was a minor order and he had rattled off the words without giving them too much thought, but now they had come back to haunt him. He was sure the young postulates didn't take the words seriously either, thinking them, if they thought about them at all, as relics from the Church's stone age. To each new group he had said: 'You receive the power to place your hands on those possessed and through the imposition of your hands, the grace of the Holy Ghost and the words of exorcism you shall drive evil spirits out of the bodies of those so possessed.' Then he would add another line that was meant to enforce this rather startling, if very superstitious, idea: 'Receive and impress upon your mind that you receive the right to place your hands upon those possessed.' Then he (and all the other Bishops all over the world) called upon those in the audience to pray that the future priests will become 'an effective agent in expelling the evil spirit from those possessed.'

'Funny,' he mused, 'I never thought anyone in my lifetime would ever have to use those special powers.' He turned toward a large coloured print of Jesus holding His heart in His hand. 'Just goes to show you,' he said aloud, 'what kind of a mess your world is in!'

There was a light rap on the door and then it opened. 'He's here, sir. I saw him come in but he stopped to talk to Brother Taddeus in the library. Just thought you'd like to know.' The door closed again.

So he was finally here. The last step was about to be taken. All these years of examination and testing and, yes, soul searching, on the part of the Church was about to come to a head. He was here and he would soon receive his assignment from his Bishop. Then his work would commence. Then the gruesome tests would begin. Then the hammer would be struck against the dynamite cap.

Bishop Rhode went behind his desk, sat in his chair,

arranged some papers and tried to look as if it was just another ordinary visitor in an ordinary day.

The door opened. 'Father Theophilus Riesinger, Your Lordship.'

A tall man appeared in the doorway. His full black cassock covered his large frame and filled the entrance way. A scraggy white beard, about six inches long and a thick white moustache hid his mouth. The hair on his face made up for the lack of hair on the top of his head, which he covered with a close-fitting grey skullcap. Small, rimless half-glasses perched on the bridge of his large nose, two lower half-circles used for reading. He pushed the glasses down slightly with one of his large, veined hands and peered over the top of their rims at the man at the desk. 'Bishop!' he exclaimed loudly. 'How good it is to see you again!' With only one or two large strides he was across the room, shaking the Bishop's hand. His Lordship didn't know whether to watch the man's large blue eyes or the bouncing of the very large silver crucifix around his neck.

'It has been a long time, Father,' Bishop Rhode stood with his hand extended across his desk. 'I think the last time we met was at the Cardinal's installation in Chicago in 1922.'

'That's right. It was. And I had just come back from a work in New Orleans. I remember how strange it was to go from such a hot place to such a cold one.' Then he laughed a large laugh that went with his large frame, 'But then I should be used to hot places, most of the characters I work with come from where it's hot.' He grinned, and the Bishop could see the uneven row of tobacco-stained teeth. 'And my accent. You notice it? It's not as strong as it used to be.'

The Bishop thought for a moment. 'No, I guess it isn't,' he admitted. 'What have you been doing?'

'I went to one of those teachers who train the voice and I said to him, "Get rid of this kraut accent of mine".

Bad enough I carried it all during the war and everybody here in the States thought I was a spy for the Kaiser. So the teacher he put pebbles in my mouth and made me talk while eating ice cream and taught me how to not roll the R's and speak like the Americans do through the nose and after awhile I got rid of some of the sauerkraut sounds. Should have done it thirty years ago! Trouble is when I get mad and start to cuss, all my old German ways come back and it takes me a day or more to sound like a Yank again.' He laughed.

The Bishop smiled. 'I'm used to accents. Most of the priests around here have them.'

'But not like mine used to be. You know, there were times when I would speak English and even I couldn't understand what I was talking about.' He grinned: dark teeth against white moustache. 'I will sit down now.' He took one of the chairs in front of the desk, his black cassock flowed over it like a water-fall. 'Yes. I had a nice trip. No, I am not tired. Yes, I like to get to the point. I didn't lose all my German ways when I lost my accent. I know why I'm here.'

'You do?'

'That Mary Lawrence woman, isn't it?' He watched the Bishop's expression. 'Hah! I thought so. I heard she was back in the hospital and I heard the hospital was in this prelacy.'

'She needs your help,' the Bishop said simply.

'She needs *His* help,' he pointed upward. 'I can do nothing if He doesn't help me.'

'I understand that.'

'I met this woman once before, you know,' the old man said. 'In 1912, more or less; they gave her to me and I chased away the devils. It only took a couple of hours. They all went away. I thought she was free of them but, obviously, she wasn't.'

'No. That exorcism was a temporary thing. I have it here in my files. She stayed normal, led a normal life for about two years, then they came back.'

'Stronger than ever, I hear.'

'A hundred times stronger than ever.'

'A hundred times?' the old man's blue eyes widened behind his half-circle glasses. 'Of course you exaggerate just a bit.'

The Bishop shook his head. 'I'm not exaggerating one iota. The woman is in a terrible condition. The demons are trying to kill her.'

The old priest shrugged. 'That's what they always say.'

'This time they mean it. They're not after just the woman, they claim to have a message for the Church as well. Prophecies for our death and destruction.'

'Who can believe them?' the old man fingered the large silver crucifix that lay resting atop his stomach. 'They always lie, those demons. You know that. Who can take them at their word? They'll tell you anything just to frighten you.'

'But this time they say they know when the Anti Christ will be born and when the Church will crumble.'

'Oh pish and tush,' Father Theophilus shook his head. 'Satan has tried for too long to destroy the Church. For centuries. You don't think Our Lord is going to permit him to get away with it *now*, do you?'

'Maybe there is nothing He can do,' the Bishop replied.

'Heresy? Do I hear heresy? And from a Bishop?' The bearded priest was not smiling. 'This eternal battle between Heaven and Hell must cease someday, of course I agree, but the winner will never be Satan! Our Lord created this world and everything in it. You know that. For Our Lord to let Satan take over the world would mean He no longer cares about the world about the people, about the innocent. I cannot believe he would give us all up.'

'Have you read the newspapers lately?' the Bishop asked.

Father Theophilus creased his brow, unsure what

216

the other man was getting at. 'The newspapers? I read them most of the days.'

'Then you see what's happening in the world – to the world – and you doubt that maybe Our Lord is not just a little tired of saving the human race . . . from itself.'

'But the prophecy starts by saying "there will be wars and rumours of wars . . ." '

'Didn't we just get out of the worst war the world has ever seen? 1918 was a mere ten years ago. And for rumours of wars look what the Soviets are doing in Russia. The Japanese are arming against the Chinese. And in your own Germany, look at the unrest.'

Father Theophilus shrugged. 'The Germans are leaderless. Without a leader they go nowhere.'

'And if one should come along, let's say in the next five years or so . . .?'

'There is none to come. I know my people. We want peace, we want to rebuild. We don't want aggression.'

'That's not what Mary Lawrence's demons say.'

'Ah!' the old man threw up his hands. 'Let me find out what they are saying. I'll get the truth of them. And of her.'

'It won't be easy.'

'You think you are telling me something I don't already know?'

The Bishop shook his head. 'No, just warning you that this case may be the most difficult you've ever had. This may be the most severe test you've encountered.'

'Your Lordship, I have cast out devils from sixteen people. Sixteen! Some of them took much time, all of them took much energy. I am not going into this case with illusions. I remember the Lawrence woman from years ago and I'm sure if they are back in her body it will be twice as difficult to rid her now as it was then. They are aware of my tricks but I, fortunately, am well aware of theirs. I have yet to meet the demon who was the match for Him.' He raised his pectoral

217

crucifix and pointed to the figure hanging on the cross. 'When He was just starting on his mission He met several demons. And He overcame them. He cast demons out of the believers and the non-believers alike. Satan himself tempted Him in the desert but He commanded Satan to be gone. He conquered every demon and He gave the gift to His priests, those of us who would come after Him, to cast out demons just as He did. Whatever I do, I do in His name. It is His name that gives me the power over evil. As long as I call on Him I cannot fail.'

'I understand all that,' replied the Bishop. 'You do recall that I too am a Catholic?'

The old man laughed. 'Sometimes we priests wonder about you Bishops.'

'When can you get started on the woman?'

'As soon as I can get to Earling.'

'Earling?'

'It's a small town . . . more like a crossroads . . . in the State of Iowa. I have decided I want to do the exorcism there.'

'In Earling, Iowa? Why?'

'First of all it's a small quiet place. I can work there in secrecy. There will be no prying noses or newspaper people or radio microphone holders. There is perhaps all of four hundred people there. And I have a very good friend who is the parish priest there, Father Joseph Steiger. Like me, he is a German, but unlike me he is a young man, in his mid-forties and with a clean-shaven face.'

'Does he know what having an exorcism in his church entails?'

'I don't know how much he knows about what goes on,' the old man replied. 'I've told him, something, of what I do and what happens when I do it. I doubt if he himself has ever assisted at a real exorcism. There is both a church and a convent at Earling. It makes no difference to me which of the two buildings we use.'

The Bishop looked at him. 'And you're sure Father

Steiger would let you take the Lawrence woman there?'

'Oh, more than sure.'

'You don't think he would raise any objections?'

'Objections? Father Joseph make objections to me? Never! We are old friends. We know one another from seminary days! Father Joseph and I are close. Not to worry. He'll let me do anything I want.'

'No!'

'But Father Joseph, be reasonable.'

'Theophilus, I will not have that woman here! Not in my church and not in my convent. Not anywhere where I am! Do you understand me?'

The old man stroked his beard and looked down at the floor. 'I told the Bishop there would be no objection.'

'Well, go back and tell him there is a big objection. I will not have my parish disrupted by your demons and devils. We are not set up for it. My parishioners won't understand it.'

'Your parishioners don't have to know.'

'Don't have to know? How am I going to keep something like that a secret?'

'Don't tell them. It's that simple.'

'Theophilus, you've lived in small towns. You know you can't keep a secret in a small town. Everybody knows everybody else. Everybody talks to everybody else. Heavens, Father, if somebody paints the inside of his outhouse bright red, the next day everyone in town knows about it. No. I have an obligation to my parish. I will not permit you to perform the exorcism here.'

'You're not giving this enough time: try to understand it.' The white-bearded man tilted his head as he said this, and looked expectantly at his old friend.

'One second is all the time I need. No, I've heard of the things that happen when an exorcism takes place. I don't want it here. Go someplace else. This is the

United States! You have a million other places, from coast to coast, to do this in. Don't pick on little Earling. We're not ready for it.'

'It wouldn't be for very long,' the older man lowered his voice.

'I don't care. Are these cases still on the increase? How come the devil is still around? You've already dispossessed him several times! How come he keeps bouncing back? Why don't you nail his pointed ears to the wall once and for all?'

The old man chose to ignore that. 'This is a nice quiet country district. That means I can do my work in a quiet manner. Now, let's get down to business. Two places are available here, either the Sisters' convent or in this Rectory.'

The younger man stared at him. 'You haven't heard a word I've said. I said "no". And besides do you really think the Mother Superior here would permit anything like that to take place under her convent roof? You don't know her, I do. There's no way she'd let you take that woman in there. And it's certainly out of the question to bring that person into my own house. My sister Therese would never permit it.'

Father Theophilus walked over to the rectory window and examined the brick church next door. He turned to Father Steiger with a smile. 'My dear friend, tell me just one thing.'

'What?'

'If Mother Lotharia is willing to have the woman in her convent, will you give me your permission to hold the exorcism there?'

'The Mother Superior give you permission?' Father Steiger laughed. 'No problem. I know Lotharia like a well-read book. She'll never go along with you. Go ahead,' he was smiling broadly now, 'ask her. If she says yes, then sure, bring your woman down. But I know what her answer will be.'

Theophilus strode from the window and gave

Father Joseph a bear hug. 'Thanks for your permission,' he said heartily. 'The case is settled.'

Father Steiger pulled back and stared into the man's blue eyes. 'What are you talking about? Case settled?'

'Before I came in here to see you, I talked with the Mother Superior about this and she gave me her consent from the very beginning. I've already made all the arrangements,' he gave the younger man another squeeze, 'provided you gave your full approval.'

'You what?'

'You didn't understand? Do you want me to translate it into German? I talked to the Mother Superior and she said okay. You said it was okay if she said it was okay. So,' he grinned between his moustache and beard, 'it's okay!'

'You, Theophilus, are a conniver!'

'The Lord works in strange ways.'

'In this case make it the *devil* works in strange ways.'

The old priest suddenly became serious. 'Oh, indeed he does my dear friend. Just you wait and see!'

'Did he make the train?' she looked up from her ironing as he came in the kitchen door. He nodded. 'That's good. I'd hate to think he would be staying here again tonight. At least it'll be calm for awhile.'

'But not for long,' he said, and took off his black suit jacket and put it carefully over the back of a kitchen chair. He ran a finger under the stiff, white clerical collar that was attached to a black shiny cotton shirt front. There were no sleeves in this shirt. A priest just slipped his arms through two openings at the shoulders, closed the back of the collar with two snaps, then tied the two cotton strings, not unlike apron strings, around the back. 'These collars must be shrinking,' he said.

'It's my cooking,' she replied. 'You've put on a little weight since I got here. I'm glad. You looked as thin as a sparrow when I arrived.'

221

'And now?' he said smiling at his sister. 'What kind of a bird am I?'

'All dressed in black like that?' she laughed. 'Like a fat old crow!' Another laugh.

'Am I as big as mama?'

'Not yet, but if you keep it up you will be. Of course some of us,' and she smoothed the sides of her dark skirt near her hips, 'manage to keep our figures. Some of us don't want to look like mama.'

'Mama was healthy,' her brother said.

'Mama was fat! Let's be honest. Mama cooked for an entire family even after we were all gone our separate ways. Unfortunately, she ate like an entire family too.'

'That was the style then. *Zoftig* was fashionable.'

'Mama didn't care about fashion,' Father Steiger's sister laughed, 'she cared about food. To her, eating was always fashionable.'

'Theophilus is a big man,' Father Steiger said. 'Not fat. Big.'

'And he doesn't eat a thing,' Therese added. 'At first I thought he didn't like my cooking, but he doesn't eat nearly enough for a man his size. He must keep going on some inner power. I never saw a man of that age who had all that get up and go.'

'He only sleeps three or four hours a night,' her brother opened the icebox door, looked inside and closed it again. 'I awoke more than once and came down to the kitchen and I could see the light from the oil lamp under his door. He said it's a habit he picked up when he was in the seminary. He reads and prays when everyone else is asleep. He told me there's not so many other people trying to get God's attention at four in the morning.' He opened the cupboard over the dry sink and looked in there, then he closed the door.

'What are you looking for?' she asked.

He shook his head. 'I don't know. Nothing, I guess.'

'You're nervous, that's your problem. It's been your

222

problem for the past few days, ever since Theophilus tricked you into agreeing to have that sick woman come down here.'

'He didn't "trick" me. I gave him my terms and he met them.'

'Uh-huh,' she said, 'and now you're stuck with your promise.'

'The lady needs help, Therese.'

'The lady needs to be committed, that's the kind of help she needs.'

'She's been committed, and it didn't do any good.'

'So now she's coming here and you and Theophilus are going to chase away her devils.'

'Theophilus is,' he said quickly. 'I'm not going to get involved.'

'Oh no. He's going to do it all by himself, right?' Her brother nodded. 'Well, if I were a betting woman I'd put good money on you being right there beside him when he does his magic.'

'It's not magic,' he said, slightly on the defensive, 'it's Church ritual.'

'Uh-huh. Well, when he does his what-ever, I'll bet you are there beside him and getting whatever there is to get, full in the face.'

'He didn't ask me to help.' He looked in the cookie jar, took out one made of oatmeal, and replaced the lid. 'He knows I have a parish to run. He knows I can't give him any time. This is *his* project. Not mine. It's just that it's happening in my parish. That's my only connection with it.'

'Uh-huh!'

'I wish you wouldn't keep saying "uh-huh" like that. It's beginning to get on my nerves. In fact everything is beginning to get on my nerves.' He picked up his jacket and left the kitchen, the uneaten cookie lying on the sideboard.

'Uh-huh,' his sister said loudly.

*   *   *

'What is it you want me to say?' Bishop Thomas Drumm looked at the younger priest, his man from the Parish of Earling. 'You've come half-way across the State of Iowa to see me and to tell me you don't like what you're getting into, yet you haven't told me what you want me to do about it.'

'I don't know myself,' Father Joseph sighed. 'I just had to talk to someone about it. I've given Theophilus my word but I wish I hadn't. I'm afraid what will happen to the parish once he gets started.'

'Happen to the parish? I'm your Bishop and I don't know what you mean.'

'It's a small town. Earling is a settlement of farmers and farmers' wives. Most of the older ones emigrated there from Germany. The younger ones have been born there but they still have that small old-country attitude about them.'

'So?'

'I don't think they could take having the devil roaming around their farmyards.'

'I thought the devil was inside the unfortunate woman,' the Bishop said. 'Not out running loose.'

'But he will get out. He will be freed by Theophilus and where will he go? Into one of my parishioners? Into an innocent citizen of Earling? It's not fair to them.'

'My dear Joseph,' the Bishop smiled. 'You don't know that to be a fact. You can't predict where Satan will choose to take up residence. If he leaves ... I mean when he leaves the Lawrence woman's body he will probably go straight back to Hell. He'll probably choose Hell over Earling. Especially when he sees how cold it gets there in the winter!' The Bishop laughed loudly at his own joke.

Father Steiger didn't smile. 'We don't know that. And what about the other things?'

'What other things?'

'The breaking of things. The terrible stenches. The obscene language. The poundings on roofs and walls.

The terrible screams in the night? What about *those* things? How can I explain them to my parishioners? Father Theophilus simply says not to tell them, but Earling is a small place. Word will get out. I can't keep it a secret.'

'Nor should you,' his Bishop agreed. 'A priest should not have secrets from his congregation. It does no one any good. You must tell them. Tell them at Mass the Sunday before the exorcism is to begin. Tell them a little bit about the woman, tell them a little bit about Theophilus and tell them a little bit about the strange things that *might* happen. Don't tell them they *will* happen, just that they *might*. Then let them go about their business and they will let the Church go about its own.'

'And that should be sufficient?'

'It should be. If not, they can come to you one by one as they please and discuss it with you. After all, Joseph, we are talking about an event that will be over almost before it's begun. Father Theophilus works very quickly. I would imagine this job will take him four, maybe five days, at the most. Surely your people can handle whatever transpires there for a few days.'

'I would hope so,' the younger man said. He paused, then looked away, then looked back at the Bishop again. 'Father Theophilus didn't say so, in so many words, but I assume he will need the assistance of the Sisters in the convent for this.'

'I assume he will,' the Bishop replied. 'The unfortunate victim in this case is female and she will have female necessities that only other females can aid her in. She will need to be bathed, to have her clothes changed, her bedding cleaned, things that neither you nor Theophilus should attempt.'

'I have my sister Therese with me now,' Father Joseph spoke up. 'She is a tremendous help as my housekeeper. I could let her do some of those things. That way the Sisters' routines will not be upset.'

'No,' Bishop Drumm shook his head. 'Your sister may

225

well be a good woman, but she is not ordained. She is not "professionally" religious. In highly difficult cases like exorcisms, there must be no lay people involved. Not even if they are good Christians and related to the priest. The Sisters have received instruction in this matter, your sister has not. One of the first things you must do is forbid your sister Therese from having any contact with the Lawrence woman once the exorcism has begun.'

'Your Lordship,' Father Joseph smiled drily, 'one doesn't *forbid* my sister anything. You don't know her.'

'Then tell her that I, her Bishop, forbid her contact with the possessed woman. That should do it.'

'And if it doesn't?'

'Then,' said the Bishop, 'we'll sic the Pope on her!' and he opened his large mouth and laughed delightedly at his own wisdom.

They were there, a good half hour before the train came into the station, huddled and fluttering their black robes and long sleeves like a pack of starlings waiting to be fed. Six of the Sisters of St Joseph stood on the station platform, waiting and worrying and murmuring about the woman who was to be their charge. The remaining nine Sisters were at the convent or the school getting it ready for the new term that would start in two weeks. The Sisters kept the farm children informed about grammar, arithmetic, social studies and religious history. The school only went to the eighth grade. That year, 1928, had been a big year. Six students had graduated. None had graduated the year before and only four were preparing for graduation next year. Classes were small because the town was small, but everyone agreed when a kid got out of St Joseph's he had a lot of learning pounded into his head.

It was the seventeenth of August and the hot summer winds parched the few inches of skin the Sisters exposed under their long black wimples. The headdress had been designed years ago, at another time in another country. Instead of soaring wings, like some orders had, this wimple had long elbow-length strips of black cloth that came stiffly out from the crown of the head, then bent and ran straight down past the shoulder. All was black, on the outside; the same black the long, full-skirted robes were made from. But inside, beneath the wimple, all was white. A Sister's face was encased in white. The stiff white material crossed her forehead, stopping just at her eyebrows. Then it ran, tightly, down both sides of her face, hiding her ears. Her chin managed to jut out just a bit, but from there on down, down her neck and into a circle down to her breast bone, the white material glared away. Eyebrows, eyes, nose and mouth. That was all anyone could see of the flesh and blood woman inside this outfit. Because most of the Sisters were Germanic, with blonde hair, blue eyes and fair skin, there was almost nothing visible at all. The sun could not reach under the wimples to tan their faces and they never added even a hint of rouge; if one glanced casually at them it was as if layers of black and white fabrics were walking down the street all by themselves.

'What time is the train due?' Sister Mundana asked Sister Ignatius.

'In about five minutes,' the Sister replied, and both of them looked again through the station window at the clock on the far wall.

'Do you think she'll be all right?' Sister Mundana said in a whisper. 'Coming all the way from Minneapolis by herself? On the train alone? I mean I haven't the slightest idea how I'd fare all alone on a train. Her being sick and all, don't you know.'

Sister Ignatius shook her head and the cloth rustled stiffly around her shoulders. 'She'll be all right. I heard Father Theophilus tell Father Steiger that the Bishop himself had escorted her to the train station and he himself had advised the conductor to look out for her. I'm sure she will be all right.'

227

'But suppose she had one of her . . . what is it you call them?' Sister Mundana peered under Sister Ignatius' wimple.

'I call them a fit,' she replied severely.

'One of her fits, then. What would the poor conductor do?'

'I understand they put her in a special compartment with a lock on the door. Any outbursts and they throw the bolt.'

'Poor thing!' Sister Mundana said softly. 'I prayed for her this morning.'

'She'll need all the prayers we can muster,' another Sister added.

'And so will *we*!' put in still another.

Father Theophilus shielded his eyes and peered into the warm Iowa summer sun. A drop of sweat rolled down his long nose and got lost in the thick moustache directly beneath it. 'I certainly hope she behaved herself on the trip,' he said softly.

'Didn't the Bishop take any precautions at all?' Mother Lotharia, the Superior of the School Sisters of St Joseph scowled at the older man. 'There are things he could have done,' she said matter-of-factly.

The white-bearded priest nodded. 'He did. He had the corridor of the train and the door to her compartment splashed with Holy Water. He also hung a cross on the window of the corridor. Should she get out, the first thing she'd see would be that cross. It should stop her.'

'I still say someone from the Diocese should have accompanied her,' Father Steiger now peered up the train tracks. 'The woman should not have been sent alone.'

'I wanted her to come alone,' said Theophilus. 'I wanted her to have the confidence that she could do things by herself. I don't want her to get the idea that she is a prisoner of the Church.'

'Well, she's not going to have much freedom here,'

Father Steiger said. 'She's not going to run around loose in this town!'

'She's not going loose, as you call it, anywhere, Joseph. She'll be under a watchful eye at all times.'

'My Sisters will see to that,' Mother Lotharia said crisply. 'I've already re-worked their assignments so that two of the Sisters are with her every minute.' Lotharia was a very competent woman. She had come to Earling as a teacher in 1919, had helped Father Steiger remodel the church and the school, and in 1926 had been elevated to Mother Superior of the Parish. Now at sixty she cut a respectful, if slightly forbidding, swathe through the small farm community. There was a local saying: 'If you want something done, do it yourself, but if you want it done right, get Mother Lotharia to do it.'

'It's not going to be easy, Lotharia,' Father Theophilus said.

'Horse feathers!' the woman replied quickly. 'We can handle anything you throw at us.'

'Anyway,' put in Father Steiger, 'it'll only be for a few days. A week at the most.'

'Exactly,' said Theophilus, 'a week at the most. She'll be here and gone again before most folks even know about her.'

Sister Mundana's voice rose over the cluster of religious figures: 'Oh! Here it comes! I can hear it coming!' She started to say something else but one sharp glance from the Mother Superior clogged the words in her throat.

'Yes,' said Mother Lotharia, 'the train *is* coming. *I* can hear it now.'

They stood silently and watched the noisy engine, streaming black smoke, come out of the flat distance, become larger and larger and finally come to squeaking and groan-filled halt alongside the wooden train platform. Then there were sudden and sharp blasts of white steam, voices shouting and a man in a blue uniform with a flat cap jumped from the one passenger coach and stood waiting.

Mary appeared at the top of the steps.

At first glance, she looked like an ordinary woman approaching forty. She was small, just a couple inches over five feet, and slim. Her reddish hair, once both her and Jeanette's pride, was cut short, coming down only far enough to cover her ears. The red was not as dark as it had been. In fact, there were streaks of a lighter red running through it. Not true red but not quite grey either. Those who had known her earlier, before all the troubles started, would have noticed the small lines that surrounded the edges of her eyes and the small creases that pointed into her lips. She had never been chubby, even as a child, but now the gauntness of her face sent her cheek-bones into high relief and her eyes, once so bright and alive, had sunk deeper into her skull as if not wanting to be any closer to the surface of the world than necessary.

Mary stood at the top of the steps.

She wore a fashionable, light brown cotton dress, almost down to her ankles, and black leather shoes with open toes, thick soles and wide, one-inch heels. She had a straw pocketbook over one wrist. The outfit, albeit her choice, had been paid for by the Diocese of Green Bay, Wisconsin.

Mary glanced at the silent group at the bottom of the steps.

She wore no jewellery. No ring or bracelet or light summer necklace. She wore no make-up. There was some flush in her cheeks, either from the excitement of having just completed a long train ride or the nervousness of arriving in Earling where 'it' would take place. She was – and yet she wasn't – looking forward to 'it'.

Mary stared down at the old man with the white beard and the black cassock at the foot of the steps. Then she smiled. 'Father Theophilus,' she said softly.

'Mary,' and the old man extended her his hand. She came slowly down the steps and onto the platform. 'Welcome to Earling, Mary,' he said.

'Yes,' Father Steiger extended his hand. 'Welcome to Earling. I am Father Steiger. I am to be your host while you're here.'

'And I,' said the Mother Superior, 'am to be your hostess. I am Mother Lotharia. You will be staying in my convent and these,' she gestured to the cluster of silent, black-robed women, 'are some of the Sisters of St Joseph. We all welcome you to Earling.' Then Mother Lotharia did something very out-of-character; she gave Mary a hug. Mary smiled. Taking their cues, the other Sisters lined up and dutifully gave Mary a hug, saying their names as they did so.

'Where is your luggage?' Father Steiger asked.

Mary pointed to the small suitcase the conductor had put on the platform. 'I only have one piece. The Bishop said I wouldn't need a lot of clothes. Actually,' she smiled again, 'I really don't *have* a lot of clothes.'

'Don't be concerned about it,' Father Steiger said. 'If you need anything while you're here you can borrow some of my sister's things. Therese is about your size.'

'Oh Father!' said Mother Lotharia, 'Therese is as big as an ox! Miss Lawrence is a small woman.'

'Therese is not that big,' Father Steiger objected. He looked at Mary again. 'Well, maybe, up here around the . . .' his hands went across his chest.

'And,' said the Mother Superior, 'down here around the . . .'

Theophilus laughed. 'It's a good thing I know you two have been friends for years. A stranger would take your arguments seriously.'

'They are serious,' the Mother Superior said and linked her arm into Mary's. 'I take them very seriously, it's when *he* doesn't take them seriously that it becomes a problem.' She smiled at Mary again. 'Come, let's get into the car. You must be tired.'

'I am a little,' Mary said. She let them lead her over to Father Steiger's new, 1928, Ford four-door sedan. It was his pride and joy, partially a gift from the parishioners and partially from his own savings. Ever since he had come to America his passion had been automobiles and he made sure that each year he had the latest model. He kept them clean, polished and rust-free and when he traded in last year's model there was never a mark on it. The car had to be black, of course. A Catholic priest couldn't have anything else but a black automobile. He wondered if after he retired his Bishop would let him drive a yellow-coloured one. Or maybe a cream-coloured one? Sometimes, and he never confessed this to anybody, he imagined this car, as he drove it over the flat Iowa roads, was fire-engine red!

Father Steiger got behind the wheel, and Theophilus got in beside him. Mother Lotharia held the rear door open for Mary and she shut it after the woman was seated. Then the Mother opened the door on the other side and sat in the backseat beside Mary.

They pulled away from the station, the back tyres making whirring noises in the gravel. With a couple of sputters the car headed past a small green park on the right with a white wooden circular building in it's centre and then down the one row of commercial buildings in Earling, with its solitary bank, farm implement store, vets and doctors. It all flashed past in a moment.

'Not very impressive after Milwaukee and Minneapolis, is it?' Mother Lotharia said.

Mary smiled. 'It'll do,' she said softly.

'Anyway,' Father Steiger said from the front seat. 'This is what you really came to see. Over there, on the left, that's all Church property. The entire block.'

Mary raised her eyes at the row of solid red-brick buildings, sitting importantly and very permanently on the Iowa soil. The stores on the main street of the town had been of painted boards with canvas awnings, tipsy and temporary with their false fronts and slanting roofs. But these buildings had been built to last. These four red-brick edifices had been braced into the earth with steel and cement and brick on top of brick until there was no doubt they had been put there to withstand anything the heathen world could hurl at them. There was a school, three floors of squareness and no-nonsense learning. Next came the rectory, red-bricked, gabled roof and an open sidewalk that ran to a small enclosed front porch. A heavy oak door kept out the uninvited. Then the church. Wide. Long. Thick. A slanted roof that rose even above the impressive rectory roof next door. The front arched doorway was almost two storeys high, and topped by a massive square tower of brick and stone that rose up past the roof, rose up another two storeys into the air and then, as if that wasn't enough, was topped with a thick pointed spire that soared higher than anything else in town. It was taller than any other landmark in Earling, either man-made or God-made. And, to the left of this imposing building, was the convent. Two storeys, red-brick, windows all around but shutters and heavy curtains over each window.

To anyone coming upon Earling for the first time, it was quite evident: Christ's Church had been established there. And nothing was going to drive it away.

Father Steiger turned his Ford into the lane beside the convent. He stopped, got out, opened the rear door and Mary stepped on Church property for the first time. 'It feels good,' she said, and smiled at the priest.

'You run along with the Mother Superior,' said Theophilus. 'She'll get you all fixed up and tucked in and after you get a good night's sleep we'll begin tomorrow.'

'Tomorrow?' Father Steiger's voice rose. 'I thought there would be a few days delay.'

'Delay? For what?'

'To get the people ready for what was to happen,' he said. 'To tell them.'

'Tell them when you choose,' the old man said. 'I begin tomorrow.'

'That is a little soon,' the Mother Superior replied. 'I thought . . .'

'That's the trouble,' said Theophilus, 'everybody thinks around here. I didn't bring Miss Lawrence down here so everyone could sit around and think about her. I brought her here so we could work. *Action.* That's what the devil doesn't like. He doesn't like *action.*'

'Will you be ready?' the elderly nun looked at Mary. 'Tomorrow?'

'I've been ready for years,' Mary said. 'Tomorrow can't be too soon.'

'There! You see?' Theophilus tugged at his white beard. 'She is ready. She knows what to expect. We did it once before, Miss Lawrence and I, and we will do it again but this time,' and he raised his crucifix to his lips and kissed it, 'this time we'll get rid of the demons for good.'

'I hope you will,' Mary said.

'I know I will,' the old priest said. 'I know I will.'

As Mary and the Mother Superior entered the convent side door, the other Sisters who had been at the railroad station arrived. They had walked up Main Street, quickly and quietly, the quintessence of decorum, until they reached the convent. Fluttering their long sleeves, they followed the Mother Superior and Mary inside.

All the black-robed Sisters were lined in the hall awaiting Mary. 'I suppose I should introduce them,' the Mother Superior said, 'even though I'm sure you won't remember half their names five minutes afterward.' They stood in two rows, like double lanes of starlings. 'This is Sister Archelaus, and Sister Primosa and Sister Serena,' the Mother Superior said. They nodded and Mary smiled. 'And here we have Lydia and Hermina. And this is Clara, Lauda and Climaka. You met Sister Mundana at the railway. She's the one who's

234

always talking.' Mundana, only twenty three, blushed deeply. 'Ignatius was at the station too, and so were Sisters Camiona, Bernadone and Agrippina.' The four, for some reason, gave Mary a slight curtsy. 'And this lady wiping her hands on her apron is Sister Eliana. Be nice to her, she's the cook.' The short, very fat older woman, smiled and extended a hand red from soapy water. 'Sometimes the things she brings up are not so marvellous,' the Mother Superior said with a twinkle, 'but we forgive her.'

'It is only Christian to forgive,' the elderly cook laughed. 'Besides, if they don't forgive they don't get nothing the next mealtime.'

'That's not quite true,' Sister Lydia spoke up. 'We get food the next mealtime but it's usually what we refused in a new disguise.'

'She can make an old shoe taste like chicken,' one of the Sisters said.

'Or vice versa,' another laughed.

'I ignore them all,' beamed the cook. 'Anyway, what do you like to eat? You are a guest in our house. You tell me and I'll fix it.'

'I really don't have any preferences,' Mary said slowly. 'I don't eat a great deal. Just whatever you fix for the others will be fine with me. I, um, probably won't be eating a lot of food when Father Theophilus starts his work. It takes a great deal out of me.'

'All the more reason you have to eat,' the cook said. 'You work a lot, you eat a lot. You gotta keep coal in the furnace.'

'I'll try,' Mary said. 'I really will.'

Mother Lotharia clapped her hands. 'All right. You've met them all. You'll be seeing a lot of them in the week you are here. Now they have things to do and you Mary . . . may I call you Mary? Good. You, Mary, let me show you to your bedroom and show you where things are.' She took Mary by the arm and steered her toward the staircase. One of the Sisters picked up Mary's

235

suitcase and came afterward. 'We have a lot of pride in this house,' the Mother said. 'There is a lot of love and dedication in here. You'll see it, I'm sure.'

In the rectory kitchen, Therese was salting a roast before it's final half hour in the oven. 'I saw her when she got out of the car with you and Mother Lotharia. I just happened to be on the other side of the church at that time.'

'Just happened to be,' said her brother.

'She's smaller than I thought she would be. From all the tales Theophilus tells, I thought she'd be a giant of a woman. She's small.' She looked at Father Steiger. 'She looks so helpless.'

'She is helpless,' he said. 'She can't control whatever it is that attacks her.'

'Does it come and go? I mean, she acted normal in the car, didn't she? She didn't have the devil with her then, did she?'

'I don't know,' he said simply.

'What do you mean you don't know? You're a priest. You're supposed to know those things.'

'I mean I don't know. She acted like a perfectly normal and perfectly nice woman. Whether the devil was with her at that time or not, who can tell? The devil works in strange ways.'

'Why would he be nice? I mean, why so docile and sweet smiling?' She tasted the broth around the beef and added a pinch of fresh basil.

'Satan is very cunning,' her brother replied.

'So what did the devil have to gain by bringing her here? I mean why let her walk into a trap? He could have done his rantings and ravings and they would have refused to put her aboard the train. Didn't the conductor tell Theophilus that she was perfectly normal all the way down here?' Father Steiger nodded. 'Then I don't understand. Why did Satan let her come here? He obviously *knows* what kind of a fight he's

236

getting himself into. I don't understand,' she shook her head, 'if I were the devil and if I knew someone was out to destroy me, I would go the other way. I sure wouldn't walk into a place knowing I would have a battle getting myself out of it.'

'We never know what Satan has on his mind,' the priest said. 'Maybe he feels Theophilus is no match for him.'

'Ah! That old man has been throwing out the devil for more years than I've been alive. Don't tell me Satan doesn't know how strong an opponent he is. Theophilus has beaten Satan many times! Isn't that right?' Her brother nodded. 'So why does Satan feel he can win this time?'

'I don't know,' and he shrugged.

'Ah! What good are you? My brother the priest! I come to you for answers and I get "I don't know". You're lucky I'm not one of your parishioners. Do you tell them "I don't know" also?'

'I tell them what I know. I can't tell them what I don't know. Anyway, we'll see what happens with this in a couple of days. She should be cured and on her way within a week. A week's not such a long time.'

Therese took the lid off the pot on the stove and stirred it. She laughed aloud.

'What's so funny?' her brother asked.

'I was just thinking. If Theophilus doesn't chase away the devil, a week of living under Mother Lotharia's roof should do it!' She chuckled. 'And a week of Sister Eliana's noddles and cornbread! That'll drive out any demon!' The deep-chested chuckle came faster.

In the convent kitchen Sister Eliana sliced off a choice piece of roast beef, and put it on a dinner plate. Then she scooped out a portion of mashed potatoes and another portion of peas and carrots and added them alongside the meat. She put the plate on a tray that already held silverware and a napkin. 'And a nice glass of milk,' she said to herself as she put one on the tray. She put her hands onto the tray's handles, lifted it, paused and set it down again. 'Almost forgot', she said. There was a stone font of Holy Water on the wall. Father Steiger would bless the water and Mother Lotharia would fill the font. It was part of the Sisters' ritual: meals were always blessed with Holy Water. Sister Eliana dipped her fingers into the water and sprinkled a few drops of it over the food on the tray. Then she smiled, lifted the tray, left the kitchen and went up to the second floor guest-room. She knocked and Mary's voice told her to come in.

'I've brought your dinner,' Sister Eliana said. 'I know you said you weren't a big eater, but eat what you can. The body needs it. Did you eat on the train?' Mary shook her head. 'Well then, all the more reason to enjoy this food now. Here, let me put it on the desk and you can sit in the chair and be more comfortable.'

Mary smiled. 'I am a little hungry,' she said softly. 'Actually I feel quite good. I've had a bath and got all the train dust out of my hair. And there's such a nice view from this window. You can see farm fields and trees. It's such a change after some of the places I've been in.' She went over to the desk, and sat at the chair. 'Um, smells good. I like roast beef. I almost never get to eat it and when I do it's usually so tough ...' She stopped smiling and looked up sharply at the Sister. 'What in Hell did you do to this pile of vomit? What's this shit scattered all over it?' She scraped a spoon across the potatoes and then threw the spoon at the wall. 'What kind of games you playing, old bitch?'

Sister Eliana turned beet-red. For a second she couldn't regain her voice. She stared at the blob of potato stuck to the wall. 'I ... I don't know what you're talking about,' she stammered.

Mary's voice rose in imitation of the elderly woman's: 'Oh, you don't know what I'm talking about!

About this water, this holy piss stuff you've splashed all over everything! You expect me to eat this junk? Me? Well, let's get one thing straight,' she jumped up and shoved her face inside Eliana's head dress, 'I don't eat food that's splashed with this shit! You understand me, old lady? You want me to eat, then you bring me decent food and cut out the Catholic nonsense! Do you hear me?' she shouted.

Sister Eliana pushed Mary away. The elder woman was visibly shaking. No one had ever spoken to her in such a way before. 'I just brought you the food the way it always is . . .'

'I'm not interested in "always" around here! Take this garbage out of here and bring me another plate without piss all over it because I *am* hungry and I *will* eat. But I won't eat anything with that damned liquid on it.' She grabbed the tray as if to throw it against the wall as well, but Eliana wrenched it out of her hands.

'I'll get you a new plate,' the Sister said slowly.

'Without that junk on it!'

'Without. I promise.' Sister Eliana backed quickly out of the door and Mary slammed it behind her. Eliana hurried down the steps, paused just long enough at Mother Lotharia's doorway to say: 'He's here already.'

'Who?' the woman looked up from her reading.

'Satan. He's here. Upstairs in that woman's body. You'd better call the Fathers. This could be a very long night.'

Father Steiger, wearing his robes, stood behind the altar table and looked at the people sitting in the congregation, very early, on Saturday morning. None of the townspeople were there and for that he was glad. He hadn't yet decided how he would tell them about Mary. He had until tomorrow's Mass to decide about it. No, the only ones at this Mass were the entire group of the Sisters of St Francis, his own sister, Therese, and Father Theophilus. They all sat together, bunched for protection in a few front pews. During the Mass he had asked for special guidance, for Divine intervention in what was about to take place in his sleepy little farm parish. He hadn't delivered a sermon, as such, just said the Mass, but he said it with such special fervour even an outsider would have seen something was troubling him. He raised his arms, made the sign of the cross and said softly: 'Missa finita est.'

Nobody moved for a few seconds, then Mother Lotharia stood up, crossed herself, and headed toward the side door. The other black-robed Sisters followed in a single line after her. Therese, wearing a black bandana over her hair and clutching at a crucifix that had been her grandmother's, stood up and followed them. Out of the corner of her eye she saw Father Theophilus move to the steps of the altar, get down on his knees and pray. The old man's lips moved, causing his white beard and moustache to flutter slightly. Father Steiger, on his way to his robing room, stopped and stared at Theophilus. He wanted to say something to the elderly priest, give him some words of encouragement, but he knew the only encouragement Theophilus wanted at that moment had to come directly from God.

The nuns had given Mary a special dress to wear. It was of plain grey cotton and hung loosely on her thin body, coming down almost to her ankles. It had long sleeves that brushed across the tops of her hands. To get into it, she pulled it over her head, giving her a loose fitting neckline. Theophilus had given the Sisters instructions on how he wanted this dress to look. It had to cover Mary's body, yet be ample enough for her body to move around in it. Above all there couldn't be any harmful hard things like buttons or snaps on it. The Sisters had made four of these outfits because Theophilus had said it would probably be necessary to change them two or three times a day.

The room they got ready for Mary that morning was

large and sparse. It was on the second floor of the convent. Its one window looked over an open field where the nuns worked a small garden. At the rear of the garden the Sisters tended a flock of chickens. The Sisters used the room for storage, sometimes for sewing and sometimes to work on special craft projects like Christmas decorations and school banners. Now the room was cleared. Tables, chairs, boxes, trunks: everything was gone. In their place Theophilus ordered a double bed made of iron. It was to have an iron head board and foot board and its frame was to be strong enough to take a great deal of pounding. Ed Messenbrink, who ran the harness shop on Main Street and who also doubled as a blacksmith, had been given the bed, by the Sisters, and had strengthened it with iron braces across the legs and under the springs. Several of his customers had been invited to jump up and down on the springs to see if it would hold. When they found out it had been the Sisters who had ordered the extra-strong frame there was more than one eyebrow raised and more than one off-colour remark smirked at. The mattress was extra thick and Theophilus has told them to make several cotton covers for it, things that could be changed quickly and washed. The Sisters had made a half-dozen covers and wondered a bit about the old priest's reasoning. There were no sheets nor blankets nor even pillows on the bed. There were no chairs or tables in the room, no rug on the wood floor. The one light bulb, hanging in the centre of the ceiling, had had its cord shortened and its naked bulb protected by a small cage of chicken wire. There were no pictures on any of the walls, no religious images, no crosses or crucifixes. The only adornment in the room was a heavy white cotton curtain over the single window. That and a galvanized metal bucket that Theophilus wanted placed under the bed.

Mary, wearing the grey gown, had walked willingly with Mother Lotharia and Sisters Lydia and Climaka to

241

the prepared room. Mother Lotharia had drawn up a list of two Sisters each day who were to assist Mary. Lydia and Climaka had been chosen for this first day because they were the oldest of the Sisters in the convent and had, presumably, seen more of the world than the younger Sisters had. Also they were both large strapping women and Theophilus had advised the Mother Superior he needed nuns with muscles as well as strong stomachs.

Mary walked into the room. She looked around and nodded to Father Steiger and to Theophilus. The room, now that the sun had come up, had plenty of natural light even with the heavy curtain at the window. She let her gaze wander slowly around the almost bare room. 'Do you want me on the bed?' she asked Theophilus.

He nodded.

Mary went to the edge of the mattress and sat on it, then Mother Lotharia raised the woman's legs and swung them into the centre of the bed. Then she raised Mary's torso and straightened her out, so she lay in a straight line. The two Sisters quickly tied the ends of her sleeves to her wrists and tied the skirt of her robe around her legs. Father Theophilus had asked them to do this so the devil wouldn't be able to lift any part of her dress and shamefully expose Mary's naked flesh. Mary looked at the old priest, smiled and closed her eyes.

Mother Lotharia reached into the huge pocket of her skirt and took out Father Theophilus' silk purple stole. It had a golden lamb embroidered on one end of it and a golden Gothic cross on the other end. The man took the stole, kissed it and placed it around his neck. Then the Mother Superior handed Father Steiger his stole. It was the same purple silk material but with three crosses embroidered in gold on one end and a cross and sunburst on the other. He took his stole, kissed it and placed it around his neck. The slashes of purple around both men's necks were the only colour in the room.

Theophilus looked at the younger priest. He raised an eyebrow. Father Steiger nodded. Both walked to the foot of the bed. Theophilus crossed himself, Steiger did likewise. 'In the name of the Father and of the Son and of the Holy Ghost. Amen.' Father Theophilus intoned. 'Amen' muttered the younger man and the three black-robed women.

'Glorious Prince of the Celestial Host,' Theophilus intoned from memory, 'St Michael the Archangel, defend us in the conflict which we have to sustain against principalities and powers, against the rulers of the world of this darkness, against the spirits of wickedness in the high places. Come to the rescue of men, whom God has created in His image and likeness, and whom He has redeemed at a great price from the tyranny of the devil. It is Thou whom Holy Church venerates as her guardian and her protector, Thou whom the Lord has charged to conduct redeemed souls into Heaven.' He looked at Mary. Her eyes were closed. Her breathing was even. 'Pray, therefore, the God of Peace to subdue Satan beneath our feet, that he may no longer retain men captive nor do injury to the Church. Present our prayers to the Most High, that without delay they may draw His mercy down upon us.' Mary's breathing came deep and regular. 'Seize the dragon, the old serpent, which is the Devil and Satan, bind him and cast him into the bottomless pit that he may no more seduce the nations.'

Theophilus looked at Mary and then motioned the Mother Superior to go nearer to her. The nun watched Mary's face and listened to her regular breathing. She looked up at Theophilus and nodded.

'Then,' Theophilus' voice rose, 'in the name of Jesus Christ, our Lord and Saviour, strengthened by the intercession of the Immaculate Virgin Mary, Mother of God, of the Blessed Michael the Archangel, of the

243

Blessed Apostles Peter and Paul, and all the Saints, and powerful in the holy authority of our ministry, we confidently undertake to repulse the attacks and deceits of the Devil.' The old priest moved a little closer to the bed. 'Let God arise, and let His enemies be scattered: and let them that hate Him flee from before His face! As smoke vanisheth, so let them vanish away! As wax melteth before the fire, so let the wicked perish in the presence of God! Behold the Cross of the Lord!' Theophilus lifted the large metal crucifix he wore around his neck and pointed it at the sleeping woman on the bed. 'Flee, bands of enemies!'

The chanted response came from Father Steiger and the three Sisters: 'The Lion of the Tribe of Judah, the Offspring of David, hath conquered.'

'May Thy mercy descend upon us!' shouted Theophilus.

'As great as our hope in Thee,' responded the others.

'Then we drive you from us, whoever you may be, unclean spirits, Satanic powers, infernal invaders, wicked legions, assemblies and sects. In the name and by the virtue of Our Lord Jesus Christ.' Theophilus started to make the sign of the cross.

Mary screamed. It was a piercing high scream that seemed to come up out of her innermost being. 'No!' she shouted and in an instant she was sitting up on her bended knees. Her small fingers now like claws as she pawed the emptiness in front of her. 'No!' she screamed again.

'May you be snatched away and driven from the Church of God and from the souls redeemed by the precious . . .'

'No!' Mary shouted, and with a single thrust of her legs she catapulted from the mattress to the very ceiling of the room. Her fingers dug into the plaster, tearing small holes in which to cling while her feet swung up flat against the ceiling where she hung like a bat.

'Oh my God!' Sister Climaka shouted.

'Get her down,' Theophilus roared.

'She'll fall and hurt herself!' Mother Lotharia screamed.

'Mary!' Theophilus shouted. He ran so he was directly under her. He made the sign of the cross. 'By the precious blood of the Divine Lamb,' he continued with the words of the ritual, 'Cease by your audacity cunning serpent, to delude the human race, to. . . .'

'No! I said no!' the voice coming from Mary's body was harsh and masculine. 'Get away! Let me alone! Get away from me!'

'. . . to persecute the Church, to torment God's elect and to sift them . . .'

'I said get away old man!' Mary twisted her head around and they could all see how her features had become distorted. Her eyes looked smaller, her cheekbones distended, her jawline pointed and jutting. 'Get your shit-filled old body away from me you old bastard!' the deep voice howled.

'She's not . . .' Mother Lotharia found it difficult to put her thoughts into words, 'She's not moving her mouth!'

'No,' Sister Lydia agreed. 'She's saying the words, but her lips aren't moving! I never saw such a thing.'

'Get her down from there!' Father Steiger ordered, but everyone was too shocked to move.

'. . . sift them as wheat,' Theophilus continued. 'This is the command made to you by the most High God,' he crossed himself according to the ritual, 'with Whom in your haughty insolence you . . .'

'I warned you!' the voice inside Mary shouted and then her mouth opened wide and she vomited out a large quantity of a reddish yellow mixture that hit Father Theophilus right in the face and spattered down over his beard and onto his robes. The old man began to claw at the stuff, pulling it away from his eyes and brushing at it before it had time to stick to his hair and clothing. '. . . in your haughty insolence you still

245

pretend to be equal . . .' This continuation of the ritual only brought down still more of the hot, sticky vomit. The old priest gagged at the stench that poured across his face. Mother Lotharia hurried to him and started wiping the stuff away with her handkerchief. Then Mary threw up again. This time it was a thin, runny mixture, green in colour, but with small lumps that looked like half-digested fish. It not only hit Theophilus but spattered over the Mother Superior as well. 'Oh, Holy Mother of God!' the elderly woman screamed and backed away toward the door.

'Let's stop this,' Father Steiger shouted at Theophilus. 'Let's stop it right now!'

'Yes!' shouted the voice from Mary's body. 'Good boy! That's a real good boy!'

'No!' Theophilus thundered, and when he opened his mouth some of the vomit found it's way onto his tongue. He spat on the floor, wiping his lips with the sleeve of his cassock. 'Get her down from there! She must be placed back on the bed! Get her down!'

Father Steiger and the two Sisters hurried to where Mary was hanging, their feet slipping in the warm vomit on the floor boards. The young priest jumped up and managed to grasp one of Mary's elbows. She snarled and tried to knock loose his grip, but lost her balance and suddenly she came crashing down onto the floor.

Quickly everyone in the room was on her, holding her, struggling with her and finally getting her back onto the mattress. 'You bunch of no-good bitches!' the voice screamed at the Sisters. 'Keep your filthy hands off me!'

'Don't you dare use such language to me!' Sister Lydia shouted at Mary, hauled back with one hand and slapped Mary across the face. 'Don't you dare talk to me like that!'

'Lydia!' the Mother Superior shouted. 'Stop that! This instant!'

246

The voice inside Mary laughed. 'Didn't hurt. I've taken worse from other frustrated virgins. At least she *claims* to be a virgin.' There was another laugh, yet Mary's lips never moved.

'I *am* a virgin!' Sister Lydia screamed. 'I am a bride of Christ!'

'Yeah?' taunted the voice. 'What about that time with you and that bakery delivery boy, huh? Gonna tell us about that time, Miss Virgin?'

Lydia coloured deeply under her dark headdress. She looked at the Mother Superior and at Sister Climaka. 'I . . .' she started, 'I am still a virgin. That time . . . that time she's talking about I was only twelve years old. We didn't *do* anything. He delivered our order and mother wasn't home, so I let him in . . . but we didn't do anything. I was only twelve.'

'But you held his thing in your hand,' the voice continued from Mary's unmoving lips. 'You held it in your hand and you looked at it.'

'But that was years ago!' Sister Lydia started sobbing. 'Nothing happened. It was years ago!' She stood in the centre of the room, her hands to her face, the tears streaming down between her fingers.

'I think,' said Theophilus, 'you had better go now.' Sister Lydia nodded. 'You go now,' he said softly, 'and you tell the next Sister to come in and take your place.' Without looking at anyone any longer, Sister Lydia turned and hurried from the room.

Father Steiger spoke up. 'I think we had better end it for today. It's not fair. You didn't tell me it would be like this.'

The old man shrugged as he kept pulling pieces of vomit from his beard. 'And if I had told you the truth? Would you have permitted me to bring the woman here?'

'No,' Father Steiger said. 'I wouldn't have.'

'So you see,' laughed the voice inside Mary's unconscious body, 'I am for real. I can do things. I know things people don't think I know. Like poor old Sister Lydia. She held it in her hand and the thought of what might have happened has stayed with her all these years.'

'You, demon, are unkind!' Theophilus thundered. 'That elderly sister did nothing to you, yet you insulted her and shamed her. For what?'

'And what did I ever do to you?' the deep voice said. 'Yet you insult me and call me names and try to force me out of this woman and back into Hell. So old man, whatever you hand out, you and your friends here had better able to take back.' Mary's body sat up suddenly and her mouth quickly spat a gob of yellow phlegm that struck Theophilus on his shoulder.

'You are scum!' Father Steiger yelled.

'Go away, little boy, and take this old fart with you,' the voice said.

'We're going,' said Theophilus. 'But just for today. We will be back tomorrow. Then we'll be ready for you.'

'And I'll be ready for you,' the voice said.

The two priests made the sign of the cross and Theophilus sprinkled a vial of Holy Water around the bed. Mary's body twisted and she cried out a couple of times, then right after the priests left the room and removed their stoles, she opened her eyes and looked at the Mother Superior and Sister Climaka who had remained beside her.

'Am I free now?' she said. 'Is it all over?'

'I thought you were going to tell them at Mass this morning?' Therese served her brother coffee and pancakes.

He sighed. 'I was going to say something, but I couldn't do it. After what I saw yesterday, I can't tell these good people what's going on here. I can't do it and they wouldn't understand.'

'I'm not so sure I understand either,' the woman

replied. 'Somebody that talks, yet doesn't move her mouth? Somebody that can jump like a prize athlete and cling to the ceiling? Somebody who doesn't eat hardly anything at all, yet vomits up buckets of stuff?' She shook her head. 'I can't understand it. Yet I saw. I saw what a mess Theophilus was when he came back here to change his clothes. And that awful stinking stuff in his beard? Poor old man. I don't know how he does it.'

'He's used to it.'

'Oh, come on Joe! Used to *that*? Who could get used to that kind of treatment? And the names she called him? And poor old Lydia?' She sat down at the breakfast table with him. She lowered her voice. 'How old did she say she was when she did that thing with the delivery boy? Sixteen?'

Her brother stared at her. 'Twelve!' he said sharply. 'Really, Therese, I'm ashamed of you. I shouldn't have told you.'

'Why? Lydia wasn't in the confessional, the devil said it out loud, and she agreed. What's the harm?'

'What's the *harm*? Sister Lydia is fifty-three years old. She deserves respect.'

'I'm giving her respect,' his sister replied. She stopped for a moment and started calculating in her head. 'That was thirty-seven years ago. Thirty-seven years! That's a long time to remember one man's thing.' She got up, shaking her head as she went to the kitchen sink. 'Must have been a real sausage to be remembered all those years!'

Her brother sat and stared in amazement.

The ritual began exactly at noon that day. Mary was led, willingly, to the room and placed on the iron bed. The Mother Superior was there, this time with Sisters Primosa and Bernadone. Both women were in their early thirties and both more than a little anxious after what they had heard had happened the day before.

The room had been put back into order. The vomit on the floor washed away, the bare boards scented with a mixture of cologne and holy water.

The two priests kissed the edges of their stoles and placed them around their necks. Then Theophilus started into the prescribed Roman Catholic ritual for an exorcism.

'In the name of the Father and of the Son and of the Holy Ghost. Amen.'

'Amen,' responded the others in unison.

'Glorious Prince of the Celestial Host, St Michael the Archangel, defend us in the conflict which we have to sustain against principalities and powers, against the rulers of the world of his darkness, against the spirits of wickedness in the high places . . .' He kept his eyes on Mary. She seemed to be asleep already. It was quite common, he had told Father Steiger, to have the possessed person slip into unconsciousness as soon as the ritual began. Steiger had suggested it might merely be hypnosis. Theophilus had only shrugged . . . 'come to the rescue of men, whom God has created to his image and likeness . . .'

'Awooooo! Yeawooo!' The loud howling sounds came suddenly out of Mary's unmoving lips. 'Aeeeiii! Awoooo!'

The two Sisters sprang to the bed, grabbed Mary's body, and pressed it down onto the mattress.

'Reawooo! Awoooo! Rooowow!' The noises sounded like animal howling. 'Reawooo!' Mary's body thrashed but the Sisters held firm.

Father Theophilus moved quickly through the Prayer to St Michael and started on the Exorcism itself. The more he chanted and pointed his metal crucifix at the woman on the bed, the more she howled.

'It's like a pack of wild dogs!' Mother Lotharia shouted over the noises.

Mary's voices howled higher.

250

'Such infernal sounds!' Sister Primosa turned her head away, not wanting to be so close to the ear-splitting screams.

'Awoooo!' Mary shouted. 'Aieawowooooo . . .' the sounds held in the air before they trailed off.

Theophilus kept up his ritual, plodding through each sentence and making the sign of the cross at all the right places. He waved his crucifix in the direction of the bed. 'Retreat, Satan, inventor and master of all deceit, enemy of man's salvation. Cede the place to Christ in Whom . . .'

'Aieawowooooo.' The high-pitched howls filled the room.

'. . . in Whom you have found none of your works. Cede the place to the One, Holy Catholic . . .'

Then the screaming started. It was as if someone had taken a very sharp knife and had plunged it into the belly of a pig. It was sudden and piercing and unrelenting in its sound of terror and pain.

Father Steiger looked at Theophilus. 'Can't you shut her up?'

The old man shook his head. 'Stoop beneath the all-powerful Hand of God, tremble and flee at the evocation . . .'

Then the cries of a baby. The sobbing, yelping, gasping-for-breath screams of a human baby being beaten. There was the loud slapping sound of hand against bare flesh, then the screams of pain coming from some pitiful tiny body. Yet, Mary lay there, eyes closed, body still, lips unmoving.

Now the cries changed. This time they were of women. Terrified women being attacked, screaming, suffering, being beaten and mistreated and killed. From the multitude of voices it sounded as if the room was filled with suffering terrorized females.

'Hey!' a man's voice shouted from outside the convent. 'What's going on up there?'

Mother Lotharia hurried to the window and looked

out. 'Good grief, there's about ten people down there. They've heard the noises.'

'What's happening up there?' another voice called out. 'Father Steiger, are you okay?'

'Yeah, is that you Father?'

Theophilus stopped his prayers. 'You better go to the window, Joseph. Let them see you. Let them know you're all right.'

Father Steiger pulled back the heavy white curtain and waved to the small crowd below. He could see others running across the lawn in the direction of the convent.

'What's all the noise, Father?' a woman called up to him.

He smiled and waved at her and made the sign of the cross.

'You people butchering up there, or what?' the farmer shouted.

Steiger opened the window. 'I'm all right,' he called down to them. 'Don't worry. Everything here is all right.'

'*Aiewowoooooo*!' the animal scream raced out the open window into the Iowa air.

'What the hell was that, Father?' a man yelled.

'Yeah! What in the world are you doing up there?'

Steiger kept the smile on his face. 'I said everything was all right. You can all go home now. It's nothing.'

The howling changed to the screams of the stuck pig. The crowd, grown now to almost fifty citizens, stared at the window and had no intention of going anywhere until they had their answers. This was Earling. Where nothing ever happened. Now that something finally was happening in their small town they sure as hell weren't going to miss out on it.

'Please! You out there!' the high-pitched, terrified sound of a woman in great distress, flew out of Mary's body and down to the crowd below. 'Please help me! They're going to kill me! Please! Get me some help! Oh

252

please, won't any of you do something? I don't want to die! Not like this!' and she screamed again.

'Father Steiger,' one man yelled up at the window, 'you better tell us what's happening in there or we'll come up and see for ourselves!'

The Mother Superior appeared in the window beside the priest. 'You will do no such thing!' she shouted. 'This is a convent and, as such, is sacred Church property. You people stay right where you are!'

'Then you come down here and tell us!' a man in bib overalls yelled at her. 'We have a right to know!'

'Yeah! . . . We do . . . It's our Church too . . . Either that or we come up there. . . .'

The priest and the elderly Superior looked at Theophilus. 'One of you go down and talk to them,' he said. 'They'll gum up the works if they're not talked to.'

'I'll go,' said the priest. 'It's my parish. I should have told them already. Anyway,' he said as he walked toward the door, 'it'll be good to get out of this madhouse for a few minutes.'

There was a minute or two of silence. 'Well,' said the voice in Mary's body, 'He's gone. What a pain in the ass he is! Where'd you find him, Theophilus? Selling vacuum cleaners somewhere?'

'Father Steiger is a good man,' Theophilus replied. 'He's a good priest too.'

'There isn't such a thing,' the voice laughed.

'One bad priest is still better than a host of you devils,' the old man answered.

'What? A man wearing skirts and listening to old ladies whispering their sins? That's being better than *we* are? Come on! We've got power. We've got abilities to do things, to make things happen! You guys just tell the poor fools everything will be better after they die and then you pass the collection plate.'

'But we have God on our side,' put in the Mother Superior.

Mary turned her face toward the woman. 'Don't give me that. I've seen what your God does and it's a helluva lot *less* than what he promises. Anyway, who asked you?'

'I'm allowed my opinion,' the Mother Superior replied tartly.

'Not around me, you're not,' the voice said. 'This is between me and the old man here. Old women like you should be put out to pasture.'

'Now that's quite enough,' Theophilus said loudly. 'The Mother is a fine woman, intelligent and honourable. She has been of great use to the Church.'

Mary spat some brown liquid into the air and there was the brief smell of chewing tobacco. 'Use?' the voice laughed. 'I can't think of anything more *useless* than an old and withered virgin!' The laugh came again with another splat of brown liquid.

'You know,' said Theophilus, 'I can't carry on an intelligent conversation with someone if I don't know their name.'

'Intelligent?' replied the voice. 'From a priest?'

'I'd like to know your name. Identify yourself, please.'

'None of your business.'

'In the name of Jesus and His most Blessed Mother, Mary the Immaculate, who crushed the head of the serpent, tell me the truth! Who is the leader or prince among you?' Theophilus thundered. 'What is your name?'

There was a sound like a dog barking, then the voice said: 'Beelzebub'.

'Beelzebub?' repeated the old priest. 'You call yourself Beelzebub?'

'You asked me my name.'

'But aren't you Lucifer, the prince of all devils?'

'No,' the voice responded, 'I'm not the prince but I *am* one of his lieutenants.'

Theophilus scowled. 'Then you were never a human

being. You are one of the fallen angels. You were part of that group who in your pride wanted to be like God.'

Mary's mouth opened into a teeth-filled grin. 'Yeah, that's right. I was one of the rebel angels, sworn to hate God and his son.'

Theophilus was still pondering this information. 'Sometimes Beelzebub and Lucifer are thought to be one and the same. Why do you call yourself Beelzebub?'

'Because that's my name.'

'But you're obviously important,' Theophilus continued, 'You've got to rank up there somewhere near Lucifer.'

'I am important,' the voice responded, 'I was once part of the seraphim. Your crazy Bible said we each had three pairs of wings. Has anyone ever tried to fly with three pairs of wings? he laughed.

'Then,' Theophilus continued, 'you were one of the very highest order of angels. Why, you and the others were attendants at the very throne of God.'

'Yeah,' said the voice, 'But that was a long time ago. Things have changed.'

'Alright,' said the old priest, 'just suppose something for a moment. What would you do if God made it possible for you to atone for your sins, for all the terrible treacheries you did to Him?'

The voice laughed. 'Do you think he'd do that *now*? Come on, old man. And you call yourself a competent theologian!'

Father Theophilus grew red in the face and immediately spoke several phrases in Latin. 'Now,' he said with a smile, 'reply to my questions if you are able!'

Mary's face turned to one side and then the other. If her eyes had been open she would have stared at the Sisters before speaking; as it was, her lids remained sealed. Then the lips smiled and out came a long reply – in the Latin language – to the priest's questions.

255

'Good Heavens!' Mother Lotharia said and crossed herself quickly.

A shot of brown tobacco liquid hit her skirt. 'Please,' said the voice, 'don't do that in front of me. If you must move your hand, pick your nose or something.'

Theophilus came closer to the bed. 'I demand to know how long you have been torturing this poor woman.'

'What business is it of yours?'

'She is one of God's children! She is a good Catholic! My mission on earth is to help unfortunate people like her. That's why!' He took a silver vial from his pocket and shook it at the bed. Drops of Holy Water sprinkled on Mary's body.

The voice inside howled and screamed, even louder than before. The Mother Superior helped the two Sisters hold Mary down.

'Since she was fourteen years old,' the voice finally replied.

Theophilus's face got red again. 'How dare you enter into such a young girl and torture her like that? How dare you?'

'We were invited.'

'Invited? Invited by whom?'

'Her father. Her very own father, that's whom. Didn't he curse her and invite us to take over? So we did. Anyway, it had to be. She had been marked since birth.'

'Marked? I don't understand,' Theophilus said.

'Marked. Promised to us. What's so difficult about understanding that? We started working on her father when he was still a boy and he promised her to us. I thought you knew all this, Theophilus. Where've you been? Had your head up your ass?'

'And so you took over?'

'Sure.'

'But who gave you the permission to take possession of the girl?'

The face grimaced. 'Don't ask such stupid questions. Satan, Lucifer, whatever you want to call him. He didn't give me permission, he *told* me to do it.'

'And so you did. You went into her and destroyed a life.'

'My loyalty is to *him*. I do what he tells me to do. He wants me someplace, I go.'

Theophilus shot a glance at the Mother Superior. 'Then,' he said slowly, 'if I understand correctly, you are here, in this room, talking to me, on *direct* instructions from Satan. Here on Lucifer's very command!'

'Of course,' the voice replied. 'It couldn't be any other way. And if you don't stop trying to get this woman's soul away from us, you will be dealing with Satan personally.'

'Is that a threat?' Theophilus asked. 'If it is, I'm not afraid.'

'Yes,' said the voice, 'it is a threat. It's also a promise. Stop this now and it will be to everybody's advantage.'

'And if I choose not to?' Theophilus asked.

'Then be prepared for Satan's coming amongst you!'

The three black-robed women gasped.

'You should be frightened ladies. You'd better do everything you can to persuade this old fool to stop this exorcism. If he doesn't, Satan himself will take over and you don't want that. Believe me ladies, you don't want that!'

The next day, Theophilus waited until early afternoon to begin the exorcism. He told Father Steiger he needed the morning to fast and pray.

Mary fell quickly into unconsciousness. Once the prayers were started the screams of stuck pigs and howling dogs and crying babies and terrified women could be heard all across the small town. There were no sessions of questions and answers. The voices inside the woman gave off sounds. There were no words.

Theophilus ended the ritual earlier than he had planned and spent the remainder of the day and the early hours of the night in the chapel praying and asking for guidance.

On the next day, Mary's body was rigid. She lay there as if carved from stone. There was no movement, no sound. At one time the Mother Superior put a mirror under her nose to see if she was still breathing. Theophilus went through the entire ritual. Actually, it was the first time he had been able to say it completely without interruption. But it seemed to do no good. There was absolutely no reaction from the woman on the bed. After the old man had said the final prayers and left the room, Mary groggily came to and was helped, every step of the way, back to her own room where she fell asleep immediately and slept through the night.

'What's going wrong?' Father Steiger asked Theophilus on the morning reserved for the fifth session. 'Why isn't she responding the way you said she would?'

'I don't know,' the older priest said. 'By now there should have been progress. All we've accomplished is to identify the devil in her and frighten the population of Earling.'

'They're not all that frightened,' Father Steiger said. 'I told them what we were doing and why we were doing it here and not in the woman's city of residence.'

'You didn't give them her name, did you? I mean, secrecy in the case is all important.'

The younger man shook his head. 'No. I just told them her first name was Mary. They understood why I couldn't identify her.'

Therese was clearing away the coffee cups. 'But

they have been asking me about her,' she said.

'What have you been telling them?' her brother looked at her. 'I'm almost afraid to ask.'

'Just that she is full of devils, that Father Theophilus is an expert and that it won't be too long before she gets cured and gets out of here. They're worried about harvesting, you know. In just a few weeks it'll be time to harvest and they wonder if her devils will wither the wheat and turn the corn black.'

Theophilus turned the palms of his hands heavenward. 'Ah, such superstition! And in this day and age. I hope you told them not to worry, that the woman was a danger only to herself?'

'I did, but I also told them if I had any harvesting to do, I'd get it done as soon as possible.'

'Therese, you didn't!' Father Steiger exclaimed.

The woman shrugged. 'I did. I wouldn't want to be out in my wheat field when her devil pops out. He might head straight for me. Then what? No, none of this being outside stuff for me. Stay in the house and keep the door shut, that's my advice to people.'

'You're impossible!' her brother exploded.

'No,' she said shaking her head, 'I'm scared. Just like all those people out there, I'm scared.'

That day too, there was no dialogue. Mary lay, as before, like a piece of granite. The only movement came when Theophilus sprinkled her with Holy Water. Then she trembled, slightly, and a muffled scream came from somewhere deep inside her.

The next day Mary was able to walk, unaided, to the iron bed. Mother Lotharia thought she was losing weight and ordered Sister Eliana to give her bigger portions at night.

'She won't eat,' the elderly cook complained. 'I bring the food to her room, place it on the desk and she doesn't touch it.'

'There must be something you can do,' the Mother replied.

'On the farm where I was a girl,' the Sister said, 'we would hold open a goose's beak and force the food down it's gullet. Is that what you want me to do?'

Mother Lotharia glared at the woman but didn't answer. All the Sisters were starting to get edgy with this exorcism business in their convent. If it had been under other circumstances she would have reprimanded Eliana, now she just walked away.

The ritual began. Father Steiger hadn't been assisting Theophilus over the past two days as he had had parish duties to perform, despite the fact that Catholic custom demanded two priests in attendance at official exorcisms. Theophilus hadn't liked it, and was glad that Steiger was present now.

The demons let the old man get half way through his litany before interrupting him with shrieks, howling and sobbing coming from the body. Two of the Sisters secured Mary's arms and legs and, more than once, thought she was about to escape.

'The glorious Mother of God, the Virgin Mary, commands you,' Theophilus made the sign of the cross, 'she who by her humility and from the first moment of her Immaculate Conception crushed your proud head. The faith . . .'

'She did no such thing!' the voice said suddenly. And just as suddenly Mary started throwing up. There would have been a bucketful had the Sisters been able to get the galvanized pail under her mouth in time, but most of the green, stringy stuff ran down her body, taking the grey colour out of her robe wherever it spread and sizzling as it touched the mattress cover. The stench was overpowering.

'Open the window, for God's sake!' Father Steiger shouted and then when nobody did his bidding, he ran and lifted it open himself. He turned back to Theophilus. 'Now look at that mess! We've got to stop and clean it up again. You know I'm getting more than a little tired of this.'

The old man shrugged. 'What can you do? What can any of us do but keep trying? You want the poor woman to be free, don't you?' Father Steiger nodded. 'Then we have to keep going. This is not something you stop and start like one of your cars.'

'Change her,' Steiger said to the Mother Superior. 'Take her back to her room and change her.'

Mother Lotharia opened the door and rang an iron cow bell that she had placed on the floor in the corridor. It was a signal that other Sisters should stop what they were doing and come to the exorcism room. In a few seconds five other black robes were fluttering around, talking, soothing, guiding the barefoot and almost conscious woman back to her room. Others stayed, stripped the mattress cover and replaced it with a fresh one, while another swabbed the still steaming vomit that had landed on the floor, and emptied the bucket.

The two priests had gone into the convent kitchen for coffee. 'You said a week,' Father Steiger sipped the hot brew and looked at the old man. 'Tomorrow is the seventh day. Tomorrow a week will be up and she doesn't seem to be any farther along than she was on the first day.'

'I know what I said. But Satan also knows what I said. If he heard me promising a week, then he'll stay longer, just to make a fool out of me.'

'How much longer?'

'Until he tires of the game.'

'And when will that be? Another week?'

'My dear Joseph, Satan has been defying God for centuries. Do you really think he counts the days?'

Sister Agrippina appeared in the doorway, announcing that Mary was back in the exorcism room.

Theophilus and Steiger took their positions at the foot of the bed. 'We drive you from us, whoever you may be, unclean spirits, Satanic powers, infernal invaders, wicked . . .'

261

The voice came out of Mary. It was laughing. 'What are you waving at me now, old man?'

'It is, as you can see,' Theophilus answered, 'a cross.'

'Where'd you get that thing? From a child's box?' and there was laughter in the voice.

'A pious lady in this community loaned me this cross,' the priest answered. 'I am using it against you today because it is her request. This cross has been in her family for years. I have blessed it at the altar of the Church. Don't negate the power of this holy sign, demon!'

'Oh, I can't negate the power,' the voice responded, 'except that cross is made of pasteboard. Since when did your what's-his-name die on a paper cross? I always thought they nailed him to a cross made of wood.'

'This is of wood!' Theophilus shook the cross violently. 'And you know quite well that Our Lord died on a cross of wood because it was your legions that nailed Him on it.'

'A paper cross for a paper god.' said the voice inside Mary. 'That figures.'

'This cross is of wood! Look, here are the grains of wood on the other side. The figure is of wood!'

'Hit it,' the voice urged.

'What?'

'Hit it. Go on, strike your wooden cross against the iron in this bed.'

Theophilus, so sure of himself, swung the cross sharply across the footboard. There was a cracking sound and everyone watched in horror as the papier-mache under the thin veneer crumbled and fell on the floor.

'How . . . how did you know that cross was made of paper?' Sister Agrippina asked the voice.

'I know everything. When are you stupid people going to realise that? Now go away, all of you. You've annoyed me enough for one day.'

'And you have annoyed us!' Father Steiger shouted.

'Good,' the voice said. 'That's the first thing you've said that's made me happy. Now tell these two fat cows to get off this body and to take it back to the other bedroom. The carnival is over for the day.'

They stood and watched for almost ten minutes but there wasn't a movement or a sound coming out of Mary. Finally the Sisters picked her up and carried her down the hall, with Sister Agrippina complaining that she was 'doing the devil's bidding!'

'I have these terrible stomach cramps,' Mary looked at Theophilus. 'They kept me awake almost all night. If it could be at all possible, I'd rather not go through it today. If you could just let me stay here quietly for one day.'

The Mother Superior spoke up. 'Sister Clara was here with her all through the night. She was in pain and didn't get more than a couple hours' sleep.'

'I had hoped,' Theophilus spoke softly, 'to have you available every day. We wanted to free you from your demon in a week.'

'I know,' she said, 'and I wanted it too, but I just feel so terrible today. Can't we delay it for a day?'

He sighed. 'I suppose so. Perhaps we all need the rest.'

'Thank you,' Mary said and tried to smile.

When Father Steiger heard the news, he grimaced and said: 'So much for getting rid of her in seven days!'

The next day Mary was no better. She remained in her bedroom. She ate or drank nothing, in spite of Sister Lydia's coaxings. Sister Serena stayed with her, watching her, nervously listening for any signal that was out of the ordinary. There was none. All there was was just a frail, slightly greying woman, ill on a single bed.

'Instead of a sermon today,' Father Steiger said as he looked out over the filled-to-capacity church, 'I want to tell you what is happening in your parish: what is happening in the convent building right next door. I want you

263

to know the truth and to be aware of what might happen.' A few people squirmed in their pews, others coughed and one woman blew her nose. 'On the seventeenth of this month, a Friday, the woman who I will only call "Mary" came to Earling. She arrived on the train from a large city in the north. She came at the bidding of the Bishop up there and with the approval of our Bishop in Des Moines. She was brought here at the urgings of Father Theophilus,' Father Steiger gestured to the white-bearded old priest in the front row. 'Father Theophilus is an honourable man, a hardworking member of the Church. Father Theophilus is also an exorcist.'

At this, heads craned, some people stood up to get a better view and almost everyone had something to whisper to the person beside him.

'He is one of the very few priests in the Church here in America who has been specially trained in the difficult art of exorcism. It is not a speciality a priest takes on lightly. It is not a pleasant task. Confronting the devil is never a pleasant task. Now many of you may scoff and say that in this modern year of nineteen hundred and twenty eight it is old fashioned, even superstitious, to believe in the existence of the devil. Yet if I asked you if you believed in the Bible you would all say "yes"; well, the Bible is filled with stories about Satan. I'm sure you all recall how Satan tempted Our Lord on a mountain top in the desert. If you believe in the Holy Scriptures you *have to believe* in the existence of the devil as well. The devil is an integral part of Christianity. As Christ is good, Satan is evil. Goodness and evil are working parts of our world.

'Right now, across the lane and inside the next building, a fallen angel resides in the body of a human being. Well you may ask how God could create such perfection as the angels and yet how they could have fallen from such grace into such depths of degradation as Hell must surely be. The fallen angel next door calls

264

himself Beelzebub. He says he takes his instructions directly from Satan, his prince of darkness. He told Father Theophilus that at one time he had been at the very throne of God, yet he chose to disagree with God and was cast out of Paradise. If I may quote from the twelfth chapter of the "Apocalypse" in the book of "Revelation": "And there was a great battle in heaven, Michael and his angels fought with the dragon, and the dragon fought and his angels: and they prevailed not, neither was their place found any more in heaven. And that great dragon was cast out, that old serpent, who is called the devil and Satan, who seduceth the whole world – and he was cast unto the earth, and his angels were thrown down with him." Now,' he looked slowly around the hushed congregation, 'call that a myth, if you choose, but it is a clear statement about the reality of Satan and his disgrace. The devil and the demons were indeed created by God but He created them for *good*. It was by their own devices and their own doings that they became evil.

'When God created Adam and Eve He gave them free will, He tested them and they failed Him. The same with these beautiful and trustworthy angels. He gave them a choice and instead of them loving Him and appreciating Him for their very existence, they were proud and vain and chose to defy him, even to do battle in such a wonderful place as heaven! Their leader, Satan, engaged in physical combat with God's archangel Michael. Satan and his followers dared hope to win through mortal combat. But they didn't. They lost. Yet the Almighty showed them love. Instead of destroying them, instead of undoing what He had created, He chose to throw them out of heaven. He could have ended their existence but He didn't. He showed them mercy and He sent them to earth, to the very bowels of the earth and gave them that territory to dwell in and to govern.

'St Thomas has the idea that this great battle came

about when God tested the angels' devotion to the coming of Jesus Christ. When God told them he was going to send the second part of the Blessed Trinity to earth in the form of a man, He asked these angels to adore a man. St Thomas feels they thought it was a great blow to their dignity that they, as angels, were far superior to any man, even in the disguise of the Son of God. So they rebelled, they revealed their own plans for dominating heaven and Archangel Michael had to fight them. Their leader, Lucifer, was one of the most noble of the archangels. The very name "Lucifer" means "the lightbearer" in Latin. But after that, men gave Lucifer other names, such as "Satan" which in Hebrew means "the adversary" and the "devil" which in Greek means "the slanderer". And all the legions of angels who fell from grace with Lucifer and who are fully committed to following his plans for complete domination of the human race are now called "demons" which comes from the Greek for "those who know" or "spirits".

'Again from the Holy Book, First John, chapter three: "He that committeth sin is of the devil: for the devil sinneth from the beginning. For this purpose, the Son of God appeared, that he might destroy the works of the devil." And what about Mary Magdalen? According to St Mark, Jesus cast seven devils out of her. Seven! The woman next door, whose name is also Mary, has only one devil. But he is a powerful one. He will not leave willingly. He has appeared in this woman on the instructions of Satan himself. It will not be easy for Father Theophilus to cast him out. The toll may be great, not only on the good Father but upon the woman Mary and indeed upon all of us here in this parish.

'One of you asked me this week if it was really the devil in this woman. If possibly she was just insane. If possibly she had invented it all. One young man told me he was reading a book about the new science called Psychiatry and that possibly this woman should be helped by medical men, not religious men.

'To those charges I answered that the Mother Church does not take up the ritual of exorcism lightly. Every person who is a little crazy, every person who has a vivid imagination, every person who sees ghosts and hears voices is not automatically considered "possessed" by the Church. A great deal of time is spent on investigation of such claims. For the Church to instigate an exorcism the person in question is studied, observed, talked to. His friends are questioned. His family is questioned. He is sent to medical doctors and mental doctors and everything possible in the man-created world is tried before an exorcist is called in. In the case of Mary she had been under observation since she was in high school. We have watched her and reported on her. I could show you a file box full of papers and scientific reports on this poor woman. I could show you documents from doctors telling how their treatments failed. Documents from other experts who were amazed at what she could do and from others who were amazed at how terribly limited she had become.'

He took a deep breath and hoped they were understanding what he was saying. 'She was interviewed by priests and nuns. She was even called into her Bishop's private study and there she conversed and answered questions about the Bible and theology and Church dogma. She answered those questions *correctly*. She astounded the Reverend Bishop with information she could not possibly have known by *normal* means. Several times, and the Bishop would be the first to admit this, this poor woman who was not permitted to even finish high school, knew more about certain subjects and ideologies than the Bishop himself knew! And,' here he paused for emphasis, 'often these discussions were not in the English language but at times in German, in Latin and even ancient Greek! Once a Polish-speaking priest talked with her for over an hour in

Polish! Another time the Bishop invited a priest from the Ukrainian Orthodox Church to interview her. The woman spoke fluent Ukrainian with him! One of the true tests of diabolical possession the Church uses is an individual's knowledge of things he could not possibly know otherwise and a knowledge of ancient and modern languages. This woman, this Mary languishing in pain next door, passed all these tests with flying colours.

'My dear friends in Earling. This woman must be helped. She has come to our community seeking a peaceful place where she can be relieved of this terrible affliction Satan has placed upon her. I ask you for your cooperation. I ask you for your understanding. I ask you for your prayers.'

'That wasn't bad,' the voice inside Mary said, once Theophilus had begun the exorcism ritual that Sunday afternoon. 'I liked how you explained me to your congregation. I really liked how you impressed them with my intelligence. Polish and Ukrainian! I speak all the languages and a lot of others you have never heard of. Anyway, you didn't preach too badly about us. Some priests go on at such lengths about us! Some priests can be so boring.'

'You heard the sermon?' Father Steiger raised his eyebrow. 'You were in my church this morning?'

'I heard it, but I wasn't in your church. I don't go into those kind of places if I can help it. No, I heard it from here. Churches make me nervous.' The voice laughed.

'Don't you think,' said Theophilus, 'that it's time you left this woman? Don't you think that after nine days you have heard enough to be convinced you have no claim on this woman's body or soul?'

'Today is the ninth day?' A smile crossed Mary's closed lips. 'I thought you were going to get the job done in seven, old man.'

'I usually do. Seven days is normally the time it takes.'

'But you didn't count on me being here, did you? You

usually deal with little demons and noisy spirits. Now you have me to contend with, one of the captains closest to Satan himself. Ain't the same thing, is it?'

'No,' Theophilus agreed, 'it isn't. It isn't the same at all.'

Mary's head jerked and the tremor ran down to her naked feet. 'What have you got in your pocket?' the voice demanded, raising it's pitch several octaves, speaking in a high, squeaky tone. 'I don't want that here! Put it outside or I'll end today's session right here.'

Theophilus turned to the younger priest. 'What's he mean? Have you something in your pocket?'

'Just this,' and he pulled out a gold medallion with a small piece of cloth glassed in its centre. 'It's a relic of the Little Flower of the Child Jesus. I've had it for years.

'Well I don't like it!' the high-pitched voice shouted.

'Why do you have it with you?' Theophilus asked crisply.

'I . . . I,' Father Steiger explained, 'just picked it up and put it in my pocket this morning. Maybe I just want some more protection.'

The older man scowled at him. 'This book and this ritual is all you need for protection,' he said coldly. 'You know the rules. I explained them to you. No one is to bring anything into the room. God and His words are all the protection you are permitted. Or need!'

'I just thought . . .' Father Steiger started to say.

'Well don't think!' the voice shouted now in its lower masculine tone. 'Your Church doesn't expect you to think. If you thought, you wouldn't be a priest in the first place.'

'That's enough of that!' Mother Lotharia shouted. 'Do not blaspheme the Church and it's pastors!'

'Why do you keep bringing this old bitch with you, Theophilus?' Mary's head turned to stare with closed lids at the Mother Superior. 'She's wrinkled and ugly

269

and stupid all at the same time. And those other two women certainly don't add any beauty to the place. Get rid of them. And get rid of that relic of Little What's-His-Name too! If not, I don't cooperate today.'

Theophilus nodded to the Mother Superior. 'You may go,' he said, 'and the Sisters also. Father Steiger and I can handle this by ourselves today.'

'I don't want to leave you alone,' the Mother Superior replied. 'Suppose she starts jumping around again? Who'll hold her down?'

'We will manage, Mother.' Theophilus replied calmly. 'Thank you. Oh, and Father Steiger, give the Mother that holy relic in your pocket. She'll take care of it for you.'

Father Steiger handed the medallion over to the older woman and without a backward glance the three Sisters left the room and closed the door behind them.

'Good,' said the voice. 'I'm glad they're gone. That old woman gets on my nerves.'

'She is a good woman!' Theophilus thundered.

'That's like saying there's a good toothache,' the voice laughed. 'There isn't such a thing.'

Theophilus raised the cross he carried and pointed it toward the bed. He resumed the exorcism ritual where the voice had interrupted him. 'Cease deceiving human creatures and pouring out to them the poison of eternal perdition; cease harming the Church and hindering her liberty. Retreat, Satan, inventor and master of all deceit, enemy of . . .'

There was a sudden rushing sound, like wind in the upper branches of a hundred trees, and then a roaring animal sound from Mary's body. 'Ahhhh!' a new voice, a deeper voice, howled out between her clasped and parched lips. 'Cease this torture! Go away and leave us alone!'

Father Steiger looked at Theophilus and he shrugged. 'Who are you?' the old man shouted. There was a silence. 'What is your name? Are you a new demon?

270

Am I still speaking with Beelzebub?' There was background noise like the purring of a large cat. 'What is your name!' the old priest shouted again.

'I am Judas.' the new voice answered.

'Who?' Father Steiger couldn't believe what he heard.

'Judas,' the voice responded. 'You asked my name and I have given it to you.'

'What Judas?' Father Steiger asked.

'Yes,' Theophilus said, 'what Judas? Are you Judas Iscariot, the Apostle?'

'The same,' said the voice, 'the very same.'

Then from out of Mary's body came such howls and shrieks that both priests put their hands over their ears. Mary started to vibrate, shaking the mattress, sending the heavy iron bed jumping up and down on the wooden floor. Then her mouth opened and a thick stream of brackish liquid came gushing out of her. The two priests leaped to one side, narrowly avoiding being hit by the foul-smelling stuff. It splattered onto the floor, sizzled for a moment, then steamed down through the cracks between the boards.

Theophilus began shouting: 'Cede the place to Christ in whom you have found none of your works. Cede the place to the One, Holy, Catholic and Apostolic Church acquired by Christ at the price of His blood!'

The mouth opened again, and again a heavy, almost congealed, greenish mess came up and out of the body on the bed. It was aimed at Theophilus but Father Steiger grabbed the old man in time and, by almost pulling him off balance, managed to get him out of the way. The vomit hit the floor and they could see it was alive with thick white worms which scattered when they landed on the wooden boards. Theophilus was still speaking but Father Steiger watched in disbelief as the worms scurried for a few inches and then vanished in tiny bursts of smoking liquid.

'Yeeessss' the word dragged out of the vomit-spattered lips. 'I am the one. That very Judas. Yeeesss . . .'

'What business have you here?' Theophilus thundered. 'Why are you here in the body of this unfortunate woman?'

'To help the others,' the deep masculine voice dragged out. 'To bring her to such despair that she will kill herself. To help her commit suicide. To help her hang herself! She must get the rope! She must send herself to Hell!'

'Then everybody,' asked Father Steiger, 'who commits suicide goes to hell?'

'No,' the voice replied slowly and under great strain, 'not everybody.'

'Why not?' the priest insisted.

'Because they have to be urged by us,' the voice drawled, 'we are the ones that urge them to kill themselves. Certain of the ones we want, we get into their minds and we urge them to hang themselves. To do away with themselves. I did, you know. I hung myself. I found a rope and I killed myself.'

'Are you happy where you are?' Father Steiger questioned.

'Leave me alone!' the voice cried.

'Don't you have any regrets?' Theophilus asked.

'About killing myself?' there was a long, low moan. 'I did what I had to do.'

'And about your treachery to Our Lord?' Theophilus came closer to the body on the bed, stepping through the blotches of still warm vomit on the floor. 'Don't you have any regrets about your betrayal of Jesus Christ?'

'You stupid old son of a bitch!' the voice howled slowly. 'Let me alone! Don't bother me! Get away from me and stop talking about your fake god. I did what I had to! Can't you understand that? I had a role to carry out and I did it. It was my own decision!' There was a long pause. 'It was my own fault.'

The fierce, terrifying howls came again, shaking the

272

room with their vibrations. Both priests stepped back and waited for the noises to stop. When they did, another voice spoke. It was easily recognizable as that of Beelzebub. 'Did you enjoy the visit?' Neither man said anything. 'It was a special treat. Just for you, Theophilus. It's not every priest who gets to meet the famous Judas. We save him for special occasions.'

'I was ashamed to meet the man who betrayed my Lord!' Theophilus said to the woman's body. 'Ashamed he would even identify himself.'

'We don't look at him that way,' the voice replied. 'I'm sorry you didn't appreciate him. I did it just for you.'

'We will take care of him the same way we shall rid the woman of you!' the old man's voice was quavering with anger.

'Not tomorrow you won't,' the voice said, 'not until the thirteenth of next month. On that day the woman will be well enough to have us back. Until then, I'm afraid, you'll have to hold onto your prayers and your holy water.'

'Tomorrow we will try again!' Theophilus was shouting now.

'Tomorrow the woman will be too sick to leave her room. Listen to what I'm telling you!'

'Then why don't you just kill her and take her soul,' yelled Father Steiger. 'get it over with. Once and for all!'

'Oh, such a child!' the voice said quickly. 'You heard Judas. It must be a suicide. She must kill herself. We have no power to *kill*, to take a life when we want one, even one promised to us the way she was. But we do have the power to get inside people's minds and to convince them to kill themselves. Oh yes, we have that ability and we use it all the time. And you would be amazed at how easy it is with most people. Just once or twice, just a small seed planted and they do away with themselves, they give themselves to us.'

273

'You're not going to get this woman,' Father Steiger was shouting now. 'She's gone through too much to hand herself over to you! We, Father Theophilus and I, have gone through too much to give her to you! Do you understand me?'

'I understand,' the voice said with a touch of sarcasm, 'but you understand one thing too. We will win in the end. We will get her away from you. She belongs to us and deep in her mind she knows she belongs to us.'

'Never!' Father Steiger shouted.

'And something else too,' said the voice. 'Theophilus, we are getting awfully tired of this young fool beside you. He is ignorant of what is happening, he refuses to stay out of what is not his business.'

'He is an ordained priest of the Holy Mother Church,' Theophilus said.

'He's also a pain in the ass,' the voice continued. 'So, a warning to him.'

'I don't listen to warnings,' Father Steiger replied.

'You'd better listen to this one,' the voice said. 'Wait until Friday.'

'That's it?' Father Steiger asked.

'That's it,' the voice said. 'You wait until Friday.'

'What Friday?' the younger priest asked. 'This coming Friday?'

The voice laughed. 'I thought you said you don't listen to warnings?' and the laugh came again, followed by animal howlings and then complete silence.

True to Beelzebub's predictions (and to no one's surprise) Mary was too ill the next day for the exorcism to continue. It was all she could do to sit up in bed and drink a little broth. For the remainder of the week the Sisters fluttered in and out of her room, putting cold towels on her forehead, changing her sheets and making sure there was no evidence of a demon anywhere around her.

The next Sunday Father Steiger gave the congregation a brief summary of what had taken place. He explained about Judas coming through the woman and told them about the seriousness of suicide. It had long been forbidden by the Church and now, he said, he understood why. 'It is the devil's way of getting a soul,' he said. 'To take your own life is to give that life directly over to Satan! Don't permit any such thought to dwell long in your mind! Should such an idea occur, throw it out immediately! Then make the sign of the cross and grab whatever Catholic image or medallion or book that is near. Make sure the devil sees that you understand what he is up to. Make sure he sees you have no intention of going along with his plans!'

Afterward, in the rectory kitchen, Therese asked her brother: 'What was all that about Judas and suicide? I distinctly recall you telling me you doubted that the *real* Judas Iscariot was there in that room with you.'

'I did tell you that,' he replied. 'I really don't know if that was *the* Judas or not. Theophilus has told me many times not to believe everything the devil says, and I just find it hard to believe that I was face to face with Judas.'

'Did Theophilus believe it was the real person?' she asked.

'I don't know, I don't know what Theophilus believes anymore. He wants so badly to end this thing that he just doesn't comment on it anymore. Like now, going off on a private retreat of his own until the thirteenth. I don't know where he is. He simply got on a train and left town. I asked him what I should do if the demons attack the Lawrence woman while he is gone and he just shrugged. He said there was nothing to worry about. That Beelzebub would be back on the thirteenth, as promised, and so would he.'

'Fine can of worms, this is,' his sister said.

The young priest shuddered remembering the things that crawled out of the vomit. 'Please, no more talk about worms.' He shook his entire body. 'Some nights I wake up and think they're crawling over me.'

By the following Sunday Mary was well enough to sit outside in the secluded backyard of the convent, and soak up the still warm rays of the September sun. Once she walked into town with two of the Sisters and had an ice cream sundae at the drug store. She didn't see (or pretended not to notice) the stares of the clerks and other customers when they realised who she was.

Theophilus returned on the afternoon of the twelfth. He walked into Father Steiger's study and announced: 'Well friend, I am prepared to begin again tomorrow. Are you?'

'In the Name of Jesus Christ, our Lord and Saviour,' Theophilus got right into the ritual, 'strengthened by the intercession of the Immaculate Virgin Mary, Mother of God, of Blessed Michael the . . .'

The scream came from one of the Sisters in attendance. They all stared. Blood was trickling out of Mary's eyes, bright red blood that ran down both her cheeks and dripped onto the mattress. Mother Lotharia hurried with a wet towel and wiped Mary's face.

The voice inside the woman laughed. 'You people are always talking about blood of this one and holy blood of that one, I thought I'd give you some of this woman's *unholy* blood. You are all so crazy about blood!' The laugh came again, but Mary's lips didn't move.

'How dare you?' screamed Theophilus, his face instantly crimson with anger. 'You have no right to this unfortunate child's blood! That blood is a gift of life from Almighty God Himself! You have no business interfering with it!'

'I don't understand you people,' the voice replied. 'We have her mind already. We almost have her body.

You have nothing. All you control is a small part of her conscience that *thinks* it doesn't want to come over to our side. She's already on our side, the foolish woman, but she's too dumb to know it. And so are you, old man, too dumb to know you've lost this battle before you began it.'

'I have pledged myself to drive you out!' Theophilus thundered.

'Look,' the voice became soft and soothing, 'you're an old man. You've had a long and tiring life. Just go away someplace and rest, why don't you? Some nice quiet monastery where they feed you three times a day and you can sit in a rocking chair and read books or just snooze. Now doesn't that sound nice?' The voice was almost purring now. 'All you have to do is make the decision. So you lose this one, Theophilus. You've won others. What's one lone woman to you? Huh? Worth getting a heart attack over? Worth all this fuss and fasting? Worth all the trouble you've put the good Father here to? And what about the good Sisters of the convent? Is this one lone soul worth upsetting the lives of all these good people? And even the people in the town? No, Theophilus, one woman isn't worth all this trouble to so many other people! And you know,' and here the voice was low and warm 'she's a stranger. Nobody knew her before you had her brought here. She had her own little life hundreds of miles away. She existed up there and nobody down here was even aware that she existed. Go on, Theophilus, call it quits. Come on. What's one soul more or less in the balance of things? The woman's going to die anyway. Sooner or later all you human beings die. Your rituals and incantations can't keep her alive forever. We'll get her eventually. And, as you know, what's a few years to us? We've been around for centuries. We can wait a few years more.'

'He does have a point,' said Father Steiger. 'I've wondered too why this woman should take up so much of our valuable time.'

'You've *what*?' Theophilus shouted. 'You, Joseph, a Catholic priest? You've *wondered* if this woman is worth it?' Father Steiger looked away from the old man. 'If one soul – one single individual soul – can be saved from Satan's clutches then it is worth it! Did not the Lord Himself tell the story of the good shepherd who left his entire flock to save *one* lost sheep? *One* lost lamb?' Theophilus put his hand on the younger priest's shoulder. 'Joseph, Joseph,' he said sadly, 'think of your vows. Think of what you promised Our Lord when you became one of his shepherds. Please, my dear friend, don't listen to that voice inside the woman. Don't pay it any heed at all! No matter how softly he speaks, no matter how convincing his words, it is still a voice straight from Hell! It is still the voice of Satan!'

Father Steiger was about to reply when Mary's body started to shake. A high female voice came out of her closed lips and she started to flail her arms and legs. Then she started rising in the air, at first just a few inches off the mattress and then higher and higher. With shrieks of their own, the Mother Superior and the two Sisters ran to the woman and helped the two priests pull Mary back down onto the bed. The body didn't resist. It seemed to be floating as if it were a feather and there had been a sudden breeze.

'That's it for today,' the old priest said, 'but tomorrow, Mother Lotharia, I think we should tie her body down. Those leather ropes I asked you to have made, will you bring them here tomorrow? We can't have scenes like this one repeated.'

They stood watching Mary's silent body, waiting for her to open her eyes and have the real owner of it return. As she began to breathe deeper and to blink her eyelids, Father Steiger made the sign of the cross and walked toward the door. He had things to do, things that needed doing in his parish whether there was an exorcism going on or not.

'Hey! You! Young priest in a hurry!'

Father Steiger turned around. Mary was sitting up in bed, her eyes closed but a finger pointing directly at him.

'Tomorrow is a Friday. Remember? I told you to wait until Friday.'

'So you did,' he replied, 'but I'm not afraid of your warnings.'

'You should be,' the masculine voice answered.

'I have the Lord on my side,' he said.

'And I have Satan on mine.'

'The Lord always works to protect me,' the priest replied.

'Perhaps,' the voice laughed, 'but my side usually works faster.'

'I think, Joseph, that you had better not go with me to the exorcism room today.' Father Theophilus had stopped by the rectory kitchen where Therese was just about to serve her brother his breakfast. 'Today is a Friday and that demon promised you something terrible on a Friday. Anything is possible with him.'

'I think I can handle myself,' the younger man said. 'The demon is no match for me.'

'Oh! You don't know, my son! Even with what you have already seen you can't imagine the extent of his tricks. No, no, no.' He shook his head and the long white beard swayed across his black clerical habit. 'You stay here, in the rectory, and take care of the paperwork that is accumulating. I can handle the task by myself today.' He held out his hand, palm toward the younger man. 'No, no. Don't discuss it. I have made the decision. Enough said.'

Therese pointed to the breakfast table. 'Will you stay and have some coffee? Maybe a couple of eggs.'

Theophilus shook his head. 'No thank you.'

'But I never see you eat anything!' the woman protested.

'The Lord is my sustenance. He is all I need.' and he left the kitchen.

'Sometimes I wonder about him,' Therese said.

'Don't,' her brother replied. 'Trying to figure out Theophilus is a lost cause.'

Father Steiger spent most of the morning in his study, sorting papers, writing letters and trying to prepare his sermon for the coming Sunday. He marvelled at all the work that had piled up in such a short time and wondered if he would ever get the peace and quiet in which to do it. As he went from one project to another he tried not to think of what was happening in the convent room. Several times the image of the woman on the bed came before his eyes, but he shook his head and forced his thoughts to the task before him. Then the telephone rang.

'I don't know how much longer my Clara can last,' the man on the other end of the line said. 'The doctor was just here. He says maybe she has until sundown. Can you come, Father? Can you come and give her the last rites before she dies?'

'Of course,' Father Steiger replied. 'I'll be right there. I'm sorry to hear about Clara. I knew she was ill but I didn't think it was so serious.'

'It is,' said the tired voice, 'believe me Father, it is.'

The priest took his leather-bound missal out of a desk drawer and slipped it into the pocket of his floor-length habit. Then he took his stole and folded it into the same pocket. There were a few seconds of looking under papers until he found his car keys and then he started for the door. He stopped, turned around and went back to his desk. There he removed his medal of the Little Flower of the Child Jesus. 'Just in case,' he said aloud and hurried from the rectory.

It felt good to be in the car and to be alone and heading away from town out into the quiet farmlands. It suddenly came to him how tightly he had wound himself ever since the exorcism had begun. He felt like a watch whose key had been turned and turned until the insides were ready to explode. The silence of the coun-

280

tryside had started, even in that short time, to unwind his coils. He smiled and waved at two children helping their father in a cornfield. A mile or so down the road, he blew his horn and waved at an old farm lady who was leading a milk cow across the dirt highway. She waved back. He ran his hand through his thick dark hair. He felt like singing, but he was on a mission of extreme unction. He couldn't do that, but he could sing to himself. He felt so good! How wonderful it was to get away from everything, including Theophilus, and drive in the opposite direction. Theophilus had spoken to him about the possibility of bringing in other priests from the area, priests who would like to witness an exorcism. It would give Father Steiger a break, the old man said. Father Steiger had been against the idea, but now that he was free of it all, if for only an hour or so, he decided it wasn't such a bad idea after all. Why not? Bring on fresh troops! This wasn't his battle after all, it was Theophilus'.

He pulled the Ford sedan into the lane and drove it up to the large, white-framed farm house. The man who had phoned was on the porch, waiting. The priest embraced him, then let him lead him to the bedroom where the old woman lay dying. Her eyes were closed and she was barely breathing. Quickly, but with all due reverence, Father Steiger put his purple stole over his shoulders, took out the missal and started reading. The old man stood silently by, staring dry-eyed at his wife. When he finished the text, Father Steiger closed the book, made the sign of the cross over the woman's forehead and touched her lips lightly with a small crucifix. Then he rose and walked from the room.

As he drove back down the lane to the dirt road he tried to feel sorry for the old lady he had just seen, but it was impossible. She had lived a full life, she had had a good marriage and good children and had been a good Catholic. She was going to her reward. It was as simple as that.

Besides, the day was beautiful. The sun was shining, the fields were full of crops to be harvested, he was in good health and he was helping others in the name of Lord Jesus. What more could a man want? What more could he want?

He slowed his car slightly as he neared the small, one-lane bridge that was ahead. It was the one spot on the road, that ran over a deep ravine, he was cautious about. The town fathers had discussed widening the bridge now that there were over fifty automobiles in the area.

He pressed his brake but nothing happened. He pressed it again. Again it refused to budge. Then in front of him he watched the cloud form. It was large and jet black and hung over the roadway just at the entrance to the bridge. It had appeared out of nowhere, had formed out of nothing, yet in this bright, sun-filled day, this black cloud blocked his way. He pushed the brakes again, still no response. Then he tried to turn the wheel, hoping to run off the road and avoid the cloud. The wheel wouldn't turn. He tugged at it, both hands turning white at the knuckles, but the car wouldn't veer from its straight path ahead. Again the brakes. Again nothing.

'Oh Blessed Mother of God!' the priest shouted. 'Archangel Michael!'

The Ford sped into the blackness of the cloud. All that Father Steiger could do was hold the wheel.

The crash came before he expected it. The tearing sound of metal against metal. The tinkling of smashing glass. The smell of gasoline, then the sensation of being tilted upward into the air, then the sinking feeling of being tilted downward, toward the ravine below. Then a silence.

The cloud still hung there. He still clung to the wheel. He could feel the car teetering on the bridgeway, swaying undecidedly, almost wondering if it should remain on the wooden planks or topple over into the chasm.

The priest held his breath as if even that minute movement could propel the car over the edge.

'Father! Are you okay? You okay Father?'

Steiger looked to one side. There stood one of his parishioners, a farmer who worked the fields on the other side of the bridge. 'I saw your car coming my way,' the man said. 'Then you hit the guard rail on the bridge. You okay?'

The priest shook his head. 'Yes,' he said shakily, 'I'm fine. Just get me out of this thing.'

The farmer reached around and put both his hands on the priest's shoulders. Then, very gently, he edged him across the front seat, then as the wrecked car started slipping forward, he yanked on the priest and both fell over onto the roadway as the automobile slid quietly into the ravine below.

'Are you sure you're all right?' the man repeated. 'You wait right here, Father. I'll run and get my old truck and I'll take you to the doctor. You look pretty shaken up.'

The priest tried to stand but his legs were wobbling and he sat quickly back down. 'That cloud,' he said, 'what caused that cloud? I couldn't see through it.'

The farmer stared at him. 'What cloud, Father? What cloud are you talking about?'

'Why, that big black cloud,' the priest's voice rose. 'The one that covered the highway. I couldn't see a thing.'

'I didn't see no cloud,' the farmer answered. 'I was standing in my corn and I saw you come down the road and then plough smack into the railing.'

'But there was a cloud,' the priest insisted, 'a huge black cloud.'

The man shook his head. 'Wasn't no cloud from where I was. You just stay right here Father. I think you need a doctor.'

The visit to the doctor was brief. Aside from a couple of cuts on his hands and a bruise on his right knee, he was fine.

The farmer drove him to the rectory but, instead of entering it, he went on to the convent. He threw open the front door and hurried up the stairs. Storming down the hallway, he came to the room and yanked open the door. The two Sisters, Mother Superior and Theophilus all turned and stared.

'Well look who's here!' the voice inside Mary's body called out. 'My, my. You look a fright, dear Father. What happened? Lose your car?' the voice laughed. 'Did you?' the laughter came again. 'Did you wreck your precious automobile?' and once more the delighted laugh.

Mother Lotharia looked at the expression on the priest's face and saw the bandages on his hands as well as the grease and dirt spots on his robe. 'In the name of God, Father,' she said quickly. 'Did you have an accident?'

He walked quickly into the room. 'Yes, I did!' he shouted at Mary's body. 'I wrecked my car and I almost got killed!'

'Pity it was "almost". But I warned you. I told you to beware of Friday. Today you pulled in your proud neck! Today I outpointed you!' The laughter came loud and long. 'Your beautiful car. Smashed to smithereens. Oh, it serves you right! It serves you so right!'

'Were you hurt, Father?' the Mother Superior asked worriedly.

'No, he wasn't hurt. Unfortunately.' the voice said. 'Just shook up a bit. We wanted to kill him but he and his damned prayers got in the way.'

'Prayers?' Theophilus spoke quickly. 'Father Steiger were you praying when it happened?'

'Not really praying,' the voice inside the unconscious woman said. 'We clouded his vision and he called out for what's-his-name's mother and that stupid angel! If he hadn't asked for their protection we would have been victorious. Pity.'

Father Steiger stared numbly at the woman's body.

284

'That's right,' he said slowly. 'That's exactly right. When I saw I was out of control I called on our Blessed Mother and the Archangel Michael to save me.' He came closer to the body on the bed. 'How did you know?'

'We know everything. How many times do you have to hear it before you start to believe it? There's nothing we don't know. Anyway, automobile accidents are always so much fun,' the voice chuckled. 'Ever since they invented that machine, we've been using it to get people over onto our side. They go out for a pleasant ride and wham! They are down there with us! And sometimes, and this is the best part, we set them up in accidents and then they have to call in lawyers and get taken to court to pay damages. Often we can ruin them physically as well as financially. Oh yes, the automobile was a wonderful invention . . . *for us!*' The laughter came again, rolling up and out of Mary's body and reverberating off the bare walls. 'Wonderful invention!'

'You see, my son,' Theophilus said to Father Steiger. 'Satan plays all sorts of evil tricks. I warned you.'

'Oh Theophilus,' the voice crooned. 'Do us a favour? Please?'

'What?' the old man asked.

'Learn to drive.'

On Saturday there was no contact with any demons at all. Mary just lay on the mattress and screamed. They were high-pitched, piercing sounds that, again, brought the townspeople to the convent. This time there was no need for the Mother Superior to go down and explain, they all knew what was happening.

Aside from her screams, Mary vomited up bucketfuls of foul smelling liquid. Some of it was clear, some was blackish with lumps of undigested meat, some was greenish and smelled so terrible the nuns put wet towels over their noses before they went close enough to clean it up. Once she even threw up some dark brown chopped leaf. Theophilus and Steiger both agreed it was tobacco.

As to how all this liquid got into the thin woman's body, no one had an answer. She hadn't been eating. The Sisters considered themselves lucky if they could get her to swallow a cup of tea or eat a slice of bread. But here were *gallons* of stuff, literal bucketfuls, so many that in the confusion everyone lost count.

Father Steiger's sermon that Sunday was directly from the devil. He spoke to them of his accident and what he had been told about Satan's use of the automobile. He warned them to drive carefully because, he said, 'you could literally drive yourself to Hell.'

The exorcism began that afternoon. Theophilus seemed tired. Steiger was still furious over the loss of his new car.

'Well gentlemen,' the voice inside Mary said in the friendliest tones, 'I have a visitor for you today. Someone I'm sure you will be happy to talk with.'

'Who?' Theophilus asked. 'Not Satan himself!'

'Of course not,' the voice answered, 'you think all the prince has to do is come to Earling, Iowa on a Sunday afternoon? No, this is a special friend of ours down here. You'll see.'

Then Mary's body shook and the nuns checked to make sure the leather thongs that they had tied her to the bed with were still knotted. A long, low howling sound came from her unmoving lips, it was similar to that of a wolf baying from a hilltop. Then came masculine screams, as if someone was being beaten with a whip. After that the sound of a man crying. Then, a voice.

'Why am I here? Who are you people?'

'This is sacred ground,' Theophilus said quickly. 'You are on soil belonging to the Holy Mother Church.'

'Ohhhhh!' the voice groaned. 'Why?'

'Ask the one who brought you,' Theophilus responded. 'He'll tell you.'

'There is no one here. I'm all alone.' Mary's head turned slowly, closed eyelids trying to see in the darkness. 'Who are you people?'

'Rather we should ask you,' Theophilus said. 'You are the intruder here. Who are you?' There was a pause and a long groan. 'What is your name?' Theophilus shouted. 'Under the command of the Blessed Virgin Mary Herself, I demand to know your name!'

The groan came again. Then slowly the name was spoken, stretched out like a stream of molasses: 'Jaaaaaacoooooob.'

Theophilus listened, then asked, 'Are you saying "Jacob"? The masculine name "Jacob"?'

'Yes. That's my name.' Again there was a groan.

'What Jacob are you? Are you the Jacob in the Old Testament? Are you a demon named Jacob?'

'No. My name is Jacob.'

'But *which* Jacob?' the old man insisted. 'Have you another name, one to help us identify you better?'

'My name is . . .' but the voice broke off and in its place came another long low wail. This one seemed to be of genuine sadness. 'I see now,' the voice said slowly. 'I see now why I am here.'

'You do?' Theophilus said quickly. 'Then tell us. We are anxious to help you.'

There was a moan that was mixed with laughter. 'Help me? You want to help me? Nobody can help me.'

'We can. We are servants of the God Most High. We can help.'

'No,' the voice responded, 'you can't help me. I am *that* Jacob. That Jacob that fathered the woman on the bed. I am Mary's father. *That* Jacob.'

'May all the saints protect us,' Mother Lotharia gasped and the other two Sisters in attendance made the sign of the cross along with her.

'You are this unfortunate woman's father? I can't believe it,' Theophilus said.

'Believe it, because it's true. I have been called up from Hell to identify myself to you. What more do you want?'

'How can we believe anything?' Father Steiger said. 'Satan and all his demons are liars. They have lied to us all along.'

'What kind of proof do you want?' the voice groaned. 'Ask me anything about myself or my daughter. Anything.'

'I know a great deal about your daughter,' Theophilus said. 'I've spent many an hour with her, talking and asking questions. I didn't begin this exorcism because I was merely curious, you know. The woman is possessed and the rituals of the Mother Church are the only ones that can free her.'

'I know she is possessed,' the voice answered. 'I wouldn't be here if she wasn't. Most of it isn't her fault. They started with me.'

'With you?'

'Yes. When I was a young man. They urged me to kill my father. I tried but he didn't die. I ran away to another town.'

'Minneapolis,' Father Theophilus said.

'Correct. But there they did things to me. They had me hearing voices and seeing things that weren't there. They tortured me with visions and sounds and I was afraid others would think I was crazy if I told them. So I didn't.'

'Not even your wife?' Father Steiger asked.

The groan came again, louder and longer. 'My wife, my dear wife. My sweet Jeanette. She was so good! What a pure, good woman she was.' The voice started crying but no tears appeared on Mary's face.

'And how did you repay her goodness?' Theophilus insisted over the sobbing.

'By drinking,' the voice finally said. 'By coming home

late and being drunk and I used to . . . used to . . . beat her! I beat that good woman! She was the best thing . . . the best thing in my life and I . . .' the sobbing grew louder.

Feeling the need to explain, Theophilus turned to the others in the room.

'Mary's father *was* named Jacob,' he said, 'and her mother's name was Jeanette. From everything she's told me her mother was almost saintly while her father was impossible.'

'I wasn't the only one impossible!' the voice said quickly. 'Mary was also impossible! She was very difficult to live with! Don't put all the blame on me!'

'How was she impossible?' the old priest asked.

'Always throwing her church lessons in my face, all that talk about him – you know – I can't say his name and about how the church was so marvellous and how I was so terrible.' The tone of the voice shifted a little. 'I brought home my paycheck regularly. When I worked, I paid the bills. I put food on the table. I bought them a house to live in.'

'As I understood it,' Theophilus interrupted, 'the house was in Mary's name, not yours.'

'Only because my bitch of a mother-in-law wanted it that way! She and Jeanette connived to keep me out of it. But I fooled them. I stayed in there after they were all dead. I got it away from Mary. She signed some papers and put it in my name.'

'Did she know what she was signing?' this from Father Steiger.

'No. She was in the midst of one of her crazy spells. I had her sign and then I put her out.'

'On the street?'

'It wasn't her house any longer. It was mine and I didn't want a crazy woman living with me! She *was* crazy, you know. Nothing anyone could do for her. Not the mental doctors and certainly not your Catholic bastards! You with your promises of pie in the sky after death! What a lot of liars you are!'

'I resent that!' the Mother Superior shouted.

'You can resent it or stick it!' the voice said. 'The Catholic Church never gave me anything but headaches. They wanted to take Mary away from me. Did you know that? They wanted her to become a nun and end up like that old prune over there. I told them there was no way. I wanted my daughter to get a job, to bring some money home. I didn't want her ending up a damned nun!'

'But look how she *did* end up,' Father Steiger said. 'Look what you did to her.'

The wailing came louder now and there seemed to be others in there with Jacob. There was loud talking, voices atop voices. Finally Jacob's came through clearly. 'It was her own fault. Granted, I damned her, but it was her own fault. Hers and yours!'

'How was it her fault?' Theophilus asked.

'With her high and mighty ways. With her church lessons and her manner of always being above everybody else. She got that from her mother, she did. Her mother always thought she came from better stock than I did. I showed them both.'

'So you damned your own daughter?'

'I did. One night me and her aunt were going at it. I had a little too much to drink, probably, and I wanted Mary to come in and join the fun. Do you think she would? Hell no! Always Little Miss Innocent. Shit, she was old enough to do it and with those tits starting to grow under her blouse.'

'So you damned your own daughter because she refused to have carnal knowledge with you?' Theophilus shook his head. 'I can scarcely believe it.'

'I damned her because she refused to fuck with me, if that's what you mean. I'm sure she was fucking other guys, but when it came time for me to get some, she wouldn't do it.'

'So you cursed her . . .'

'I did.'

'And damned her?'

'I did.'

'And wished her soul into Hell?'

'I did.'

'And you're not sorry?'

'Not at the time, anyway . . .' and the low moaning started again then slowed down. '. . . anyway, I was drunk. I didn't know what I was doing.'

'You knew!' the Mother Superior yelled.

'Oh, fuck you!' the voice snarled, then spat a gob of pale brown phlegm that hit the Mother Superior on the breast. 'Stay out of this. You know anything about fucking?'

'After you kicked Mary out of her own house?' asked Father Steiger, 'Where did you go? Did you stay in Minneapolis?'

'I didn't kick her out of her house, I told you she signed the place over to me. I kicked her out of *my* house.'

'Where did you go then?'

'I sold the place and went to Arizona. I lived there for a few years. The weather was better than in Minneapolis. I never saw Mary after that. Never wanted to. The girl was crazy! I mean, who in their right mind would want a crazy person living with them?'

'Did you go to Arizona alone?' asked Theophilus.

'None of your business,' the voice shot back.

'Did you not go there with your own sister-in-law? A wanton woman you were living with as if you were married? Did you not go there with your own wife's sister? A sinner no better than one of the dogs in heat on the corner?'

'Yeah. I went with Minna. Why not? What's so wrong with that? She was free, white and over twenty-one. She didn't have no strings on her and neither did I. So what?'

'Where is this Minna person now?'

'She's dead.' the voice said simply. 'Something with

291

her lungs. It came on quick and it killed her. So I stayed on by myself.' The wailing started again, then died down. 'I really missed her when she died. It seems that everything I loved, I lost. Everything and everybody. All taken away from me. All.'

'You have never repented for your sins?' Theophilus asked.

'What good would it have done?' the voice replied. 'Who was I going to repent to? Some old ass in a black robe like yourself? Shit, don't make me laugh. You don't want repentance, you want money and blood.'

'So how did you die?' Father Steiger spoke up.

'They said it was cancer. Of the liver. And of a few other places. I was in a hospital when it happened and,' he laughed, 'want to hear something funny? They called in a damned Catholic priest and he gave me Extreme Unction, or whatever you call it, and I *still* went to Hell! Ain't that a pisser? Shows you how worthless your rigmarole is!' there was more laughter, but weaker.

'Extreme Unction was given you and you went to Hell anyway?' Father Steiger looked at Theophilus in amazement.

'When a man has sinned as wickedly as this man did,' the old priest explained, 'not even the ritual of Extreme Unction can save him. Anyway, he only did it as a last resort, as a way of making one final attempt to stay free of Hades. He didn't really want it. He couldn't have thought it would really work.'

'Nothing you people promise ever really works. I know. The only thing that's real is down here, where I am. This is reality and that is what people have to know. Your church and all its bullshit is exactly that: bullshit! Stop lying to people. There is only one prince and true ruler of this world and his name is Satan!'

'That's blasphemy,' Theophilus shouted.

'No,' said a completely different voice, one they all recognized as Beelzebub. 'That's not blasphemy, it's reality. Worldly reality,' he laughed. 'Did you enjoy your visit with Jacob? Were you surprised? I knew you would be, but then where else would a soul like Jacob's come after death? He was a perfect candidate for us! Perfect! And you know, Theophilus, when we do things we do them *perfectly*.'

'It's all in her head,' Therese said to Sister Serena when the two met in front of the rectory. 'I've heard the brain can do strange things and, as far as I am concerned, she's imagining it all.'

The young, black-robed Sister shook her head. 'Oh, I don't think so. I was there one afternoon assisting the priests and I saw her do things and heard her say things that just couldn't have been made up. She may be a little crazy, yes, but what is happening to her is from something outside herself. Poor woman, we all feel so sorry for her.'

'I did too, at first,' Therese replied, 'but now that I see the toll she's taking on my brother, I'm not so sorry as I used to be. He's not getting his regular work done, he's lost his appetite, he finds it very difficult to sleep at night and he says he hates to get up in the morning knowing what he has to go through in the exorcism room.'

'But surely Father Steiger understands he is doing the Lord's work?'

'He understands he is doing old Theophilus' work. Now *that* he understands! He didn't ask to have that woman brought here, you know. It was all Theophilus' doing.'

'It'll be over soon,' the Sister said hopefully. 'It's just a matter of a few more days or so.'

'It was only supposed to last seven days in the beginning. Now look! That woman has been here a month today. A whole month! And nothing accomplished!'

'It's not easy to be rid of the devil,' Sister Serena replied piously.

293

'Well,' Therese shook her head,' if we can't get rid o
the devil, at least we can try to get rid of the body he
resides in. The woman came on a train, she can leave on a
train.'

'But that would be terrible!' Sister Serena was
shocked. 'After all she's been through!'

'And my brother? He's not been through anything too?
No Sister, if Theophilus can't get rid of the demons by the
end of this week, my brother is going to get rid o
Theophilus and that woman.'

That day Mary had to be helped, almost carried, from
her bedroom to the exorcism room. Theophilus had spen
part of the morning with her, trying to explain that Jacob
had come through yesterday and what he had said. But
while Mary blinked her eyes and tried to smile, the
priest knew she wasn't understanding anything he was
saying.

They put her on the mattress, then strapped her arms
and legs with the leather ropes. The two Sisters in atten
dance thought that was a little unnecessary, seeing as
the poor woman could barely raise her hand, let alone
her entire body.

Theophilus and Steiger were wearing their purple
stoles, one man held a missal, the other a large wooden
cross. The older man began the ritual and the others in
the room listened with diminished interest. It had all
been going on far too long. 'Stoop beneath the all
powerful Hand of God, tremble and flee at the evocation
of the holy and terrible Name of Jesus, this Name which
causes Hell to tremble, this name to which the Virtues
Powers and Dominations of heaven are humbly submis
sive, this name which the Cherubim and Seraphim
praise unceasingly, repeating: Holy, Holy, Holy is the
Lord, the God of hosts.' He paused, then looked at the
others. 'Oh Lord, hear my prayer.'

In response they chanted: 'And let my cry come unto
Thee.'

'And with thy spirit,' he replied.

At that moment Sister Primosa let out a scream. 'Look! Look what's happening!'

It had started with Mary's face. The features had began to distend, change, transfigure until there was nothing recognizable there at all. Then the tiny body started to puff up, as if someone were filling a tyre tube in short fast spurts of air. The arms were next, extending themselves like rubber snakes, slithering down to where her twisted fingers touched her ankles. Then her legs began to swell at the calves and at the thighs as if they were the legs on a stuffed doll whose joints were tied at the ankles and knees. The thin grey smock she wore stretched tightly over her enormous body. And the Sisters were frightened that it would burst and reveal the naked flesh underneath.

Theophilus managed to regain his composure. 'Get out of that woman!' he shouted. 'In the Name of all that's Holy, leave her this instant!'

Mary continued to expand, sounds of stitching giving way came from the grey smock.

'You may torture her,' the old priest shouted, 'but you cannot take her life! You admitted as much! You told me she would have to hang herself! Do you remember those words?' There was no answer from the grotesque body. 'You said you could not kill her, that she would have to do it herself! Then leave! Stop this inhuman suffering! Leave her now!'

Some sort of purple steaming liquid starting streaming from Mary's twisted and swollen mouth.

'Give me the water,' Theophilus ordered. Sister Primosa handed him the bowl containing the Holy Water. He dipped his hand into it and started flicking the clear water onto the agonized body.

'Noooooooooooo!' the scream came from deep within. 'Stop thaaaaaaaat! That burns!'

'Then get out!' Theophilus thundered. 'By the power given me by our Blessed Lord Jesus, I command you to get out! At once!' and he threw the entire contents of the bowl onto Mary's body.

The sound was like someone letting the air out of a balloon as she shrank back to her regular size. The smell was so disgusting Sisters Primosa and Hermina ran vomiting from the room.

'You see?' Theophilus said to Father Steiger. 'He obeyed me. He left the body. Brought her down to normal!' The old priest had a smile on his face. 'I think we are starting to beat him. I think it will all be over very soon.'

The younger man looked first at the pitiful woman on the bed then at the man with the white beard. He started to say something, then shook his head and walked out of the room.

'They were at it again in my bedroom last night,' Father Steiger confronted Theophilus on his way to his prayers that morning. 'I got very little sleep.'

'I'm sorry Joseph,' the old man said, 'but did you put on your stole and sprinkle the room with Holy Water?'

'I did,' the younger man answered, 'but I did it at three thirty in the morning. When I should have been sleeping.'

'Same sounds?'

'Like rats scurrying in the walls, yes. And the banging on my bedroom door. I got up twice thinking that something was wrong and Therese needed me.'

'Unusual,' Theophilus admitted, 'I'll make note of it.'

'I wish you'd make it go away,' Father Steiger said with a slight edge in his voice, 'not just make note of it. Maybe you're not concerned because I'm the one being bothered and not you.'

'I'm concerned, but obviously they are trying to get to you instead of me. They figure if you get upset enough you'll ask me to leave.'

'And take the woman with you,' Father Steiger added.

Theophilus raised his eyes above his half-round glasses and looked at the young man. 'Ah, then you have thought of it. I'm not surprised. But,' and he shrugged, 'you know it's all the work of the devil. You certainly won't heed his calls. Of that I'm positive.' He laughed, turned and went through a side door into the empty church.

'Don't be too positive old man,' Steiger said aloud, 'this is still my parish and I'm still in charge here. Not the devil and certainly not you!'

The exorcism ritual began at exactly ten a.m. It wasn't very effective. No sooner had the old priest commenced droning the litany than Mary's body started to arch up on the mattress. Her back came up slowly in a curve, pushing her shoulders down and twisting her face until her forehead was touching the mattress. All words stopped, all eyes were on her as her ankles twisted slowly around so that her feet were flat on the mattress but pointing at her head. She was almost like the letter 'O'. No sound came from her. No voices, no screams, no vomit. She stayed like that for almost two hours until Theophilus decided there was nothing to be gained from continuing for the day. As he and Steiger left the room, her feet twisted back into the proper position and she lay calmly on her back once more.

The next day was more of the same, except this time she flipped over onto her stomach, arched her head backward and her feet forward until they met, in the centre of her back. She looked like a wooden puppet fallen into a grotesque heap on the floor. They heard no bone cracking, saw no sign of discomfort on her face. And, like the day before, there wasn't a sound.

'Theophilus, I'd like to talk with you.'

The old priest looked up from the book he was reading. Father Steiger had come to his small guest room in the rectory. He had never done that before, he'd

297

always respected the elder priest's privacy. 'Yes, of course. Come in. Please.'

'I'm not sure how to begin this,' Father Steiger didn't sit, just stood in the centre of the room. 'I don't want to sound negative nor harsh but it's just that . . .'

Theophilus finished the sentence for him: 'That you've had enough.'

'Yes,' Steiger nodded. 'I have. You know I didn't want you to come here. You know that you pulled a fast one by getting the Mother Superior to agree before I did. You know that the only reason you've stayed on is because I gave you my word. Well, I feel you have taken advantage of that word. You and your charge have taken advantage of me and of everyone in this parish. You came here to do a simple exorcism. Well, it didn't take. The woman is still possessed and if you ask me is *worse* than when she arrived. You told me it would take a week. A week is seven days. She has been here a month! The poor soul doesn't eat, barely sleeps, is kept like a prisoner and she looks like something that has been dead and left unburied for three days!' He paused while Theophilus continued to look at him. 'And I have been visited by your demon friends too!'

'My friends? When did they become friends of *mine*?'

'You seem to be on a first name basis with most of them. Beelzebub and Judas and Jacob and God knows who. You've been dealing with them for years, it's no wonder you know them personally. Anyway, they keep me awake at night. They wrecked my new car. Therese tells me they have turned all the sugar in the kitchen to salt. Did you ever have a morning cup of coffee with two teaspoons of *salt* in it?' He didn't wait for a reply. 'And just now, in my office, came the last straw. I had written a two-page letter to the Bishop reporting on how things were progressing here. It had taken me all morning to write it. I chose my words carefully and

298

was extra careful with my penmanship. And do you know what they did?' Again he didn't wait for an answer. 'They made the ink bottle rise into the air and dump it's entire contents over the letter! Not only is the letter ruined but also several other papers and some books that were nearby!' He paused as Theophilus rubbed his mouth with one hand. 'Are you smiling under that hand?' he shouted. 'Do you think it's funny? Do you? Everything around here is going crazy and you think it's funny! My parishioners are getting upset! Several of them have come to me to ask when this will all be over. When that woman will leave town. I have to keep smiling and telling them "soon" when I don't know what "soon" even means anymore!' He paused, took a handkerchief from his back pocket and wiped his brow. 'I'm sorry but that's the way things are.'

'What do you want me to do?'

'I want you to get rid of the demons in that woman!'

'I have been trying to do just that, but I've not been very successful.'

'Then both of you just leave. Take her back to Minneapolis or wherever, but go. Both of you.'

'We have a session planned for tomorrow. Remember?'

'Of course I remember. But it's your *last* session here in Earling. Cure the woman tomorrow or get out.'

'This is not you speaking, Joseph. These are words that Satan has put in your mouth.'

'I don't want to hear about Satan! I'm tired of hearing about him. I just want the peace and quiet we had here before you came. That's all. If wanting tranquillity is a Satanic desire, then so be it.'

'Satan is doing this to create a rift between us. He figures that he will remain triumphant in the woman if we argue and you tell me to leave. Listen to what you are saying, my son. These are the devil's desires, those are his words. Not yours.'

'Look, Theophilus, words are words no matter who

says them. Now watch my mouth. These are my words
Cure her tomorrow and then leave! Both of you!'

Friday, September 20, 1928. The day that Father
Joseph Steiger hoped would be the last day.

'What are you waving that thing at me for?' the voice
inside Mary said loudly. 'What is it supposed to be?'

'You know perfectly well what it is,' Theophilus
replied. 'It's a crucifix with the Lord Jesus Himself
upon it!'

'You're sure?' asked the voice.

'Of course I am.'

'Well, I'm not. There's something wrong with that
thing. It's got what's-his-name with both feet side by
side.'

'What's wrong with that?' the old priest asked.

'Well, when he was hammered onto that pile of
wood, they pounded one foot atop the other. That silly
thing has one foot beside the other, not the way it was
at all. I wish you Christians would get your symbology
straight.'

'No one can be sure how the Lord's feet were
placed,' this from the Mother Superior. 'Catherine
Emmerich writes that they were atop each other, but
nobody really knows.'

'You again! Well, *we* know how it was done because
we were there. We saw it.'

'You mean you *did* it!' Mother Lotharia said loudly.

'Oh no, we didn't do it. We let the humans do it. The
Romans did all the nailing. We just encouraged them.
And watched. It was quite a day for us. We worked a
long time for that day.'

'But He arose,' Sister Mundana said vehemently,
even though she (the convent chatterbox) had been
warned to keep silent while in the room, 'He arose and
showed the world He had thwarted you!'

'And you believe that,' said the voice.

'We *all* do!' replied Theophilus.

300

'Santa Claus, mermaids and a risen saviour! It's always amazing what nonsense human beings will believe in. No wonder there's so many churches fouling up the world. Everybody wants to believe in a fantasy and so they go to those churches every Sunday morning.'

'Christ died for our sins and then on the third day He arose!' Sister Mundana was not about to be silent.

'He did huh? You were there? You saw him?' the voice inside Mary was sarcastic.

'Of course I wasn't there!' the young Sister said.

'Then how do you know what's-his-name did those things?'

'Because the Bible says so!' the Sister was almost screaming at this point.

The voice groaned. 'The Bible! That damned book again! When you people get backed into a corner, you always quote the Bible! Do you know what a chopped up and fictionalized publication that is? Do you know how many people – all belonging to your dear Catholic Church by the way – have thrown out passages they didn't like and stuck in things from their own point of view? Do you know? Some of your Popes and Cardinals had a field day redoing that book! And you still quote it with sugar in your mouth and revere it and claim it is the truth. Well, it's not.'

'When have you ever known the truth?' Theophilus asked. 'And when have you ever *told* the truth?'

'Theo, are you doubting my word? Are you calling me a liar?' There came false, play-acting sobs from the woman's body. 'And I thought you trusted me.'

'Just about as far as I can throw you,' the old man replied.

'And that's not very far, is it?' the voice laughed. 'You can't even budge me out of this woman's body, let alone *throw* me.'

'You are a liar and a thief!' Theophilus shouted. 'You lie about the Good Book and you steal innocent souls.

301

There is nothing about you we can trust! Nothing!'

'Here's something you can believe,' the voice said. 'It's really not for you. It's for that young idiot beside you.'

Theophilus looked quickly at Father Steiger. 'Prepare yourself,' he said quickly. 'Be ready for any event.'

The voice inside Mary abruptly changed from the harsh masculine one to a soft feminine one. It was a voice choked in tears. It was difficult, at first, to understand the words.

'Joseph, my Joseph! Is that you? Are you really here with me?' It was small and frail and the words were in German. 'Why don't you reply? Joseph, I have come such a long way to see you again. Please Joseph, talk to me. Talk to me again.'

Theophilus looked at Father Steiger. 'Do you know this woman?' he said.

The other man looked puzzled. 'I don't think so,' he said softly. 'I'm not sure.'

'You don't know me Joseph?' the voice rose to a wail, then came back down. 'The curse of motherhood! When your own son doesn't even know you!'

'Son?' Steiger looked stunned. 'You call me your son?'

'My own little boy. My own baby Joseph! Ahh, it's so good to be with you again. Such a long time. All these years.'

Theophilus put his hand on the younger priest's shoulder. 'Don't be taken in Joseph. Don't let him get to you.'

'How many years Joseph, my baby? Such a time gone by, such a time that passed. And Therese? She is here with you. She is also fine? My Therese?'

Father Steiger started shaking his head, backing away from the bed and the lifeless body on it. 'No,' he said under his breath. 'No. This is not my mother. No I'm not believing this. I cannot accept this.'

302

'My own Joseph,' the voice crooned, 'what's not to believe? Here I am. Your mother. You remember me? You remember your mama, Joseph?'

'Of course I remember my mother,' the priest answered, 'but you are not her. Not my mother! My mother is in heaven. My mother is not in hell! My mother is not with Satan!'

'I am, Joseph my child. I am! I'm with Satan. I have been since the moment I left the body. It surprises you? It surprises you that I'm here instead of being up there in heaven? We don't all go up there, my son. Many, many of us are down here. You would be surprised to see who is down here with me. All sorts of people even I would never have guessed.'

'My mother was a good Christian woman. There wasn't a Sunday when she missed a Mass. She did nothing to put herself in hell. No, you are not my mother. My mother was a saint, an angel.'

The masculine voice came back, suddenly. 'Your mother was nothing of the kind! Your mother was a whore!'

Theophilus reached out and steadied the younger priest.

'You remember Herr Lutkens? Well, do you?'

Father Steiger was so angry he could barely speak. 'Yes. He rented a room from us. For several years.'

'At night,' said the voice, 'when your stupid old father was sound asleep, your sainted mother would slip into bed with Herr Lutkens. And why not? Your father couldn't get it up.'

'That's not true!' Father Steiger shouted. 'That's a lie.'

The woman's voice returned. 'It's true, Joseph. I did that. And your father never knew.' She laughed. 'He wouldn't have cared anyway. What did he know about sex? Almost nothing.'

'And then when your father died,' the male voice said, 'how long did it take your angelic mother to marry

303

another man, a Herr Wegerer, and you know they fucked. That's where Therese came from, not from under a cabbage.' There was laughter, in fact it sounded like several people laughing in there.

'No!' Steiger screamed. 'It's all a lie! It's all a trick!'

'It's no trick, my baby boy,' the feminine voice said. 'It's real. But you can help me.'

Father Steiger shook his head and the others could see there were tears on his eyelids, tears ready to fall.

'You can help me,' the feminine voice said, 'you must help me. I want to get out of here. I want to go to the other place, up there. Only you can help me, my son. Only you.'

The tears started down his face. He didn't care if they saw them or not. Timidly, he approached the bed. 'How? How can I help you?'

'By stopping what is happing to this woman. Stop this old man here from trying to drive me and all the others out of her. Please stop him! He is dangerous. The old man is crazy, my son. That old man would see you all dead before he would give up!'

'Don't listen to him!' Theophilus said loudly. 'Remember the source!'

'Listen to me,' the voice said, 'your own mother. Listen to me. Stop this terrible thing he is inflicting on this Mary woman. Stop it and send him away and I shall be free. I shall be free, my son.' The voice started sobbing. 'I'll be able to get out of here and go up there. But only if you stop that madman. Only you can bring me out of this place. Only you. Only my little boy, my Joseph!' The crying continued even louder.

Father Steiger came next to the bed and, trembling, put one hand on Mary's body. 'Mama?' he whispered. 'Mama is that really you?' The sobs became deeper, making the answer incoherent. 'Mama? Have you come back, mama?'

Theophilus took him by the arm. 'Don't listen Joseph!

I've warned you of Satan's tricks. That is not your mother! Please believe me.'

'Joseph, my little boy. Believe *me*.'

'I don't know who to believe,' the priest cried out. He put his hands over his ears and hurried toward the door and the freedom he would find outside it. 'I don't know *who* to believe!'

Theophilus avoided Father Steiger for the next two days. He deliberately stayed in his room, coming out only when he knew the younger priest would not be met in the hallways. And he was busy making preparations, ready to take Mary back to Milwaukee. He had phoned the Bishop there, had explained the exorcism was not working and asked to be taken off the case. Bishop Rhode was surprised that the old priest had failed but not too surprised when he heard Father Steiger had wanted her out of his parish. He had written to Father Steiger telling him how difficult it would be, but obviously the Father had not heeded his words. Or, the situation was worse than the Bishop himself had imagined.

This time there was no large party at the station in Earling, Mary did not get the collection of nuns and priests at her departure. She was so ill she was unaware she was going anywhere. The Sisters had bundled her in blankets and put her in a wheel chair. The September mid-day air was already chilly, a sign that mid-western winter was about to descend and isolate the small farming community.

The town's only doctor drove them the few blocks to the station. Father Theophilus sat in the front seat with the driver, stony-faced and mute. Mother Lotharia had helped load Mary and the folding chair into the back seat where Sisters Lydia and Archaelaus sat side by side with the almost unconscious woman. They had volunteered to travel with her to Milwaukee, to make sure she reached the hospital safely, and then to come back to the convent. The Mother Superior had told them to take a few days vacation if they wanted to, to see the sights up there, but neither Sister wanted to be away any longer than was necessary. The world was a terrible place. There was safety behind the convent walls.

Therese was in the rectory kitchen making bread when she heard the train whistle. She stopped long enough to think of the woman being bundled aboard and the double good luck of having Mary and Theophilus leave town at the same time. She smiled, crossed herself, leaving a wisp of flour on her forehead, and went back to her bread board.

Father Steiger was in his study when he heard the whistle. He went to the window. He saw the streams of white and black inter-mingled smoke coming from the engine. He saw the streams go farther and farther away from town, heading north. He reached into his coat pocket and took out the Little Flower of Child Jesus medallion. He stared at it, rubbed it's surface with his thumb and walked over to the silver crucifix that hung on the wall. 'I'm sorry,' he said softly. 'I'm sorry for the woman and I'm sorry that I hurt Theophilus. I know I've lost a friend. I couldn't help it. It was becoming impossible. I'm sure,' he said, reaching out and touching the agonized figure lightly, 'I'm sure you understand.'

The final week of September passed uneventfully. Farmers took the last of the late vegetables from their fields, shocked their cornstalks and stockpiled fodder for their animals. Father Steiger worked on his backlog of paperwork and tried not to think about what had happened. Mother Lotharia and the Sisters cleaned the exorcism room with a vengeance, getting on their knees with hot water and lye soap scrubbing the floor, dismantling the bed and burning the stained mattress. They kept candles lit in all four corners of the room for seven days. They were almost as severe in the cleaning of the guest room where Mary had slept. They congratulated themselves on a job well done, yet in the back of their minds was the thought that they had, somehow, failed the poor woman.

In October there were ripe orange pumpkins in every field. The convent school was in full operation and the new furnace worked wonderfully. At the end of the month there was a Halloween parade downtown with children dressed as witches and goblins and skeletons. The town fathers discussed it and it was decided that in view of what had taken place earlier, no one should come dressed as the devil. It just would not be the thing to do that year. Three little boys who had worn devil costumes the year before had their mothers resew them into pirate outfits.

The snow started falling on the afternoon of November second. It was light at first then grew heavy as the night came on. By morning people were out with shovels for their walks and ploughs for their lanes. It was a usual happening for Earling and the citizens had adapted long ago. As much as they disliked the snow they knew it would be followed by spring and then summer and then the wonderful smells of autumn harvest. And some folks actually *liked* the snow.

It was during that month that Therese said to her brother: 'You recall old Frau Winkler?' The priest nodded. 'Back in Germany?' He nodded again. 'Well, she is a cousin to Herr Lutkens.' Father Steiger looked at her sharply, to see where this was leading. 'Well, after you told me that terrible story about mama and Herr Lutkens I wrote to Frau Winkler. I remember her coming to the house to visit with Herr Lutkens before he died. And I told her what that Lawrence woman had spread about mama.'

'Therese! You didn't!'

'I did. I wanted to get to the bottom of the thing. So,

today I get a reply and old Frau Winkler must be still laughing. She knew her cousin very well, they grew up side by side in the same village. Anyway she says that the reason Herr Lutkens never married is that he didn't have a pee-pee! When he was a very small boy he was bitten by a mad dog, right here. Right on the pee-pee! His little thing had to be cut off. All he had down there were two marbles and a hole!'

'So mama couldn't have . . .' the priest said.

'Mama couldn't. Nobody could! Poor Herr Lutkens. All those years with no pee-pee. It makes you think. It really makes you think.'

'So all that stuff the demon said about mama was untrue.' Father Steiger frowned, then smiled. 'What a relief. It was all a lie. Theophilus said it was. You know Therese, Theophilus said it was a lie and that I had to prepare myself for the devil's lies.'

'But you believed that one.' she said.

'I don't know whether I believed it or not,' he said, shaking his head, 'but the voice. Now *that* was so believable! It sounded just like mama's voice! It was uncanny.'

'So are you going to tell Theophilus?'

He stopped smiling and looked at her. 'No,' he replied simply. 'I haven't had any communication with him since he left. It's better this way.'

'He used to be a friend,' she said.

'I know, and I valued his friendship. But things changed.'

'You mean *you* changed.'

'No,' he shook his head, 'things changed us. This whole event changed me a great deal and I know it changed Theophilus. His failure changed him. He was a tired and beaten man when he left. He and I are not the same people, but,' he tried a half-smile on her, 'I suppose an experience like this one would change anybody. Anyway I'm very happy you wrote to Frau Winkler. Thank you.' He kissed her on the forehead and went back to his study. Later, she thought she heard him whistling.

It seemed to the Sisters at the school that no sooner did they take down the Thanksgiving decorations and have the windows clean, than it was time to put up the Christmas things. Not only at school, but all over town, windows were gleaming with candles, paper stars and silver tinsel. Figures of Father Christmas stood side by side with figures of the Holy Family. There were creches brought from Germany. Tree ornaments were sorted out and repaired. Women got ready to make fancy cookies and elaborate, twisted breads and those fruit cakes that had been ageing quietly since June were inspected and doused with additional rum or whisky . . . just in case.

Father Steiger was on a stepladder inside the church helping some of the Sisters hang the decorations when Therese yelled at him. 'The telephone! You're wanted on the phone!'

He looked at his dusty hands and at how much work was still to be done. 'Tell them to call back later,' he shouted to her. 'I'm busy right now.'

'I think you'd better take this call,' she said. 'It's the Bishop.'

He sat in the warm railway waiting room, the day after the call, waiting for the train from Des Moines. His car, a temporary loaned by one of the parishioners, waited outside in the snow. The Bishop had been very short on the telephone. Would Father Steiger be in Earling the next day? Would he have time to talk to his Bishop? Could he pick his Bishop up at the train station in the morning and deliver him back again for the afternoon train to Des Moines?

When Bishop Drumm got off the train, Father Steiger marvelled at how spry he still was. He didn't know exactly how old the man was but he did know he

309

had received his ordination at the turn of the century
He had been a priest for eighteen years then consecrated a Bishop for the last nine years. He liked Bishop
Drumm. He was a smart man as well as a wise leader
He discussed things with his priests and almost never
made demands. His talent lay in the fact that his
priests all admired him and did things because they
respected him. And he could smoke and drink with the
best of them.

They rode the few blocks to the rectory and the
Bishop told of what he had seen from the train window
and what kind of people he had met in the dining car
He was always meeting 'the strangest' people and he
loved every minute of it. In the telling he could make the
most boring encounter sound fascinating. He started
telling the young priest about two elderly maiden sisters who were on their way to Nebraska to bury their
ancient mother. 'It seems,' said the Bishop, 'that mama
had run a gambling hall and saloon during the Civil
War and had made a fortune. Her two daughters
wanted the money now that the old lady was dead but
needed me to tell them, imagine *me*, if the money still
had sin in it. They didn't want to bring sin back home
with them, but they sure wanted to bring that money
back! Imagine those two greedy old girls worrying
about sin. At their age!'

'So what did you tell them?'

'To bring it all to me and I'd bless it, but if some of the
sinful bills stuck to my fingers, not to worry. I'd just
keep them inside the Diocese where they wouldn't
harm anyone.'

By the time they got to the rectory Father Steiger
was laughing. It felt good. He realised he hadn't really
laughed in a long time.

The Bishop was ushered into Father Steiger's study
where he had a 'bit of warmth in a glass' and lit up a
cigar. Therese came by with a pot of hot tea and they
greeted each other as old friends. When she left, he

310

motioned Father Steiger to sit down. 'Now,' he said, 'I know you're curious to hear why I'm here.'

'As a matter of fact, yes. I've been wondering why you couldn't tell me on the phone.'

'Too many busybodies on the phone. When I make a long distance call I never know if the operator has hung up or not. Seems they all want to hear what the Bishop is up to! And besides, I like to get out of the office once in a while. A day in the country suits me fine. Train was warm and comfortable and I'm looking forward to the meal on the way back. The train cook promised to make me beef and noodles and you know how I love noodles!' He held out his empty glass. 'Possibly a wee bit more of that warmth, if you don't mind.' Father Steiger gave him a little more brandy, sat down and waited. 'It's about that Lawrence woman. She's dying.'

'Oh?' the younger man shifted uncomfortably in his chair.

'Yes. Bishop Rhode called me a couple of days ago. She has never fully recovered from whatever happened to her here. She has been under sedation and lock and key at the hospital ever since she arrived back there. She tried to kill herself, you know.'

'Kill herself?' the younger priest was startled. 'I didn't know.'

'She ripped up some sheets one night and tried to hang herself.'

All the air seemed to go out of Father Steiger's body. 'Hang herself?'

His Bishop nodded. 'The doctors still can't figure out where she got the energy to do it. She hasn't eaten hardly a thing for months. By all natural laws she should have been dead of starvation by now.'

'But he doesn't want her to go that way. Not by starvation.'

'He?' the Bishop looked at him over his brandy glass.

'Satan. He told us. The only way he wants her dead is if she hangs herself. Now he's forcing her to do it.'

Father Steiger got up and walked nervously to the window. He looked out at the snow-covered earth. 'And he will do it. I don't doubt it. Not for a moment.'

'That would be suicide and you know how the Church feels about suicide.'

'I do indeed and so does Satan. We don't approve of it but he does. It figures.' He decided to pour himself a brandy. 'Well, I feel very sorry for the poor woman. It's the worst case I have ever seen. I wish we could have done more to help her, but it's too late.'

'What do you mean "it's too late"?' asked the Bishop.

'She was here for almost a month and a half. Theophilus and I worked on her for seventeen days, in two separate intervals, and nothing happened. She got worse and went back to where she had come from. We tried.' He drained the liquid in his glass.

'She went back where she came from because you threw her out.'

Father Steiger whirled around, facing his Bishop. 'Now wait a minute. Don't blame this woman's attempted suicide on me! And don't blame me that Theophilus couldn't do anything. He tried but the devil was too much for him.'

'And for you as well.'

'Yes,' Father Steiger said rather loudly, 'for me as well! That pair disrupted this parish, created havoc in the convent, frightened the citizens, kept me awake night after night, made Therese angry and caused me to wreck my car. And all in less than two months. Yes, it was too much for me. I freely admit it! I was very happy when they finally left.' He found himself pouring more brandy into his glass. 'And so was everyone else.'

The Bishop took a couple of long puffs on the cigar, watching the smoke drift through the air and waiting for the priest to calm down. 'Well,' he finally said. 'I'll tell you why I am here. I have a request.'

Father Steiger just looked at him. Waiting.

'I want you to permit Theophilus to bring the woman back to Earling.'

For the first time in a long while Father Steiger was aware of the ticking of the wall clock. It was the only sound in the silent room.

'You want me to *what?*'

'Let the woman come back and allow Theophilus to complete the exorcism she needs.'

The younger man found it difficult putting his thoughts into words. 'In all respect to yourself, Your Lordship, and to the office which you hold, I cannot comply with your request. I do not want that confusion back in Earling. I won't have it again.' He shook his head and stared out of the window, not wanting to look at the face of the man sitting across from him. 'I won't have it,' he said again.

'If you refuse, you'll be sending that woman to suicide.'

'I don't care. I won't have a repeat of this ghastly August and September. And if that kills the woman,' he turned back to the Bishop, 'then I'm sorry.'

'As your superior, I could order you to.'

'I know, but you won't.'

'That's true,' the man sighed, 'the decision must be yours.'

'Look, Bishop, let me explain. Please.' He sat down at his desk chair and faced the man. This was *his* desk and he felt secure behind it. 'I am aware that the woman will probably kill herself. It's something the devil wants. It's almost inevitable. But I'm also aware of the incredible problems having her back in Earling would cause. As pastor, I can't inflict – willingly inflict – those problems on the parishioners nor on the Sisters. You have no idea of the abuse they took from that woman. Or from the voices inside that woman, I should say. You have no idea of the extra work, the mental stress she put on the good Sisters of St Francis. I'm surprised some of them didn't ask for a transfer.

313

They listened to the filthy language, they had to dig the dried vomit and excrement from the very floor boards of the room. They were insulted. Lies were made up about them and during it all they were expected to go about their other duties, to teach school, to tutor special students, to visit the sick and dying. I mean, it was a terrible imposition on them.'

'The Mother Superior agreed willingly,' said the Bishop. 'She knew what the risk would be.'

'In all respect, Bishop, Mother Lotharia had no idea what she was getting into when she told Theophilus it was okay with her. She had never assisted at an exorcism before! Lotharia came to Earling as an ordinary school teacher eight years ago. She was made Mother Superior just two years ago. She never dealt with the devil, unless it was some devilment in one of her pupils. She walked into this with all ignorance. Good will and good intentions, but in ignorance. I doubt if she would agree to do it again.'

'Shall we call her?' the Bishop asked. 'Shall we get her opinion?'

'If you choose,' Father Steiger said rather coolly. 'She should be in her study at the convent. I'll have Therese fetch her.'

When Mother Lotharia saw the Bishop, she grew flustered. 'Your Lordship,' she said, kissing his amethyst ring, 'what an unexpected honour.'

'His Lordship has something to ask you, Mother,' Father Steiger said. 'Please sit down. You'll need it.'

Bishop Drumm got right to the point. He explained what was happening to Mary in Milwaukee, what the doctors had said and how he wished the exorcism to be completed before Mary died.

Again, afterward, there was silence. Finally Mother Lotharia said: 'And me? What do you want from me in all this?'

'Your approval to have the poor woman come back to Earling for one last try to free her,' Bishop Drumm said.

She shot an anxious look at Father Steiger. 'And what do you want Father?'

'I'm against it as I'm sure you'd know I would be.'

The woman in the black robe and the large silver cross around her neck lowered her gaze. Her brow wrinkled several times and her fingers twitched. 'I . . .' she started to say and then broke off. 'Probably if I had more time to come to a decision, Your Lordship . . .'

'There isn't a lot of time left,' the visitor replied. 'The doctors say it's a matter of days at the very most.'

'I should consult with the others,' she replied slowly. 'They are the ones who will have to take the brunt of it all.'

'You're the Superior here,' the Bishop replied dryly, 'you make the decisions for them.'

She nodded. 'I know. I made one before about the Lawrence woman and lived to regret it.'

'You regretted trying to help that tormented soul?' the Bishop raised his voice in surprise.

She shook her head. 'No, not for trying to help her. I regret that we tried and *failed* her.'

'Now you have another opportunity,' the Bishop replied.

Mother Lotharia looked at Father Steiger. 'I know how you feel about it. I know what horrors we all went through, but our failure to help this woman when she trusted us to do so has bothered me ever since she left.'

'And you are willing to go through all that again?' Father Steiger couldn't believe what he was hearing.

'But this time,' the woman answered, 'it won't be so difficult. I know what to expect. I know how to handle her.'

'The other Sisters feel the same way?' the Bishop asked.

'Yes, We've talked about nothing else. Mary needs another chance.' She looked up at Father Steiger, her eyes pleading. 'And so do we Father. We also need another chance.'

315

'But if it fails again?' the young priest asked.

'But if it doesn't,' she said, 'if it works . . .'

They carried Mary off the train on a stretcher. She had been unconscious the entire trip. Theophilus was with her and had sat up with her in the private compartment the train company had provided upon the Bishop's request. Mother Lotharia and two of the other Sisters loaded her into the back seat of Father Steiger's borrowed car. They worked quietly and quickly, the freezing air that came across the open, snow-covered fields was bitingly cold. Theophilus wore a heavy overcoat and had his white beard covered with a dark scarf. Father Steiger stomped his feet to keep them warm as he waited for the Sisters to finish. Somehow they managed to get themselves into the back seat as well. Then he got behind the wheel, Theophilus sat in front with him. They drove, in silence, to the church grounds. Again, Father Steiger watched as the women took Mary from the back seat and carried her into the convent.

Theophilus and the younger priest went into the warmth of the rectory.

'I'm sorry,' Father Steiger said. 'I behaved like an ass the last time. It won't happen again.' He extended his hand to the old man. 'Are we still friends?'

'I know what pressures you were under,' the other replied. 'I've seen it before with other pastors in other cases I've been on. The devil works in strange ways, I try to warn people but they always have to find it out for themselves. Very often Satan even surprises me, and look how many years I've been taking him on!' He smiled. 'No, I won't shake your hand. Instead give me a hug!' He reached out both arms and embraced the younger man. 'I'll do it this time Joseph,' he whispered, 'I promise.'

Father Steiger showed Theophilus to his former room and told him to rest before supper. Theophilus

316

npacked the small black satchel, the only luggage he
arried, and hung his spare cassock in the closet. Then
e took out his purple stole, his cross and his Bible. As
e placed them on the dresser he started to cough. It
/as a deep rattling cough and he fumbled quickly for
is handkerchief, then spat in it. When the coughing
ubsided he opened the handkerchief. Yes, just like the
ther times, there was fresh blood in it.

'he fifteenth of December was a Saturday. There was
o school, all the Sisters could be in attendance, if
ecessary. They had reassembled the iron bed, bought
new mattress and spread newspapers on the floor
round the bed. This time if there was vomit to be
leaned up, they would just throw away the papers.

This morning Mother Lotharia was there along with
isters Lydia and Hermina, the oldest and the youngest
f the lot. Both had volunteered.

Fathers Theophilus and Steiger stood at the foot of
he bed looking at Mary's unconscious form. Even
wathed in the grey robe the Sisters had made for her
ast visit, they could see how thin and frail she had
ecome. Her small body had deteriorated to almost
ones underneath her yellowish skin. Her eyes had
unk deep into her skull and her cheekbones stood in
igh relief. Her face had no colour, even her lips were
rey.

The two men glanced at each other, Theophilus nod-
ed. They crossed themselves, put their stoles around
heir necks and Theophilus opened his missal.

'In the name of the Father and of the Son and of the
Ioly Ghost. Amen.'

'Amen,' the others responded, crossing themselves.

'Glorious Prince of the Celestial Host, St Michael
he Archangel, defend us in the conflict which we have
o sustain against principalities and powers, against
he rulers of the world of this darkness, against the
pirits of wickedness in the high places. Come to the

rescue of men, whom God has created to His image and likeness, and whom He has redeemed at a great price from the tyranny of the devil. It is Thou whom Holy Church venerates as her guardian and her protector. Thou whom . . .' Theophilus intoned the Prayer to St Michael the Archangel who defeated Satan and cast him from Heaven into the earth. When he came to the second part of the exorcism ritual he said the names of Jesus, the Virgin Mary and those of Saints Peter and Paul with special fervour. The others listened to every word, mentally emphasizing each of the ritual pleas and beseechings. They had heard it all before, but this time there was more of an urgency. Mary was dying and Satan had to be thrown out of her before she did.

'Retreat, Satan, inventor and master of all deceit, enemy of man's salvation. Cede the place to Christ in whom you have found none of . . .'

'Oooooooooohhhhhhhhhhhh!' The moaning came from Mary's closed lips. Then a long, deep cry, like a baby lost in the bottom of a well. Then her body began to twitch, her legs moved rapidly under the grey robe and her fingers twisted like claws. The Sisters rushed to her side, ready to hold her down if necessary.

Then came the laughter. It was as if a dozen or so people were having a party inside Mary. There were snatches of conversation about the weather, bits of gossip about someone's wife and a man started to tell an off-colour joke. Then came the scream. High and piercing and so shrill the Sisters put their hands to their ears to drown it out. That was followed by a female voice: 'What kind of a mess is this?'

'Mess?' repeated Theophilus. 'Who are you?'

'What is all this? What's happening here?' The voice was feminine but low and rather harsh. The tone was more of wonderment than fear. 'What are all you people doing dressed in black? Somebody die? Did I miss anything?'

'Who are you?' insisted Theophilus.

318

'I mean, one minute I'm one place and the next minute I'm here! What's going on? Why are you crazies
standing around watching me?' Mary's lips never
moved. 'I don't like this place. Boring.'

'I asked you to tell me your name' the old priest said.

'My name? Why? Who's this old bastard?'

'I am Father Theophilus and I am a member of Christ
Jesus' army here on earth. I demand to know your
name.'

'Will someone get him out of here?' the voice said
sarcastically. 'Old fart.'

'By the power of the Blessed Virgin Mary, I demand
to know your name! Identify yourself or suffer the
consequences!'

'Suffer the consequences? Shit, that's all I've ever
done.' The voice sighed. 'Okay, I don't know what good
it's gonna do you, but my name is Minna. Satisfied?'

Theophilus scowled trying to remember why that
name was familiar to him. 'Minna?' he repeated.

'Well, I'm not Little Red Riding Hood, that's for
sure.'

'I seem to recall hearing of a Minna,' the old man still
wore a puzzled frown, 'but I can't recall where. Do you,
Father Steiger? A Minna?'

'I've never known anyone named Minna,' the other
priest said.

'Perhaps she is connected with Mary,' the Mother
Superior suggested.

'Not the *Virgin* Mary!' the voice laughed. 'That's not
me.'

'No,' said Mother Lotharia, 'the Mary on the bed.
Mary Lawrence.'

There was a long pause when nothing came from the
body. Then: 'Mary *Lawrence*? You've got Mary in
here,'

'Do you know her?' Theophilus asked.

'Damn right I do. The little bitch.'

'How do you know her? Are you related?'

'She's my niece. Jacob's girl and she's a pain in the ass. Never could stand that brat. She always knew so much.' The voice was almost angry.

'Wait a minute,' Father Steiger said, 'are you the woman Mary's father went to Arizona with? After he kicked her out of her own home and sold it?'

'It wasn't her home. It was *his*. My foolish mother gave Jeanette money to buy it. Money I should have inherited. But it went to Jeanette. As far as I was concerned, that place was really *mine*. Anyway, she got crazy and had to be booted out. Pious little brat. She was so goody-goody she wouldn't have said the word "shit" if she had a mouth full of it!'

'So you're the one,' Theophilus said slowly. 'You were there when her own father cursed her and gave her to the devil.' She didn't answer. 'Remember? You and Jacob wanted to have sexual relations and Mary refused to join in? You recall that?'

'Well, it wasn't exactly the way it happened. Jacob was getting fed up with her bitchy ways. Anyway, we were both drinking. I don't remember it clearly.'

'And now you see where your sinful ways have taken that poor child,' Theophilus said loudly. 'Your curses have put her in the arms of Satan!'

'And me? Where do you think I am? In Never-Never Land having tea with Alice and the White Rabbit?' She began to moan, softly. 'This ain't no picnic where I am. I am in Hell! My life was a hell and now I'm in Hell. You think that's so fine? You think I'm happy here?' The crying grew a little louder.

'Why are you there? I mean,' Father Steiger asked, 'there must be a reason. Don't they tell people why they are sent there?'

'I'm not here because of Mary. That's for sure. I didn't do anything real bad to her. She just annoyed me, that's all. I'm here for something else.' The crying was a little louder.

'What else?' the younger priest demanded. 'What

320

could you have done that would make your soul spend eternity in Hell?'

The sobbing grew in loudness. 'My babies!' the voice cried. 'What I did to them! My babies!'

'Babies?' Mother Lotharia asked. 'You had babies?'

'I killed them!' she wailed.

'You killed your own babies?' Sister Hermina gasped. She had never spoken to a murderer before. How many?' She was intrigued and didn't see the sharp look she was getting from the Mother Superior.

'There were three of them' the voice moaned. 'No, wait, there were four. I killed four little babies!'

'Are you sorry now?' Hermina asked.

'Sorry? Of course I'm sorry. They say I should have repented while I was alive, but I didn't. I died not being sorry at all. It was only after I got here that I became sorry.'

'Were you a Catholic?' this from the elderly Sister Lydia. 'Did you have Extreme Unction when you died?'

'I was born a Catholic,' the voice said, most of the sobbing had subsided, 'but I didn't go to church. My sister Jeanette went all the time. I had other things to do. And yes, I got that Extreme Unction bullshit in the hospital, but it didn't do any good. The fool of a priest mumbled something over me but I couldn't answer him. I was already out of my body and floating over it, watching his antics while he named all his saints.'

'Out of your body?' Young Sister Hermina was conducting her own interrogation. 'What do you mean by that?'

'I mean I was out of my body. That's what I mean. I was dying and I was floating over myself.'

'Why, I never heard of such a thing,' the Sister gasped. Then to Theophilus: 'Father, is this another of Satan's tricks?'

Minna's voice became peeved. 'Don't you teach these silly nuns anything? Everybody knows you go out of your body when you die. I mean, I didn't know it

321

when *I* was alive, but when I died I saw how it work
Pretty nice too, no pain, nothing. You'd think at lea
your *church* would know those things!'

'Some things are not meant to be known,' sa
Theophilus.

'Bullshit!' replied the voice. 'You don't want peop
to know too much. It would be bad for business.'

'You are still an unrepentant sinner!' said th
Mother Superior. 'One would think being in Hell woul
have changed your ways.'

'Being in Hell only makes me want to get out of Hell.
doesn't change my ways. Learn that fact too, old lady

Theophilus got closer to the inert form on the bed.
am prepared to offer you salvation,' he said, 'a way ou
of Hell and into Heaven. Even for sinners like yoursel
there is hope.' He reached into his cassock and took ou
a round flat silver container, like a woman's compac
'In here I have a blessed wafer, the blessed Host, th
bread of eternal life. Let me place it on the poor lady
lips so that you take it into her body.' He bent over th
bed and reached to put the wafer on her parched gre
lips. Suddenly something grabbed his arm, twisting
and making him cry out in pain. The wafer fell onto th
floor.

Immediately Mary began to vomit. She spat up cu
fuls of greenish, steaming, stinking stuff. The fir
charge of it hit Theophilus right in the face. When h
managed to pull back, the second spout flew across th
room and spattered the Mother Superior and Siste
Hermina. Their black robes sizzled where the gree
liquid hit. Mother Lotharia clucked and pushed the tw
Sisters from the room. Father Steiger grabbed Theo
philus and wiping his face with a handkerchief, led hi
out of the room as well.

'Save your tricks for someone a lot stupider, ol
man!' the masculine voice inside Mary shouted. 'Shov
your Host up your ass! Just because we let you brir
the woman back here doesn't mean we have weakene

322

any!' Then came high-pitched laughter followed by the sounds of dogs barking and then the baby crying far, far away. But it was all wasted on an empty room, everyone had gone. 'Good riddance!' the voice said.

Mary lay like that for about five minutes, then several Sisters came fluttering in to clean up the cold vomit and carry her back to her room.

Father Steiger stood behind the pulpit looking at the congregation. They, in turn, looked up at him. They sat bundled in sweaters, heavy jackets and woollen trousers, their winter coats, scarves and gloves hanging neatly in the cloakroom just inside the big wooden door.

'I look around me this morning,' he said, 'and I see the decorations announcing the birth of the Christ Jesus. In ten days it will be Christmas morning and we will commemorate again the most sacred event the world has ever known. There will be presents and fine food, decorated trees and singing, family gatherings and visits with old friends. Yet while that sacred day approaches, we have Satan right next door.' He gestured to the left, toward the convent. 'Evil has returned to Earling, Iowa. I gave it my permission to come back.' There was some murmuring from the group, some puzzled glances.

'You all will recall the case of the woman named Mary. The possessed woman who was here in August and September of this year. You will recall how we worked on her, how we exhorted the devil to leave her and how we prayed for success. You all know it didn't work. The woman grew weaker while Satan grew stronger. Havoc reigned in this parish and confusion was the norm. It was a difficult time for Earling and it was a very difficult time for me. Father Theophilus Riesinger,' and he pointed to the old man in the front row, 'did everything in his power to exorcise the poor woman. He might have succeeded if I had not let my

passions rule my head, if I had not refused to cooperate
any longer. I gave him a time and an ultimatum. When
the time that *I* prescribed had elapsed I asked him to
leave and to take the unfortunate woman with him. I
should never have done that. I listened to the devil's
own thoughts inside me and made invalid everything
that Father Theophilus had accomplished.' He paused,
hoping they were understanding what he was saying.
'Yes, *I*, your priest and your confessor, listened
to Satan's urgings and obeyed them. I am guilty
and I confess. Your confessor is confessing to
you.'

There were several coughs in the audience and more
than one person turned to whisper something to
another person. There was the uneasy rustling of
handbags and rosaries and hymnals.

'Bishop Drumm came to me, he personally made the
trip from Des Moines, to convince me to permit the
woman named Mary to return to Earling so that Father
Theophilus could carry out and complete what he was
supposed to do. I gave my approval as did the Mother
Superior. The good Sisters of St Francis want to help
the woman too, in spite of the fact that the demons
inside her insult them and commit unspeakable acts
upon them. You know,' and he smiled, 'I can't help but
be reminded of the symbology in all of this. One thou
sand nine hundred and twenty eight years ago, another
Mary came to a small town asking to be delivered of a
burden. Now here, to this parish, at the same time of
the year, another Mary comes asking to be delivered of
another burden. This time it's not the beloved Christ
child; instead she asks to be relieved of the hated and
feared Satan himself. If I had been in Bethlehem all
those years ago I could not have refused that Mary in
her time of need; now, here in Earling, I cannot refuse
this other Mary either.'

324

Immediately following the Mass, the two priests along with three of the Sisters started on the exorcism. This time there were only screams and howls of pain. No words came clearly, just the horrendous shrieks and deep pitiful sobbings. And the vomit. It poured out of the body almost unceasingly. Mary had eaten nothing since she had arrived but the Sisters in attendance later told the others that there had been eighteen bucketfuls of the stuff.

'Are you all right, Father?' Therese knocked on Theophilus' door. 'Do you need some help?'

The door opened, he was wiping his mouth with a handkerchief. 'Very kind of you my dear,' he said trying to smile, 'but I'm fine.'

'I heard you coughing as I was coming up the stairs,' she said.

'I'm sorry to have disturbed you.'

'No, you didn't disturb me, but you did worry me. Shall I call the local doctor?'

He shook his head. 'No, no. I'm in no need of him. It's just the winter weather and the fact that I'm an old man. Old men get these things you know,' he said with a smile, 'you mustn't worry about old men.'

'Well,' she said, not at all sure he was telling the truth, 'if you need anything, you call me. If I'm not in the kitchen, I'll be in my room, but call me anyway. Understand?'

'Yes,' he smiled again, 'but not to worry. Please.' He closed the door.'

She went directly into her brother's study. 'And there was blood on his handkerchief,' she said emphatically. 'I saw it.'

'You foolish people really think we are going to let you survive? That we are going to permit your church and your Bible to give up our hold on the earth?' The voice inside Mary had identified itself as Beelzebub. 'We got

325

thrown out of Heaven and were given the earth! Given it, old man, we were handed the bloody place! It's ours! It was to make up for getting thrown out from up there. And now you're trying to throw us out *again*? You think we're going to go peaceably?'

'Our Lord commands us to get rid of you,' Theophilus said. 'You are the enemy. You and your legions are the curse of mankind!'

'Whose fault's that? Huh? We were sent here, we were told it was eternal banishment but that the place belongs to us. To us.'

'The Heavenly Father never meant it that way,' Mother Lotharia said.

'How do you know, old bitch? How would you like to be kicked from pillar to post being told one thing and then later being told something else again? This building here, for instance. You black-birds all live here. Right?'

Mother Lotharia stiffened at being called a 'black-bird' but simply said: 'Correct.'

'So you live here. They tell you it's yours to stay as long as you want. Then they change their minds and tell you to take your things and get out. Just like that! And when you don't go, they send in idiots like this old man and this younger fool to drive you out. Would you like that? Well, would you?'

'It's not the same thing. Jesus Christ put us in this house because we are doing His work. And the people on earth are His people. He protects us and we worship Him for it.' The Mother Superior tried to keep her voice level.

'We were here before what's-his-name was,' the voice said loudly. 'We've been here for thousands of your years. He is a newcomer. He shows up here – on our earth – and promptly tells everybody to kiss his behind and throw us out. Some nerve, if you ask me. It's not his. We offered it all to him. Did you know that? We took him up in the sky and we pointed out the rivers and

326

everything and told him he could have it. We offered him the whole thing! It was ours to offer him. He understood that. He knew it wasn't his. He knew it was ours. And you know what he did? He refused it! Said he didn't want it. Threw our offer back in our faces! Then he turns right around and tells everybody it's *his* world! After he turned it down! His world! The nerve of some people!'

'Perhaps He didn't like your terms,' Father Steiger said.

'It was our offer because it was our property. He didn't like it? Then tough shit. Go somewhere else, why didn't he?'

'Because God sent Him here to free us from the likes of you,' Theophilus said.

'Uh huh, and he had no more right to do that to us than what you are trying to do now with this woman.'

'This woman is a member of His Church. Therefore she is sacred to Him.'

'His church! Please!' Some brown liquid was spat into the air. 'Don't prattle on about your damned church. It's no match for us.'

'The Church is the foundation stone of salvation for all humanity!' Mother Lotharia was getting tired of all this blasphemy. 'Christianity will rid Satan and his henchmen from the earth!'

'Yeah,' the voice laughed, 'and then where will Christianity be? Ever think of that? Without Satan there is no need for Christianity. Get rid of Satan and the fear of Satan and you've gotten rid of the reason for your church. Without us there would be nobody to fear, nobody to point at and accuse. Your religion would be as flat as a pancake if you didn't have Satan to blame on everything. No, no old lady, we don't need you but you sure need *us!*'

'The Holy Roman Church will prevail!' Mother Lotharia found herself shouting.

'The Holy Roman Church will prevail, la da de da!'

the voice mimicked her voice. 'Some prevailing it's doing. We're just being nice in keeping you alive. Let me tell you something. Down in Mexico, you know? Down there? What did we do just ten years ago? We got rid of your wonderful Holy Roman nonsense. We tried an experiment and it worked. We got the federal government to close you people down, to shut your churches and open your convents. We made you crooks give back millions of dollars worth of property and gold and stolen jewels. We made them arrest your priests. We had many beaten up, some were even killed. Many others were deported. We made them do the same to the nuns. Many were thrown out of the country, some got killed and some got fucked.' There was a laugh. 'That last bunch we did a favour. They never would have known what it felt like if we hadn't had it done to them.' There was another laugh. 'You three prunes better hurry up if you intend to try it. If you don't, you'll have to find some guy that's blind.' Another laugh. 'Or else blind and lost his sense of smell!' Several voices laughed inside of Mary on that one.

'Stop that kind of talk! Instantly!' Theophilus shouted. He reached for the bowl of Holy Water and threw it's contents onto Mary's body. There were screams of pain and howls like wounded animals, then everything went quiet.

'I'm sorry,' Theophilus said to the others in the room. 'I couldn't take any more of it, not the way he was insulting the Sisters. I probably shouldn't have . . .' but he broke off and started to cough. He pulled a stained handkerchief out of his pocket and covering his mouth, he hurried from the room, the exorcism over for the day.

On Tuesday, the eighteenth of December, both Minna and Jacob made an appearance. The two seemed to be inside the emaciated body at the same time. Usually one would speak and then the other, sometimes both voices could he heard talking over one another. The Sisters did a great deal of crossing themselves that morning.

'We both had Extreme Unction, so what?' Jacob's voice was demanding. 'It didn't do any good. We still ended up in Hell.'

'Because you were not repentant of your acts while you were alive,' Theophilus insisted. 'You must be sincere when you repent. Just going through the motions isn't enough.'

'Why not?' Minna asked. 'You priests go through the motions all the time and you don't believe half the things you say.'

'How can you say that?' the younger priest spoke up. 'You admitted yourself that you never went to church. How do you know what priests believe or don't believe?'

'Because of the ones I see down here!' Minna said with a laugh. 'There are lots of you guys running around down here.'

'Not Roman Catholic priests!' Mother Lotharia said angrily. 'They must be Orthodox or Episcopalian or something.'

'They are turned-collar frauds just like all R.C. priests. They screwed up on earth and they are down here with us, the baby-killers and the wife-beaters. They're no different and neither are all of you.'

'We have the right of the Lord behind us,' Theophilus replied.

'And we've got the fires of Satan at our asses,' Minna said. 'Frankly, one's just as bad as the other.'

Then came loud laughter and Mary's body started to curl into the foetus position. Quickly her knees pulled up to her chin and her arms wrapped around her legs. The Sisters hurried to help her but found they couldn't move her limbs. Sister Serena said later they felt like steel bars: 'Cold and hard, unbreakable.'

Mary's body stayed like that for a half hour, giving Theophilus time to go through the entire exorcism ritual again. He prayed, called on all the saints in heaven and crossed himself at all the right moments. It was only at the last line: 'That Thou wouldst crush down all enemies of Thy Church, we beseech Thee to hear us,' that Mary uncoiled and lay flat on her back again.

Minna's voice was the first one heard. 'Maybe we could make a deal,' she said.

'The Church does not make deals,' Theophilus replied.

'Cut out the shit,' Jacob said, 'of course it does. It's made deals with people for centuries.'

'With *people* when necessary, but not with demons!'

'We're not demons,' Jacob answered hotly, 'we're people.'

'Not any longer, you aren't. You've died and gone to Hell. You have become a demon!'

'Oh, your church and it's terminology.' Jacob laughed. 'Okay old man, if it makes you any happier you can call us demons.'

'You can call us stringbeans or hollyhocks, if you want to,' Minna laughed.

There was a pause. 'Well,' Jacob's voice said, 'you want to hear the deal or don't you?'

'I will hear it,' the old priest replied,' but that is not a promise that I will buy it.'

'Agreed,' said Jacob. 'Okay, it's this. My daughter is dying. We all know that. You want us out of her. In fact you've been trying for years to get us out of her. But you know while we, Minna and I and some of the others are inside her, we stay out of Hell itself. Although we are damned we are not right there in the middle of Hell when we are in her body.'

'There are different grades of Hell?' this from Father Steiger.

'Yeah. Some places are better than others, if you can

330

imagine it. Being here in Mary's body is about the best place we could be. The worst place would be the exact centre of Hell. That's where the fires are. That's the worst spot of all.'

'So?'

'So, we are asking you to make a deal. Mary is dying. We seem to be getting weaker. I'm not saying you are going to win this battle, but from our point of view, you are ahead on points. We, Minna and I and some of the others, will leave this body if you don't demand we return straight into Hell. Let us stay at the same level we are now and we'll go.'

'Go where!' Theophilus demanded. 'Into another poor creature like your daughter? Torment another innocent child of the Church?'

'We'll just go. Okay? We promise not to disturb anyone. Just let us stay until Judgement Day. Okay?' All eyes in the room were on the old priest. He didn't say a word. 'Well,' Jacob spoke up again, 'how about it? Don't command us back to Hell and we'll leave Mary's body.'

'How can you do that?' Father Steiger asked. 'Aren't you under orders from Satan or one of his henchmen? How can you defy their instructions like that?'

'We're not defying anything,' Minna replied. 'You people can't possibly understand the rules here, how this place works. If you let us leave peaceably, we won't bother any more human beings.'

'What will you be doing instead?' Father Steiger asked.

'Lots of things. There's lots we can do, possession of a body is only one of them.'

'How can we trust them, Father?' the Mother Superior asked Theophilus. 'Will you believe the word of the devil?'

'We are not the devil, old crow!' Jacob yelled. 'We are trapped souls. We are humans who have been sent to Hell. Can't you understand?'

331

'Not very well,' she shook her wimpled head.

'When you get over here, when you arrive in Hell, you'll soon catch on,' said Minna. 'It doesn't take long.'

'I have no intention of going to Hell!' the Mother Superior said loudly.

'Neither did I,' Minna laughed, 'neither did I.'

'Think about it,' Jacob commanded. 'Think about the deal, old man. It's either that or we keep up the fight until my daughter is a piece of dead meat.'

'You would do that to her?' Sister Serena asked in astonishment. 'Your own daughter?'

'I wanted to do worse,' Jacob moaned. 'It's too late to be forgiven now, but I wanted to do worse.'

Then Mary's body again swiftly contracted into the foetal position. Theophilus re-read the entire exorcism ritual and when she relaxed and there were no more voices coming from her, he ended the session for the day.

'I put his tea and bread roll by the door,' Therese said, 'but he hasn't touched it. It's still sitting in the hallway.'

'I thought I heard him coughing in the night,' her brother said. 'He woke me up once.'

'He is not well, Joseph. He doesn't sound right. Maybe it's worse than we suspect. He is an old man.' She dried her hands on the dish towel. 'And he has been through hell in these few months.'

'Yes,' her brother replied, 'literally through Hell!'

Father Steiger knocked on the old priest's door. 'Are you all right? Don't you want your breakfast?' he called. There was no answer. 'Theophilus! Can you hear me! Are you all right?' Still no reply. 'Theophilus, I'm coming in. Be prepared because I'm going to open the door.'

Theophilus was lying on the floor; dried blood from his mouth had trickled onto the rag rug near the bed.

332

'Therese!' Father Steiger shouted down the stairway to the kitchen. 'Call the doctor! Quick!'

Doctor Gambee listened to Theophilus' heart, then took his pulse. 'The man is exhausted,' the young doctor said to Father Steiger and Therese. 'He must stay in bed and take nourishment until he recovers. It may take a month or more. We are not dealing with a young man, you know.'

'A month?' Therese said what her brother was thinking. 'We can't wait a month!'

'I'm afraid you'll have to,' the medical man replied. 'He has a congestion in his lungs. His heart is beating too rapidly to suit me and from the looks of his eyes his red blood count must be very low. You say he hasn't been eating?' Therese nodded, 'then that explains his weak condition. He needs broth and cereals. Even a little red wine would help. But mostly he needs rest.'

Theophilus opened his eyes. 'I'm fasting,' he whispered. 'I cannot eat.'

'You'd better cancel your fast,' the doctor said, 'and start taking in food. Like sensible people do.'

'I have given my word. I must fast until the demons have left the woman's body.' He closed his eyes and sighed.

'I am well aware of what's going on, Father Steiger,' the young doctor said, 'and I've read enough about what you are trying to do here to know what an incredible toll an exorcism takes on its priests. But Father Theophilus does not have any energy left to be expended. He is near physical collapse. Why, he *did* collapse. Fainted on the floor. You've got to convince him of the need for food and rest.'

'I have a mission to complete,' the old man said without opening his eyes. 'If I fail, the woman dies.'

'If you don't take care of yourself first,' the doctor said without smiling, 'you'll go before she does.'

'If that is the will of the Lord,' he said, 'then so be it.'

'The doctor is right, Theophilus,' Father Steiger

333

came closer to the bed. 'You must take care of yourself first. Then the woman.'

'You think' Theophilus asked in a trembling voice, 'that while I lie here enjoying the luxury of this bed and eating good food, Satan will stop tormenting that poor child? Now that I'm down, you think Satan will patiently wait for me to get back up, wait for me to have the strength to challenge him?' He shook his head and his white beard rustled across the top of the bed quilt. 'Satan won't wait. Satan is very clever. What is happening to me is part of his scheme. He wants me out of the way. He wants me to stop tormenting his demons, his messengers from Hell. 'No,' he struggled to sit up, but Father Steiger pushed him back down. 'No, I cannot lie here while he destroys that woman. My own soul would roast in Hell if I permitted that.'

The doctor opened his bag. 'I'm going to give you some powders,' he said. 'I want you to take them.'

'I told you I'm fasting! Please, respect my penance for the Lord.'

'These powders are not food. They are just some medicines that I want you to wash down with a little water. The Lord says you can have a glass of water, doesn't he?'

Theophilus glared at the young doctor. 'Yes, I can have water.'

Dr Gambee motioned Therese to pour a glass of water from the pitcher that was on the dresser. She brought it to him. Quickly he opened a paper packet and poured an amount of white powder into the water, then he put his finger in it, stirred it, and it dissolved. 'Drink this, Father,' the doctor said. 'There's no food in there. You're not breaking your promise to God.'

Theophilus squinted at the glass in the man's hand and saw that it was almost clear. Therese lifted Theophilus' head and as the doctor held the glass to the old man's lips, he drank. Then he sighed, and Therese lowered his head back onto the pillow.

'We'll leave you for now,' Dr Gambee said, 'but I'll check in on you tomorrow.'

'No need for that,' Theophilus said.

'You let me be the judge of that,' the man said. 'Your job is to take care of souls; mine is to administer to bodies.'

'Yes,' the old priest sighed, 'and you see what a mess I have done with that woman's soul.' He closed his eyes and they all left the room.

In Father Steiger's study, Dr Gambee wrote out two prescriptions. 'Have these filled and make sure he takes them with water this afternoon and before bedtime tonight.'

'What is this stuff?' Father Steiger asked.

'There are some vitamins in it, but it's mostly a relaxant. It'll make him sleep. He needs to get more sleep.'

'If he has been fasting,' the priest said, 'then he probably has been staying up all night praying. They go hand in hand.'

'Well, with these powders, he'll find it very difficult to keep his eyes open. He needs rest. Lots of it.' The doctor put on his heavy grey coat and a cap with ear muffs. 'I'll be back tomorrow morning,' he said and he left the rectory.

Therese looked at her brother. 'Wonderful!' she said sarcastically. 'Six days till Christmas and we have a possessed woman in one house and a half-dead priest in another! I wonder what Santa Claus is going to bring us next year?'

The Wednesday night service took on special meaning. Because it was almost Christmas, the church was almost full.

'Tonight,' Father Steiger said, 'I want to tell you what has been happening to the woman called Mary. I want to inform you of her progress but I have some sad news regarding our dear friend the exorcist, Father

335

Theophilus.' The priest went on to tell of Mary's terrible health and of the demons that came through her. When he started talking about Theophilus and how ill he had become there was a rustling and murmuring that swept slowly over the congregation. He said that the old man was exhausted and was under the care of Dr Gambee and that the doctor had said it would be possibly another month before the priest would be well enough to continue the ritual.

'What we need now are your prayers,' he said. 'We need prayers and we need fasting. I know the Christmas season is upon us, but it is Satan's way of testing our mettle, or laughing at us and trying us to the last degree of our patience. The Sisters have all promised to fast and I will do the same. To fast and pray and ask that the woman be delivered from her demons and that Father Theophilus be delivered from the valley of death. As I bless you all and send you back to your homes in the middle of this winter night I ask you to remember these two souls, both battling to stay alive, both battling the forces of evil for your salvation.'

When the Mass was over and most of the parishioners gone, five men awaited Father Steiger as he came from his robing room. He stopped short. He had been planning on turning off the lights, not having a discussion.

The first man, overcoat on and hat in hand, opened the dialogue: 'We are very sorry to hear about the priest,' he said.

'Yes,' said another man, 'it's too bad.'

'We were hoping,' said a third, 'that it would all be over by now. That things here could get back to normal.'

'What with Christmas coming and all,' a fourth said.

Father Steiger nodded. 'I was hoping for the same thing. But just as it looked as if we were close to victory, this illness came on. It'll put us back a bit.'

'You said a month,' the fifth man spoke up.

'The doctor said a month,' the priest replied, 'it could be sooner.'

'Father,' one of them said, 'we don't want this thing to drag out.'

'Yes. We don't want to have the devil in our town for another month.'

'There's no telling what will happen to our families,' one said.

'To our children.'

'The nuns teach our children. Why couldn't a demon get inside one of the Sisters and she carry it to the school?'

'Or a demon get out of the convent and enter into one of us?'

'My wife is going to have a baby. The demons could go into our baby as the child is being born. I read of that happening, some place.'

'Believe me,' said the priest with a smile, 'that could never happen.'

'How do you know?' one of them asked.

'Yeah. You don't have any answers about this. You've told us so.'

'There can be no harm to any of you,' the Father insisted. 'I have his word.'

'Whose word? Satan's?'

'No. Father Theophilus.'

'Hah! No harm to any of us he says and yet he himself has been laid low by the devil! How can we believe you?'

'You must trust me,' the priest said. 'Trust my knowledge and trust my office in the Holy Church.'

'And if one of them gets into my newborn? What'll happen? Same thing? Screaming and puking and hollering while old Theophilus drives the demon away? Not to my baby, Father. I won't sit around waiting for the devil to grab my child.'

'I've given you my assurances,' the priest replied crisply,' what more do you want me to do?'

337

'The same as before.'

'Yeah.'

'Get rid of the both of them.'

'Like you did before.'

'Put them on a train. Get them out of Earling.'

'I can't do that,' Father Steiger said. 'Not again. Not this time.'

'You get rid of them,' one man said, 'or we'll figure out a way to get rid of you.'

'I am your priest!' Father Steiger shouted. 'How dare you speak to me like that!'

'And we are your congregation. In the end it must be our decision on how our parish is run.'

'Only the Bishop can replace me!' the priest was angry now. 'Not you people!'

'The Bishop is in Des Moines. We don't have time to go to Des Moines.'

'Then what else can you do?' Father Steiger asked.

'This is a small out-of-the-way community.'

'People don't pay attention to what happens here.'

'Not even when accidents happen.'

'Accidents?' the priest's voice rose in disbelief. 'What do you mean "accidents"?'

'If you don't get those two out of here, you'll see.'

'Yeah. You'll see.'

'Get them out!'

'Now!'

'Before Christmas!'

Therese opened the door for the doctor. He hung his coat in the hallway and went directly up the staircase to the old priest's room.

'He slept almost all day, yesterday,' she told him. 'I did manage to get a cup of tea down him along with the powders last night. But he didn't eat anything at all. He says he promised the Lord.'

Dr Gambee knocked once on the door, then without waiting to be invited, went in. He went directly and sat

338

on the edge of Theophilus' bed. 'How are we feeling this morning?' he asked cheerily.

'I know how *I'm* feeling,' the old man replied, 'I don't know how you are.'

'Did you sleep last night?' the medical man asked. Theophilus nodded. 'Good. Therese tells me you didn't eat anything. That's not being a good patient.'

'It's being a good Christian. I made a pledge to the Almighty that I wouldn't eat until I had rid that woman of her devils. I cannot go back on that pledge just because *you* don't like the idea.'

'You must think of your body,' the man insisted.

'Doctor, I must think of her soul. If I fail her, her soul will be lost for eternity in Hell. My body is a temporary thing. It was born to die and be destroyed. But her soul will never die. That's why it's important that I save it. Save *my* body? What for? For the undertaker?'

'You are a very stubborn man, Father. I'm glad all *my* patients aren't like you.'

'And I'm glad all *my* patients are not like Mary Lawrence.'

'How many persons have you exorcised in your career?' the doctor was preparing another packet of his powders.

'Sixteen. The Lawrence woman will be my seventeenth.' He sighed. 'And my last.'

'Your last?' the doctor smiled. 'I don't think so.'

'Young man, don't try to fool an old fox. I know I'm dying. I know I have but months . . . possibly weeks . . . to live. I am not going to be one of those priests who sit around a monastery and get a letter on their hundredth birthday from the Pope. No, I am going soon, but I want the satisfaction of knowing the Lawrence woman has been saved.'

'You are a very dedicated man,' the doctor replied, lifting Theophilus' head so he could drink the medicine.

'Not dedicated, sir. Promised. When I became a priest I promised our Lord Jesus Christ that I would

serve Him with all my strength for I believe His cause i
right.'

'And you still believe He is right? After all thes
years? After what you have seen and what Satan ha
told you?'

'Yes, because I don't believe Satan. Satan is a liar
Satan will pervert any truth around to his way of think
ing. He has tried very hard, in my career, to make me
renounce my belief in the Lord, but he hasn't suc
ceeded. I understand his tricks. I know his goals. Many
people refer to him as the Prince of Darkness. I always
think of him as the Prince of Lies.'

'You will get some sleep today?' the doctor asked
'Maybe take a little tea with some sugar in it?'

Theophilus turned to Therese. 'How is the woman?
Is she still alive?'

'Yes Father. The Sisters are taking good care of her.

'Fine,' he sighed. 'We will begin again tomorrow.'

'Tomorrow?' The doctor shook his head. 'Oh no you
won't. Tomorrow you're going to stay right here in this
bed. Don't make any plans for tomorrow.'

'Don't tell me what I will or what I won't do, young
man. I have already made concessions to you by taking
your medicines. You should consider that sufficient.'

'We want your body to get well,' the man said.

'It's not what you want,' Theophilus said as he
closed his eyes. 'It's what the Lord wants. It's His body
He can take it anytime He chooses.'

'He still won't eat a thing,' Therese said to the Mother
Superior. 'Such a stubborn man! And he looks so terrible, all thin and pale.'

'He must conserve his strength,' Mother Lotharia
agreed with the doctor. 'If something should happen to
him, if he should die before . . .'

'Oh, don't say that Mother,' Therese crossed herself.
'If Theophilus should die and leave Mary here . . .
the way she is. What would happen to her?' Therese

bviously had never considered this possibility. Mother, what would happen to us? How would we handle that woman then?'

'We would have to send her back to Milwaukee, I suppose,' the Mother Superior answered. 'We couldn't let her die here in Earling. How would that look? Everyone would say we killed her.'

'But she's dying anyway,' Therese said.

'Yes, but better she should die back up there, where she came from.'

Therese was about to say something else when Sister Archelaus hurried into the rectory kitchen where the two women were talking. 'Mother,' she said out of breath, 'come quickly. The woman has revived.'

Both Mother Lotharia and Therese scurried from the rectory side door, across the back lot behind the church and into the side door of the convent. The Mother Superior had her heavy woollen habit on, but Therese just threw a shawl over her cotton housedress. Neither of them minded the cold. They hurried up the stairs and into Mary's bedroom.

Mary was on the bed, her eyes were open and she was trying to smile at the number of Sisters who had run to her room when they heard the news that she had regained consciousness. They parted to let their Mother Superior get over to the bed. Therese followed right behind her.

'Mother,' Mary tried to talk but she was so weak it was only a whisper.

'Yes, my dear,' Mother Lotharia put her hand on Mary's forehead. 'Are you feeling better? Would you like something to eat? Something to drink?'

Mary looked around at the others in the black habits with the white cowls under their wimples. 'I . . . I didn't know I was back here,' she whispered. 'When . . .?'

'Seven days ago,' the Mother replied. 'On the train. You were very ill.'

'And . . . the Fathers . . . have they . . .?'

'Yes. Every day but two. Father Theophilus has bee
ill.'

'And have I . . . inconvenienced . . . this time . . . a
of you?'

The Mother Superior smiled and patted Mary's tw
thin hands. 'Of course not. You have been the perfec
guest.' She laughed lightly. 'You are welcome her
anytime.'

'I always feel so safe here,' Mary said slowly. 'Yo
are all so kind to me.'

'We want to help you,' the Mother replied. 'That'
our main desire. Don't you fret about it. Now, are yo
sure we can't bring you a little broth? Maybe som
oatmeal?'

Mary shook her head. 'I'm really not hungry,' sh
said.

'But you haven't eaten since you arrived here,' th
Mother said soothingly. 'Let us bring you something.'

Mary turned her head to look at the others in th
room, when her gaze stopped. Her eyes grew wide. Sh
lifted a trembling hand and pointed at the ceiling. 'D
you see . . . that?' Her voice was almost inaudible.

Instantly every eye in the room was looking at th
spot where she was pointing.

Sister Mundana was the first one to speak 'Look
roses! Can you all see them?' Her voice got higher. 'Th
roses! See them? Can you see them?'

They nodded and murmured in agreement. Yes, the
could all see them. A wreath of white roses floatin
calmly against the ceiling, directly over Mary's bed.

'Holy Mother of God!' said Sister Primosa.

'Blessed Jesus!' said Sister Lauda.

'It is a sign from God,' said Sister Serena.

'Who would have believed it?' said Therese. 'Look a
them! White roses!'

Mary began to smile. She reached out and tugged a
the Mother Superior's habit. 'Can you hear the voice?
she asked. 'Can you hear what he is saying?'

Mother Lotharia tilted her head slightly, as if that would help her hear better. She shook her head. 'No,' she said slowly, 'I don't hear anything.'

'The voice,' Mary insisted. 'Can any of you hear it? Hear what he's saying?'

The Sisters looked at her, then back to the wreath of roses and then back at Mary again. No, none of them could hear anything.

'A man's voice,' Mary said, 'and he is telling me . . . he wants you to know . . . that . . . "Do not lose courage. The priest especially should not give up hope. The end is soon at hand." That's what the voice says,' she smiled broadly now. 'He says the end is soon at hand.'

Therese hurried toward the door. 'I'd better go get my brother.' She took another look at the flowers on the ceiling and hurried back to the rectory.

By the time Father Steiger got to Mary's room, the vision was gone. Mary had fallen unconscious and the Sisters were scattered about the room, on their knees and giving thanks for the miracle they had all witnessed.

'Joseph! Joseph? Are you awake? It's almost sunrise.' The pounding continued on Father Steiger's bedroom door. 'We are wasting time! We have work to do.'

Father Steiger managed to get out of bed, grapple with the sleeves of his robe and finally open the door. 'Theophilus!' he said in amazement. 'What's the matter? Are you worse?'

'I'm fine,' the old man said. 'Don't concern yourself with my health. It's not important. Come, get dressed and have your coffee, if you must. We have things to do.'

'But the doctor said . . .' Father Steiger was trying to wake up.

'That doctor is a young fool. What he says is of no importance to me. Come on now, for God's sake. We haven't much time.' He turned and walked back to his room and shut the door.

Therese poured Joseph a second cup of coffee. 'Eat some of that omelette. You don't have to rush off so fast.'

'I feel guilty having this coffee,' he said quickly. 'Theophilus is already in the church, waiting for me.'

'He is killing himself,' the woman said simply, 'just as much as if he was driving a knife through his heart.'

'I don't know where he gets the energy, I really don't. Flat on his back, hasn't eaten a thing, almost dying and now he's up and dressed and can't wait to get started on the Lawrence woman.'

'It's almost over,' Therese said. 'The voice told Mary that, remember?'

'I'd like to believe it.'

'You mean you don't? Joseph, I'm shocked! It was a message from the Lord. It said "the priest especially should not give up". And you don't believe it?'

'How do you know it came from the Lord?' he asked her 'It's probably one more of the devil's tricks. Has she ever got a message from the Lord before? Of course not. So why should this one be any different?'

Therese came over to him. 'I think, Joseph, when this is all over, that you should have a serious talk with yourself. Sort out in your own mind what you believe and what you don't. Perhaps you have a decision or two to make.'

'About what?'

'About who you are and what you are doing with your life.'

'I know all that. My life has been settled.'

'Until Mary and Theophilus arrived it had been. Maybe you have to make some new choices. Can you?'

He pushed past her. 'Sister dear, if I'm anything, it' that I'm stronger in my beliefs than ever before. I've always known there was a God in Heaven but I always doubted a real Satan in Hell. I don't doubt any longer

It was just ten minutes before nine that morning, December 21st, 1928, when the nuns placed Mary's unconscious body on the bed. That day, aside from the two priests and the Mother Superior, four Sisters were in attendance. Theophilus had asked for volunteers, saying that he intended to continue until the demons had fled and would need Sisters who could come in and relieve the others when they became too tired to continue.

The stoles were in place, the Holy Water in a large bucket against the wall, and each Sister held a large wooden crucifix. Father Steiger carried his medal of The Little Flower of the Child Jesus and Father Theophilus wore a crucifix containing a relic of the True Cross loaned to him by his Bishop in Wisconsin. Theophilus intoned the opening prayer to St Michael, then went on to the Exorcism text itself. Finally he reached the final prayer: 'From the snares of the devil, deliver us O Lord. That Thy church may serve Thee in peace and liberty, we beseech Thee to hear us. That Thou wouldst crush down all enemies of Thy church, we beseech Thee to hear us.'

A groan came from Mary's unmoving lips, then several loud shrieks as if someone was being beaten with a whip. Then much laughter and the noise of bones cracking.

'So you recovered, did you Theophilus?' the masculine voice of Beelzebub filled the room. 'You don't look very well.'

'I have recovered sufficiently to get back to you, demon,' Theophilus said loudly. 'These are your last hours inside that poor woman's body! Your end is near. Her salvation is at hand!'

There was laughter and then something like a large cat purring. 'What good is all this wasted energy, Theo? What can you hope to gain by putting yourself and all these good people through this trial and torture? One woman's soul? A soul that was promised to

345

us even before the body was born? There are a billion souls out there for us to take, if you don't let us have this one. Just think what we could do in China? All those people, all the confusion we could cause.'

'Like you are doing in Mexico,' Theophilus stated. 'And in Ancient Rome. And in the Crusades. And during the Great War.'

'The what war? You call it the great war?' Now the voice laughed loudly and long, shaking the room with the reverberating sounds. 'You call that a great war? You people haven't seen anything yet. You want to know what we've got planned? What will put your "great" war into shadow?'

'I don't want to hear anything you're planning to do,' Theophilus replied, 'unless it's to tell me you're getting out of this poor woman!'

'Oh, you'll be interested in this. At least your children will!' The voice laughed again. 'Your children Theo! How many do you have? Any with this old crow over here?' Again, much laughter from several voices.

'Beelzebub, leave that woman's body at once! In the name of Christ Jesus, depart!' Theophilus had to shou over the laughter.

'Anyway, let me tell you what's going to happen. In more than five years from now, but less than ten England will have a terrible political upheaval. The think they're so smart and above it all but we will wor! on them and we'll shake them right where it hurts, i their high and mighty Royal Family. Oh yes, don't loo so surprised Theo, there is no home too grand that w cannot enter. In one year great England will have thre kings. Three of them! Isn't that wonderful! They lov their kings so much, we're going to give them three One will die and another will take over but one of the will walk away from the throne. One of them wi refuse it and for what?' Here Beelzebub laughed, 'Fc worldly pleasures, pleasures of the flesh! How's tha Theo? Did you like that one?'

'I refuse to believe anything you tell me. That story could never happen. Not in England.'

'Okay, now let me tell you what else is going to happen. In about three years there will be much trouble in Europe. One man will appear and take over a large nation. He'll do it by lies and then by force, but he'll eventually be the supreme leader of the country. He'll raise an army and he'll have those machines that fly in the air too. Not flimsy things like in your "great" war, but fast things and they will drop death and destruction everywhere. Tens of thousands of humans will die and millions more will be displaced.'

'That sounds horrible,' Sister Mundana said quickly. 'I can't believe it.'

'Believe it,' Beelzebub said, 'because it's true. This one man will destroy Europe. The world will never be the same after him.'

'Good always overcomes evil,' Theophilus said. 'The forces of good will prevail, and this tyrant shall be deposed.'

'Yes, yes he will,' said Beelzebub, 'but he will leave behind him chaos and instability that will last for generations. It'll be so much fun,' he laughed. 'All that turmoil and death and your precious church doing absolutely nothing to stop him. In fact, your church leaders will turn the other way. They won't want to get involved.'

'And the Vatican?' asked Mother Lotharia, 'will it be destroyed too?'

'Unfortunately not. We would like it to be, of course, but this man is not strong enough for that. We are not strong enough . . . yet . . . to accomplish that. But the countryside all around it shall be bombed and in flames and the leader of the Italians shall hang upside down like a dressed hog, in a public square.'

'I can't believe you,' spoke Father Steiger. 'Surely God would not permit it.'

'God has nothing to do with it,' Beelzebub said almost with a snarl, 'this is our plan, not his.'

347

'What you're predicting is . . .' the Mother Superio
was interrupted.

'Not *predicting*. Stating actual facts!'

'. . . that the Antichrist will come to earth and sha
be vanquished. That will clear the way for Blesse
Jesus to return.'

'Who said anything about the Antichrist? Theo, di
you hear me mention the Antichrist?'

'No,' the old priest sighed, 'I didn't.'

'If that old bitch didn't have that thing over her ear
she might hear better. No, the Antichrist is not thi
man. I said in three years this man will start makin
himself known. No, the Antichrist is just about to b
born. He will make this man in Europe look like a
amateur.'

'Will the Antichrist also be from Europe?' Fathe
Steiger asked.

'No. He will be born in what you call the Middle Eas
He will appear suddenly on the world's political scene
coming from nowhere and taking command. He will nc
be formed from either mother or father but jus
appear. Oh yes, later on he will invent some obscur
parents and pretend he was born naturally, but wh
will be able to prove it?'

'And he also will wage war?' asked Sister Ignatius.

'War? You mean like your "great" war?' the voic
laughed delightedly. 'It will be the worst war the eart
has ever seen. Millions will die from long metal thing
that fly faster than aeroplanes through the skies. The
won't even need men inside them to find the exact ta
get. And when they explode . . .' his own gleefulnes
interrupted him '. . . when they explode on the eart
they will kill thousands at a blow! In some places *mi
lions* at a blow! Won't that be something to see?'

'Get thee into Hell, Beelzebub!' Theophilus thur
dered. 'Leave this woman at once!'

'How can you banish me into hell, Theo? I have to b
here to prepare the way for the Antichrist. I have to b

348

here to welcome him. We know more than you think, Theo. We know the signs of the times. We know what will come to pass.'

The Mother Superior hesitated before asking the question everyone else in the room wanted to be asked: 'When,' she said, 'when is this terrible destruction coming?'

Beelzebub paused. Mary's head twisted and her closed eyes seemed to stare at each religious figure in turn.

'This is the last century,' Beelzebub said. 'When people will write the date as the year two thousand, the end will be at hand.'

There was a strange silence in the room, then Sister Mundana spoke up: 'That's only seventy-two years from now.' She turned to Sister Ignatius. 'I won't see it, I'll be too old by then.'

'None of you in this room will see it,' Beelzebub replied, 'but think of those born in the years to come. Think of little babies born in the forties and the fifties and the sixties and seventies. They'll all see it and they'll all suffer together at the same time. They will see the end of their world and the beginning of Satan's rule!'

'But Jesus will prevail!' shrieked Sister Mundana. Then to Father Theophilus: 'He will prevail, won't He?'

'Of course, Sister. Jesus always prevails,' said the old priest.

'Don't be so sure of yourself, Theo,' Beelzebub said. 'Your precious what's-his-name has been losing popularity lately. Your churches have not been as full as they used to be. Oh yes, we monitor all those things. In another fifty or sixty years your churches will be almost empty. People will get tired of praying and not getting results. By the end, by the year 2000, he will have very few followers. He will be unable to save the humans from the fate they deserve. He will be powerless.'

349

'God the Creator is never powerless,' shouted Theophilus. 'He will protect his children.'

'*If* he wants to,' Beelzebub said smoothly. 'Perhaps by that time he'll be so fed up with all of you that he won't care what happens. I know I would be if I were him. I'd have written you off years ago! Dumb bunch of upright animals!'

'God will prevail! Jesus will prevail!' Theophilus hurried to the bucket of Holy Water by the wall and came back with it. He cupped his hands into it and threw the liquid onto Mary's body. 'God will prevail!'

The voice inside Mary began to scream. Others joined it, howling and crying in pain.

'Don't' yelled a woman's voice and they all knew it was Minna, 'don't do that! It burns!'

'Let us go!' This time Jacob's voice was heard. 'Let us out of here! Don't hurt us any more!'

In answer Theophilus lifted the bucket and splashed its entire contents across the bed. Mary's body rose about two feet into the air, feet kicking and hands clawing. The Sisters grabbed her and tried to force her back onto the soggy mattress. They shoved down on her but she remained there, hovering and clawing and spitting up long strings of something green flecked with blood.

'Clean blankets!' shouted Theophilus to the Sisters. 'Hurry, put clean blankets on the bed. They won't bring her back down if her body rests on Holy Water! Hurry Mother Lotharia, get some dry blankets and put them under her!'

Sisters Ignatius and Lauda ran from the room, lifting their long skirts so they could travel faster. In a couple of minutes they were back with three thick woollen blankets. Quickly they spread them over the wet mattress. Then Mary's body lowered, slowly, onto them.

For the next few hours Theophilus called on the Devil to leave. Sometimes there were bits of conversation but mostly just long stretches of silence broken

350

with intervals of screaming, sobbing, shouting and animal noises like dogs barking and wolves howling.

The Sisters had tied Mary to the bed, with a leather rope across her ankles and another under her breasts. They weren't tight, she had some room to move if she chose, but after settling back down on the mattress she hardly stirred at all.

When the bell rang in the convent for six o'clock vespers, the four Sisters were replaced by four others who had been freed of their duties that day and instructed to remain in their rooms resting and praying for the ordeal ahead.

'Hadn't you better go with them, Mother?' Father Steiger asked the elderly woman. 'You must be tired too.'

'No. I'll be all right. I want to stay here. I belong here.'

'As you choose,' he said, and smiled at her.

Shortly after eight p.m., Mary vomited up a large ball of hair. It was as big as an orange and was composed of matted blonde, brunette and red hairs. They were tightly compacted and covered with a film of yellowish slime. Mother Lotharia picked it up, using a towel, and put it in a pail under the bed.

Just before eleven-thirty Mary opened her eyes, stared at the group around the bed, and then tried to speak. It was the first time she had ever broken through to her conscious state during the exorcisms. 'I . . . I'm dying,' she whispered in her own voice. 'None of this has done any good.' She sighed deeply. 'I'm dying.' Then she closed her eyes, there was another deep sigh, and her body stiffened.

'May the saints preserve us all!' Mother Lotharia hurried to the side of the bed and felt Mary's pulse. She looked up at the two priests, frightened. 'She gone,' she said simply.

One of the Sisters began crying, the other three crossed themselves and started mumbling prayers.

351

Father Steiger put his hand over Mary's heart. He shook his head. Then he took her pulse. 'She's dead, Theo. We were too late, We failed her.'

'She didn't even have Extreme Unction,' Mother Lotharia lamented. 'At least we could have done that for her.'

Theophilus stood at the end of the bed, scowling. He shook his head. 'She's not dead. It's another of Satan's tricks. He's tried them all and now this!'

Mother Lotharia took a small mirror from her habit and placed it under Mary's nose. After a minute of silence, a long minute for them all, she said: 'It's true. The Lawrence woman is dead.'

'And I say she isn't!' Theophilus grabbed the refilled pail of Holy Water and sloshed some of it out onto the body. 'Vade Satanas! Begone Satan!'

The screams were loud and immediate. Mary's body bucked and thrashed under the leather ropes. 'Leave us alone!' several voices shouted. 'Don't do that!'

'Out of that body!' the old priest shouted. 'Get out! Now!'

This was followed by more screaming and howling and the new sound of someone clanging two pieces of metal together.

'You see?' said the old priest. 'You see? I was right! I know all of Satan's tricks and he *knows* I know!' He threw more Holy Water on Mary's body and as she writhed under the ropes, and the noises came from deep inside her, Theophilus said to everyone in the room: 'Come on. Let's begin again.' He took his place at the foot of the bed, Father Steiger stood wearily beside him. The four Sisters and the Mother Superior took their positions alongside the bed. 'In the name of the Father and of the Son and of the Holy Ghost. Amen. Glorious Prince of the Celestial Host, St Michael the Archangel, defend us in the conflict which we . . .'

He got all the way through the ritual, there was no movement or noise from the bed.

'Once more,' he said. 'We shall say it again.'

Father Steiger looked at the Mother Superior. He could see the lines of exhaustion on her face. 'Mother, are you sure you want to remain here? You look so tired.'

'I have a duty, Father. Surely you must understand that.' She didn't smile.

'Yes, I do. All right Theophilus, we're ready. Begin again, please.'

Theophilus kissed the edge of his stole, crossed himself and started: 'In the name of the Father and of the Son and of the Holy Ghost. Amen. Glorious Prince of the Celestial Host, St Michael the Archangel, defend us . . .' His voice, old and scratched and weak, said the words again. Even though his energy was at its lowest he intoned the ritual with feeling and command.

Father Steiger glanced at the others in the room and saw that they were all tired. They had each thought of their bed. They all wished this thing was over and done with.

And again: 'In the name of the Father and of the Son . . .'

There were the glimmerings of daylight creeping around and under the white cotton curtain over the window. Father Steiger glanced at it. He had stopped counting the numer of times Theophilus had intoned the ritual. Theophilus knew it by heart and he was sure he could recite it by now himself.

'Seize the dragon, the old serpent, which is the Devil and Satan, bind him and cast him into the bottomless pit . . .'

Father Steiger wondered what they would do with the body when the woman finally died. It would be shipped back to Milwaukee, of course, but should he tell his congregation? Should they know that everything they had done for the woman had failed? That *he*, their pastor, had failed?

'Cease by your audacity, cunning serpent, to delude

353

the human race, to persecute the Church, to torment God's elect, and to sift them . . .'

Of course, there would be a full enquiry, Bishop Drumm would see to that. Maybe he would be transferred to another parish, be sent out of Earling altogether. He couldn't blame them if they did that to him. The Church's history has been one of heroes, not failures and he, definitely, was a failure.

'The glorious Mother of God, the Virgin Mary, commands you, she who by her humility . . .'

Father Steiger could see the red arch of the rising winter sun as he looked through the window curtain. It was another day. He wondered if Therese would check his room before she made breakfast. He pictured her in the kitchen, filling the coffee pot with cold water and then throwing in a handful of coffee grains before she put it on the stove-top to boil. God, how he'd like a cup of coffee now! Maybe a slice of buttered toast with some of Mrs Muenchrath's strawberry jam. God, that's good jam! His thoughts were interrupted by the sight of Theophilus picking up the bucket of Holy Water and aiming it at the bed.

'No!' the voice inside Mary screamed. It was the first sound there had been in hours.

'Then leave!' Theophilus said loudly, his voice now hoarse. 'Leave!'

'Not back to Hell!' Minna's voice was unmistakable. 'Let us stay up here until Judgement Day, don't send us back to Hell!'

'Not to Hell,' a male voice cried out. 'We promise!'

'Promise what?' the old priest tried to shout.

'Let us go and we won't bother anyone. Ever! Please!'

'How do I know you'll keep your promise? Who can give me that assurance?'

'I will!' This new voice, this powerful masculine voice, filled the room almost instantly. Along with it came a strange odour, like burning chemicals.

354

'Who are you?' Theophilus asked. 'Who are you to make promises?'

'I am the one you have been battling all these years, Father Theophilus. I am your arch enemy. I am the one you call the Prince of Lies.' A thin layer of sulphurous smoke started forming around Mary's body.

'At last,' said the old man, 'after all these years. Satan himself!'

'I thought we would win this time,' the voice shook the room, 'and we would have if I was not bound and held back from doing so many things on earth. I will win them all one day, Theophilus. You'll see. One day I'll be ruler here. One day there will be churches erected to me. I am the rightful heir to this miserable planet and it will all be mine.'

'Never' said the old priest loudly, 'Jesus Christ will never permit it!'

'There will come a time, Theophilus, when your precious what's-his-name just won't give a damn. There will come a time when he will wash his hands of all humans. He has tried so hard to make something of this mismanaged zoo and has failed. He won't admit that, not quite yet.'

'He will never abandon us. We are His children.'

'Children should learn to grow up and to handle their affairs by themselves. Children should learn to live with each other as responsible adults, not kill each other for gold or politics. Children should learn that there comes a time when the parent just can't do any more and that's when the parent walks away.'

'He has promised to protect us,' Theophilus shouted.

'He has tried to protect you for almost two thousand years and you have done nothing to improve yourselves. You've done nothing to show him that you care about anything above your navels. You are a miserable lot. You're all nothing but a bunch of animals who accidently got more intelligence than you should have.'

'We are created in God's image!' Mother Lotharia said angrily.

'That's what you like to think, I know. It helps your egos to tell each other that. Really, do you think the Almighty gets old like you do? That his skin wrinkles and he loses his teeth? That he has white hair? Do you think he eats and then defecates what his body can't absorb? Made in his image? No you're not. As much as I dislike him, I have to admire him. He looks nothing like you. The human race was a mistake, then it became an experiment. That experiment is failing. Wait until your year two thousand. You'll see.'

'I can't believe you,' Theophilus said slowly.

'Then that is your problem. Now, about my workers inside this body. Let them go. Permit them to roam the earth until the day God ends his experiment and you can have the woman back. You've fought for her, Theophilus, you've earned her.'

The old man looked at Father Steiger. He was standing open-mouthed as he listened to all this. Theophilus glanced at Mother Lotharia, her eyes where closed in prayer. The four Sisters were doing the same. 'The decision seems to be mine,' he said to Satan.

'It's always been yours,' the voice replied.

'All right,' Theophilus said, 'I'll make you a deal, as one of your demons called it. You will give me your promise the entities inside this woman will not bother any other human until judgement day?'

'It is yours. I have given it.'

'When they leave her, I demand that they tell me their names. Their sign to me must be giving me their names. Agreed?'

'There is no problem with that. I agree.'

Theophilus looked at Father Steiger, then at the still-praying Sisters. He took a couple of steps backwards, away from the bed and raised the silver crucifix containing the relic of the Cross he wore around his neck. He pointed it at Mary's body.

'Then in the name of the Most Blessed Trinity, in the name of the Father and of the Son and of the Holy Ghost I command all of you to depart and never enter this woman or any other human again! Vade Satanas! Begone Satan!'

Suddenly, with incredible speed and force, Mary's body sat upright on the bed. She had broken the leather rope around her chest and as she continued to rise up, the rope around her ankles snapped as well. Then only her heels were touching the bed and she tottered back and forth as if she was going to rise up to the ceiling.

'Pull her down!' Father Steiger ordered the Sisters. 'Grab her! Pull her down!'

Theophilus began touching her body with his True Cross crucifix. He touched her face, her hands, her feet and her abdomen crying loudly: 'Depart, fiends of hell! Begone Satan, the Lion of Judah reigns!'

At that moment, all the rigidity in Mary's body vanished and she crumpled back down on the bed.

Then an ear-shattering scream filled the room and voices began shouting 'Beelzebub . . . Judas . . . Jacob . . . Minna.'

'Out, demons from Hell!' Theophilus thundered, waving his cross in the air above the bed.

'Beelzebub!' came the scream.

'Judas!'

'Jacob!'

'Minna! My name is Minna!'

Theophilus stumbled around the bed, looking at the far wall, his attention near the window. 'Leave!' he shouted hoarsely. 'Out! Out of here!'

'Beelzebub . . . Judas . . . Jacob . . . Minna . . .'

'In the name of the Holy Trinity, out of this room! Out of this holy place!'

'Beelzebub' came the name again, but softer and farther away.

Then 'Judas' also from a distance.

'Jacob'. It sounded as if it was coming from outside the building.

Then 'Minna' very faintly. 'Minna' again almost inaudible.

Then nothing.

Mary sat up. She opened her eyes. Then she moistened her lips with her tongue. She looked at her hands and touched her chest. Tears came into her eyes. She looked at the faces around her and reached out a trembling hand toward Father Theophilus. 'I'm ... I'm free ... My God, my sweet Jesus ... I'm free!' She burst into tears and started to sob and the Sisters hurried to her side.

Then a terrible smell filled the room. It seemed to be there all at once, coming from every corner, filling every breath. Mother Lotharia ran to the window, threw back the curtain and raised the sash. She bent out into the open air, trying to fill her lungs with the freshness. Quickly she turned and shouted to the others. 'Fathers, come here. Look!'

Father Steiger hurried to the window and looked down to where she was pointing.

The dozen or so chickens that the Sisters raised behind the convent were flapping and squawking and running in mad circles, clawing at each other with their feet. Then, one after the other, they flew headlong into the brick wall of the coop, until none were left alive. Gradually their feathers settled on to the ground.

Father Steiger turned back into the room and said, 'Theophilus, come here and see this. What do you make of it?'

Father Theophilus didn't hear him. He was on the floor and he wasn't breathing.

Epilogue

Father Theophilus recovered from his illness and went on to exorcise several other possessed Catholics. He never wanted to talk about the Earling case, even though he permitted interviews with Rev. Carl Vogl for his booklet *Begone Satan*. It was the one case that bothered him. Why did it take as long as it did? Should he have permitted the four entities to remain on earth? Why did they immediately enter into that flock of chickens? Why did the chickens kill themselves? If the entities survived, did they go elsewhere? Did they keep their promise to him and not enter another human being? If not, *where* did they go? Who have they since destroyed? Father Theophilus died in a home for retired priests in Mount Calvary, Wisconsin. He was 73. The year was 1941.

Father Joseph Steiger stayed on in Earling. He too never talked about the case, refused to give any information to reporters or the curious. He worked to enlarge the school and in 1930 built a new series of classrooms. In the next few years his health failed and on November 8, 1938, while actively doing parish work, he died. He was buried in Earling. He was 57 years old.

Therese Wegerer stayed on in Earling and was housekeeper to Rev. Peter Bissen who took over after Father Steiger died. She never married. She died and was buried in Earling in 1944. She was 56 years old.

The highest toll was taken on the Sisters of

St Joseph. All of them were psychologically scarred by what they had been through. After Mary left the convent they asked to be transfered to other parishes. The Mother Superior, Lotharia, left right afterwards as did Sister Primosa, Sister Serena, Sister Ignatius, Sister Clara and the chatterbox Sister Mundana. By the end of the 1930 school year, only three of the original fifteen remained.

As for the woman Mary, very little of her is known after that. The Church has pulled a curtain over her. She stayed with the family of John and Magdaline Schimorowsky, of Earling, 'for several weeks to make sure she was fully recovered', recalls their son James Schimorowsky. Supposedly, she went back to Milwaukee and led a normal life. There was one minor 'flare-up' after that and she was quickly exorcised, but not by Father Theophilus. She returned to Earling several times to say novenas of Thanksgiving in the parish church. One rumour has it that she became the housekeeper for a priest in Minnesota, thus fulfilling her dream of being part of the religious life.

And the prophecies? Satan's predictions to Father Theophilus? In the year 1936 England did have three kings. King George V died on January 20, 1936. His son, Edward VIII, assumed the throne that same year but abdicated for the love of a divorced American woman, Wallis Simpson. His brother, George VI, assumed the throne on December 11, 1936.

There was indeed a man who arose and took over a large European nation a few years after 1928. He did indeed change the course of history with his armies and his war planes. The world has never been the same since Adolph Hitler.

The Antichrist? The one who will bring the world to its knees and destroy civilization as we know it? The man who will end it all when the year 2000 is written? He will, said Satan in 1928, come out of the Middle East and have to invent obscure parents. He will not be born

360

of them. He will rise rapidly on the international scene and then send 'planes with no pilots' (missiles) onto large cities killing millions. Does anyone living today sound like that?

Bibliography

Official Catholic Directory. P. J. Kennedy & Sons. N.Y. 1982

Progress Is Our Future. Earling, Iowa. Centennial Committee. 1981

FATHER GOMMAR A. DE PAUW, *The Traditional Roman Catholic Mass.* Catholic Traditionalist Movement Publications. N.Y. 1977

MARTIN EBON, *Exorcism: Fact Not Fiction.* New American Library. N.Y. 1974

REV. THEODORE GEIGER, *Mary Crushes The Serpent.* The Theotokia Press, New Haven, Conn. 1934

MALACHI MARTIN, *Hostage to the Devil.* Readers Digest Press. N.Y. 1976

JAMES L. MONKS, *Great Catholic Festivals.* Henry Schuman. N.Y. 1951

REV. JOHN J. NICOLA, *Diabolical Possession and Exorcism.* Tan Books and Publishers. Rockford, Ill. 1974

JEFFREY B. RUSSELL, *The Devil.* Cornell University Press. N.Y. 1977

LESLIE SHEPARD, *Encyclopedia of Occultism & Parapsychology.* Gale Research Co. Detroit, Mich. 1978

REV. CARL VOGL, *Begone Satan.* Tan Books and Publishers, Rockford, Ill. 1973

WILLIAM WOODS, *A History of the Devil.* G. P. Putnam's. N.Y. 1974

MINE TO KILL
by David St. Clair

On Wednesday, 28th August, 1878, Esther Cox, a plain, unassuming girl from the town of Amherst in Nova Scotia rode out in a buggy on her first date. Storm clouds lowered on the horizon; later there was lightning and torrential rain. Esther returned at nightfall, soaked through and too distraught to speak to her family: her innocent trip had turned into the beginning of a personal nightmare.

At first there were rustlings in her bedroom at night, then unseen hands gouged a terrible message on her wall: ESTER COX, YOU ARE MINE TO KILL!

On the third night, Esther leapt from her bed. 'Oh, my God', she screamed, 'I'm dying! Please dear God! I'm dying!'

This is the chilling story of a girl's possession by malevolent spirits. Like CHILD POSSESSED (also available in Corgi paperback), everything in this book actually happened.

552 12587 3

CHILD POSSESSED
by David St. Clair

This is a true story. Nothing has been added in th
interests of sensationalism. What happened in the sma
town of Watseka, Illinois, between the years 1865 ar
1878 may strain credibility, as well as shock. But it d
happen

Mary Roff, a gentle, unassuming 19 year old girl, di
suddenly on the morning of July 5th, 1865, in the town
Watseka, Illinois. Her death was strange, but her li
had been stranger. For several years she had be
subject to sudden, unaccountable "fits" – But dea
brought to an end her sad and disturbing case . . .

Thirteen years later, in 1878, Mary Roff reappeared –
the living body of Lurancy Vennum . . .

0 552 11132 5

THE EXORCIST
by William Peter Blatty

The terror begins unobtrusively. Noises in Regan's room, an odd smell, misplaced furniture, an icy chill. Easy explanations are offered. Then changes begin to show in eleven-year-old Regan – severe and frightening. Medical tests shed no light on her symptoms, but it is as if a different personality has invaded the child.

Father Damien Karras, a Jesuit priest, is called in. Is it possible that a demonic force is at large? Might exorcism be the answer?

Made into a terrifying film, THE EXORCIST remains the most famous novel of satanism and possession written in recent times.

0 552 09156 1

A SELECTED LIST OF HORROR TITLES
AVAILABLE FROM CORGI BOOKS

The prices shown below were correct at the time of going to press. However Transw○
Publishers reserve the right to show new retail prices on covers which may differ from th○
previously advertised in the text or elsewhere.

☐	09156	1	**THE EXORCIST**	*William Peter Blatty* £2.○
☐	12186	X	**PSYCHO 2**	*Robert Bloch* £1.○
☐	08272	4	**PSYCHO**	*Robert Bloch* £1.○
☐	13135	0	**POLTERGEIST II**	*James Kahn* £1.○
☐	12691	8	**WHAT ABOUT THE BABY?**	*Clare McNally* £1.○
☐	12400	1	**GHOSTLIGHT**	*Clare McNally* £1.○
☐	11652	1	**GHOST HOUSE**	*Clare McNally* £1.○
☐	11825	7	**GHOST HOUSE REVENGE**	*Clare McNally* £1.○
☐	13148	2	**APRIL FOOL'S DAY**	*Jeff Rovin* £1.○
☐	12587	3	**MINE TO KILL**	*David St. Clair* £2.○
☐	11132	5	**CHILD POSSESSED**	*David St. Clair* £2.○
☐	10471	X	**FULL CIRCLE**	*Peter Straub* £2.○
☐	13000	1	**THE INTRUDER**	*Thomas Altman* £2.○

ORDER FORM

*All these books are available at your book shop or newsagent, or can be ordered direct fr○
the publisher. Just tick the titles you want and fill in the form below.*

Transworld Publishers, Cash Sales Department,
61–63 Uxbridge Road, Ealing, London, W5 5SA

Please send cheque or postal order, not cash. All cheques and postal orders must be i○
sterling and made payable to Transworld Publishers Ltd.

Please allow cost of book(s) plus the following for postage and packing:

U.K./Republic of Ireland Customers:
Orders in excess of £5; no charge
Orders under £5; add 50p

Overseas Customers:
All orders; add £1.50

NAME (Block Letters) ....

ADDRESS ....

....